RO -36096

MAN IN SPACE

**The United States Air Force Program
for Developing the Spacecraft Crew**

MAN IN SPACE

The United States Air Force Program for
Developing the Spacecraft Crew

Edited by

KENNETH F. GANTZ
Lieutenant Colonel, USAF

With a Preface by

GENERAL THOMAS D. WHITE
CHIEF OF STAFF, USAF

DUELL, SLOAN AND PEARCE
New York

Library of Congress Catalog Card Number 59-9375

MANUFACTURED IN THE UNITED STATES OF AMERICA
VAN REES PRESS • NEW YORK

Contents

Editor's Introduction

By law the United States Air Force provides the National forces for offensive and defensive air operations. These forces are charged with maintaining general air supremacy.

This fundamental responsibility is not limited to any altitude. It extends as far from Earth as the mission demands. Where the atmosphere of Earth gradually thins into airless void, there comes no detectable dividing line to mark the transition from air operations to operations in space.

For the air-breathing gasoline engine the supercharger lifted the air operations of World War II to thirty thousand feet and beyond. Air-breathing man had put on his oxygen mask when he climbed half as high. As the planes lifted yet higher into the thinning atmosphere, the rocket engine came to give them power from fuel that bore its own oxygen for combustion. And when the air thinned so that wings did not bite and lift, flight surged on higher under the thrusting power of the rocket missile until it was spent and bound by the chain of gravity into Keplerian trajectory in space.

To signify the indivisibility of its boundless field of operations above the surface of the earth, the Air Force has named it the "aerospace." Already in response to its mission of gaining and maintaining air supremacy, it has operated flying vehicles under what its biomedical scientists call "space-equivalent conditions." In 1956 Captain Iven Kincheloe flew the experimental aircraft X-2 nearly 24 miles above the earth. In 1958 Major Howard Johnson took the combat-operational F-104A interceptor-fighter to more than 17 miles. The X-15 now very near readiness is designed to be test flown a hundred miles out, in the vicinity of the low orbit points of the man-made satellites. A rocket research aircraft with an inertial guidance system, the X-15 is expected then to attain manned flight as far as 300 miles out.

The Air Force also provides the Nation's intercontinental ballistic missiles and its land-based intermediate-range ballistic missiles, together with the operational forces to employ them. These strategic bombing vehicles, such as Thor and Atlas and the more advanced Titan and Minuteman, travel through both "air" and "space." Our defense against their enemy counterparts involves operations in both air and space, in the aerospace. Our defense against enemy piloted vehicles of the X-15 type will necessarily be an aerospace defense operation, calling for both missiles and piloted craft. And as more sophisticated vehicles evolve from the X-15, replacing the simple ballistic missiles with the spacecraft of internally controlled power and maneuverable flight, the aerospace crews must also progress in capability to man it.

The United States Air Force has been historically concerned with the physiological and psychological problems of the flying man. And as with the aerospace itself, no detectable dividing line has appeared in the passage of its interest and investigation from the man flying in air to man flying in space. While this book is concerned with the current Air Force program in the biomedical and behavioral sciences of putting man himself in space, the roots of the know-how and successes it presents run deep into the pioneering Air Force work in "aviation medicine." As the Air Force has followed its vehicles ever higher, it has examined ever more precisely the physical and mental powers of its crews to endure alien stresses increasing into the yet unknown. It has devised protective gear fantastically complex, proceeding step by step from the simple oxygen mask to the full-pressure suit and the space capsule.

For studying what it terms the "human factor" in flight operations, the Air Force has three major centers.

The School of Aviation Medicine, USAF, a component of Air University at Randolph Air Force Base, Texas, has the dual mission of training aviation medical personnel for the USAF and of conducting basic exploratory research of medical flight problems. Historically concerned with the physical demands on aircrew members, Air Force aero medicine has paced manned flight since 1918 to higher and higher altitudes, entering immediately after World War II the physiological studies and related investigations preliminary to manned flight from the region of earth's atmosphere into space itself. In 1949 the School formed the world's first Department of Space Medicine.

The Aero Medical Laboratory in the Wright Air Development Center at Wright-Patterson AFB, Ohio, is operated by Air Research and Development Command, which has primary responsibility for the technical superiority of Air Force equipment. As aeronautical progress exerted increasing demands upon the crew and particularly upon the pilot, research into the human-factor requirements for flight looked more and more to the marriage of man and machine, called for surer knowledge of human capabilities and for "human engineering" of the vehicles and mechanisms the man had to operate. The Aero Medical Laboratory, founded in 1936, is charged with developing the devices and equipment indicated by the basic research of the School of Aviation Medicine as needed for the survival, well-being, and efficiency of man in flight.

The Aero Medical Field Laboratory at Air Research and Development Command's Missile Development Center, Holloman AFB, New Mexico, got its beginning in 1946 as a testing facility of the Aero Medical Laboratory for its early high-altitude experiments in space biology and later for biodynamic tests in g stresses with the rocket sled. Holloman's specialty is experimental employment of new human-factor equipment. Inevitably the circle closes back to basic research at the School of Aviation Medicine and Aero Medical Laboratory, as field tests reveal new requirements.

This book is intended to give a professional review of the current investigations of the U.S. Air Force into the problems of putting its aerospace crews into outer flight. Its chapters have been written by top Air Force scientists and ranking officers at work with the research and planning, and it is as authentic and as complete as security permits. With one exception * the chapters were originally composed for article publication in a special "human factor" issue

* Chapter 4 by Brigadier General Don Flickinger on "Biomedical Aspects of Space Flight" was edited from his lecture in Denmark, 23 October 1958, before the NATO Advisory Group for Aeronautical Research and Development. The Appendix IV on "Project Mercury and the National Space Program" was selected from data issued by the National Aeronautics and Space Administration and from a statement to a Congressional Committee by its Administrator, Mr. T. Keith Glennan. Also included in Appendix IV as a ready introduction to Project Mercury is an unofficial roundup article from *Air Force/Space Digest* the magazine of the Air Force Association.

and in other current issues of *Air University Quarterly Review,* which is the professional journal of the United States Air Force in strategy, tactics, and techniques. At the publisher's request addressed to the Department of the Air Force, the material of greatest interest was selected and integrated by the Editor of *Air University Quarterly Review* for public dissemination as a comprehensive report from those intimately involved in the human-factor aspects of space operations and the related "human engineering" of the equipment.

The immediacy of the material to the public interest is revealed by demonstration in almost every day's newspaper of the rapid progress in space technology. Talking satellites, lunar probes, and the projection of missiles beyond the influence of Earth into orbit round the sun have had far more public attention as the visible genesis of the space age than have the immense difficulties of putting man himself in space and the successes in their solution that are described in this book. But successes with both man and machine are the essentials of the developing age of space exploration, as they are of the operations of the U.S. Air Force.

Our current stage in America's progress into this newer age is reflected by Project Mercury, the intent of which is to put a manned space capsule into orbital flight round the earth and to recover the capsule and its occupant safely. Project Mercury is under the management of the National Aeronautics and Space Administration developed by the Space Act of 29 July 1958 from the National Advisory Committee for Aeronautics, which for two generations had contributed signally to the progress of aeronautical science. A special appendix has been added to the chapters on the Air Force program to depict the aims and status of Project Mercury, for which NASA is already selecting the crewman from a list of meticulously screened volunteers.

That such a selection by name is now possible, that Project Mercury can be contemplated for immediate execution, is due to such extended and painstaking research as is sampled in this book.

The attention of the reader is invited to the fact that the opinions and conclusions conveyed in *Man in Space* reflect the understanding and opinion of the authors and the selection of the Editor and do not necessarily carry the official sanction of the Department of the Air Force.

K.F.G.

23 March 1959

Preface

THE INEVITABLE CLIMB TO SPACE

General Thomas D. White

After centuries of groping through the fundamentals of earth-space relationships, man is now invading the space envelope of his own world, which is in turn a stepping stone to the universe beyond. A very recent and fundamental part of this progress has been the discovery and development of air power. The successful accomplishments of air power which have been achieved over the last fifty years have been keystones in the foundation of our nation's space program. This era, which we call the age of air power or the air age, is in reality only a period of transition, a prelude to the inevitable dawn of the space age.

Air and space are not two separate media to be divided by a line and to be readily separated into two distinct categories; they are in truth a single and indivisible field of operations. Space is the natural and logical extension of air; space power is merely the cumulative result of the evolutionary growth of air power. It would be more accurate, rather than to speak of two separate and distinct eras, to adhere to a more descriptive frame of reference, one which would clearly show these phases of man's entry into the universe in their proper perspective. Precisely speaking, we are and have been operating in the "Aerospace Age."

Within this same frame of reference, then, the equipment developed during the transition period also might be called aerospace equipment. In comparison with man's earth-bound activities before the first flight of the airplane at Kitty Hawk, the P-40—an early

World War II fighter—was, for all intents and purposes, a pioneer space vehicle. The F-51, the F-80, the F-100, and now the F-104, to mention but a few, likewise were the evolutionary forerunners of the future. Each succeeding improvement in structure, design, and propulsion has provided a means toward greater achievement. Experimental models like the X-1, the X-2, and the X-15 comprise additional rungs on the ladder to space. The degree of application of each of these vehicles to the exploration of space is merely relative to the point in time and technology at which they are applied. From the first military aircraft to enter the inventory—the Wright brothers' pusher-type, skid-equipped airplane—to the futuristic X-15 unveiled in 1958, Air Force goals have changed in degree only; the basics have been constant—greater speed, longer range, and higher altitude.

Although the basic requirements have remained unchanged, improvements and advances in Air Force equipment have been revolutionary. There are few resemblances between the first airplane, the World War II combat planes, and the B-70 and the F-108 which are under development today. Airframes and power plants are being developed which tax the credulity of even those who have been closely associated with the progress in these fields. Supporting systems to meet the rapidly growing demands of increased speed, range, and altitude are so complex that we are strained to support and maintain them.

There is, however, one element in the aerospace program whose nature has not changed—that is man himself. As each new goal in our march of progress has been won, we have been faced with the problem of adapting man to his new environment, and man by the very nature of his basic design is not readily amenable to engineering change. He is primarily a sea-level, low-speed, one-g, 12-hour animal. He represents the weakest link in our aerospace development to date, and his establishment in the hostile environment outside his own world will not be easy.

The question has been asked many times—why man in space? If man is, in fact, the soft spot in the development of our aerospace capability, why do we not eliminate him from the entire effort? The capability of remote instrumentation to obtain information from space already has been demonstrated in the recent satellite and lunar-probe projects. Surely developments can be anticipated which will further reduce the need to risk human life in our space activities.

This type of thinking is correct up to a point. The marvels of science and the inventive genius of man can be predicted to gather more and more knowledge of space through remote efforts. Knowledge so gained will represent the majority of that available in the early stages of space exploration. But despite all the efforts of industry and the genius of science, certain limits are automatically imposed where the machine is involved. A machine cannot think nor can it reason. Although certain computers closely approach this capacity, even the most sophisticated of these machines cannot replace on-the-spot human judgment and selectivity.

Man must operate in space, employing his logic, his common sense, and his good judgment as he encounters the unexpected and the unknown. Furthermore our spaceman must be as functional in space as he is in present-day air operations. In the event of military operations in space, man's presence and ability to perform in space could spell the difference between defeat and victory. His on-the-spot presence, then, will not only be necessary for purposes of scientific research but to ensure national survival.

The design and development of equipment necessary to achieve the space goals of this nation are a matter of time, effort, and ingenuity. This has been proved in many other fields, which if taken in their own context, were equally as imposing as the obstacles we face today. The problems of sufficient thrust and range and of adequate aerodynamic characteristics can logically be expected to be solved. In the same way the solutions to the problems of placing the judgment and moral fiber of man in space will be forthcoming.

From the day man invented a machine which left the ground and employed the principles of aerodynamics in its flight he was destined eventually to journey into space. His early efforts were confined to the lower fringes of the space envelope surrounding the earth; his more recent explorations have reached deep into this envelope. It is inevitable that man will go beyond these temporary limits to still greater achievements far out into space itself.

Headquarters United States Air Force

CHAPTER 1

The Threshold of Space

Major General Dan C. Ogle

Since man's time began, many generations have stood at thresholds of new eras. New worlds have always been hard to conquer. It is hard to step beyond the comforts of status quo. Yet for those with vision and ambition the future has always appeared stimulating and bright. To be dynamically alive to the challenges of the future, man must feel the magnetism of attainable goals and have faith in reaching them.

Columbus dared the edge of the sea to give us a new world; William Harvey suffered ridicule and scientific ostracism for teaching the circulation of the blood; van Leeuwenhoek's crude microscope upset fixed traditions of microbiology; and more recently a group of men meeting in secret under a college stadium caused the invisible atom to react with a force that will affect man for all time.

Throughout time, man and history have worked hand in hand to give substance to his dreams, and few men contemplating the heavens and the stars have not felt their compelling attraction. Man's phantasies of defying gravity, his dreams of flying, have been fulfilled by increasingly extravagant accomplishment during the past fifty years. The stimulation of dreams and vision, spurred by a will to survive in a highly competitive world, now beckons him into space, from which he confidently plans to return. The era of space exploration now at hand has captured universal interest and imagination, and there is ample evidence that man's faith and scientific ability will sustain him in this limitless achievement.

Exploration of space is no longer phantasy. Based on present knowledge we believe prospects are good for engineering both man and machine for successful orbiting flights. We believe such flights

1

are attainable from the standpoint of cost and human endurance, and we also believe such flights are practicable from the standpoint of value received.

Exciting as it is, planning for the space age has gotten off to a slow start. While there are the few who objectively face the challenges of new eras, there are many of each generation who feel they have just missed a great period of development or progress by having been born too late. Like the nineteen-year-old Alexander, they cry because there are no new worlds to conquer. There are yet others who look neither forward nor backward, who have no interest in cumulative knowledge, who abhor the future and cling tightly to the present. These latter are like the centenarian who, on being interviewed concerning the changes he had seen in his lifetime, replied, "Yes, I sure have seen many changes and I've been agin every one of them."

There will always be new worlds to conquer if we but will. Indeed the brightness of our future will become dangerously clouded unless we now determine the goals toward which we will apply our intellect, our energies, and our will. Our society is being challenged in many areas—in politics, ideology, religion, philosophy, and significantly at this time, in science. Any race, society, or nation that would outlive another must outperform its rivals.

We cannot afford to be second-best in the conquest of space. To be second is to invite the bonds of subjugation, the humiliation of inferiority, or the oblivion of destruction.

In a message addressed to the then Soviet Premier, Marshal Nikolai A. Bulganin, President Eisenhower made a proposal to solve what was, in his opinion, the "most important problem which faces the world today"—the proper use of outer space. He proposed that in this "decisive moment in history . . . we agree that outer space should be used only for peaceful purposes." His reasoning is unassailable. Both the Soviet Union and the United States, he noted, were using outer space for the testing of missiles designed for military purposes. Such a course of action if continued could lead to the "potential destruction of the human race itself. . . . The time to stop is now . . . There are about to be perfected and produced powerful new weapons which availing [themselves] of outer space would greatly increase the capacity of the human race to destroy itself." The President implied that the path to destruction or the peaceful exploration of these new frontiers was a matter of human choice: "Should not outer space be dedicated to the peaceful use of mankind and denied to the purposes of war?"

The President was reflecting the opinion of our highest military leaders who have stated that we must progress as rapidly as possible toward the conquest of space, perfecting the utilization of manned vehicles as well as ballistic missiles. If space is to continue as a symbol of freedom, then its use for the purposes of war must be neutralized. General Thomas D. White, Chief of Staff of the United States Air Force, has repeatedly affirmed the truism that the nation which controls the air and space above controls the ground under it as well. The control of "high ground" has long been a major factor in determining military advantage. In our time this vantage point may become the surface of the moon itself.

In reaching the objective of extraterrestrial "high ground," there must be a progressive development and employment of Air Force experience in manned flight. Each advance in the development of flying vehicles has added new environmental hazards and stress problems for pilots and passengers alike. These have been solved only by the joined efforts of medicine and engineering, a combination science as old as aviation itself.

To adapt man and vehicle for space it will not be enough merely to meet the tolerances of safety; we must also guarantee the tolerance of efficiency and reasonable comfort if successful flights and survival are to be ensured. In anticipation of space flight, medical scientists in the Air Force have been studying the diverse aspects of space medicine for several years and are now convinced that, from the standpoint of human tolerance and rational functioning, short-duration flights such as limited orbiting are physiologically acceptable and presently attainable.

Scientists tell us that from a space vehicle during daylight hours it will be easy for man to observe terrestrial detail with considerable clarity. They tell us also that such a traveler will have the capability of directing destructive missiles. While the functions of space vehicles are not now altogether apparent, scientists such as Dr. Edward Teller and Captain Howard T. Orville, USN Ret., of the Federal Advisory Committee on Weather Control, speak of the possibility of eventual modification of the earth's weather. The Weather Control Committee's report to President Eisenhower implies that, while an international race to control the world's weather sounds fantastic, it may be that this race has already begun. The committee asserts that the importance of research in this field can hardly be overemphasized and concludes: "Few areas of science have implications so profound to all mankind as the study of the atmosphere and the phenomena which occur in it."

Scientific discussions thus far presume that human beings will ride as passengers in space vehicles orbiting about the earth as man-made satellites are already doing. If so, there is much yet to be done in the field of space medicine to prepare both the vehicle and the man for the ordeals he will encounter if he is to retain efficient operation and control of his space destiny.

As man plans his conquest of space he faces his most limiting conscious spatial confinement. While in thought and dream he envisions the stars bounded only by the dimension of time, he must embark upon his celestial excursions encased in a cramping capsule of natural environment, as close fitting and sustaining as the womb that gave him life on earth. Though he dreams of the boundless freedom of the heavens, if he is to travel there he must be capable of a most exacting, tedious, confining, and skillful performance if he is to survive.

Space medicine, which is but an extension of aviation medicine, will ensure that all is done that can be done to promote the safety, efficiency, and comfort of those who orbit the earth or who may later escape the chains of gravity and soar into true space. The preventive medical aspects of aviation medicine and space medicine must encompass also the science of adaptive and protective medicine. Such efforts will cut across the scientific disciplines of astronautics, electronics, physics, chemistry, and all the life sciences.

To be effective, space medicine must be wedded to space engineering, the "hardware" department. For in the development of increasingly high-performance aircraft there has been a proportionate increase of interdependence between man and machine for the survival of either. In rocketry, as in atmospheric craft, human safety and human escape measures are highly desirable. Yet there comes a point of performance where the failure of either man or machine serves to destroy the other regardless of safety and escape provisions. It is easy to see then that in spacecraft design, and in selection and training of space flyers, little can be left to chance.

When earth-bound man achieves his sought-for freedom in the limitlessness of space, he must be capable of the most exacting human performance and must possess the highest degree of stress tolerance in all creation.

In space we lose the adjusting influence of the cycling between day and night. In space there is no oxygen, no barometric pressure, no ambient air, and no atmospheric filter protecting us from cosmic and solar radiations. There is no molecular diffusion of light, and no medium for transmission of sound. There is no support from the substance of air and no stabilizing influence of gravity. Although these subjects will be more thoroughly treated in the following discussions, it is appropriate to give initial thought to one example of the engineering problems involved in space flight—design requirements for a space cabin.

A space cabin must have provisions for appropriate and continuous pressurization, for temperature control, humidity control, and control of atmospheric gas concentrations. It must provide for the elimination of poisonous gases and noxious odors, for the elimination or reconstitution of the waste products of metabolism. It must supply emergency oxygen and possibly escape oxygen. All this is in addition to the requirement for power and controls for the mission which someday must provide for possible landings away from the earth but which must always provide for a safe return to a selected terminal here below. This is but a brief mention of the many problems which must be solved by the combined efforts of engineers and space-medicine experts.

In addition to the engineering features of a space cabin, scientific attention must be given to the space traveler himself. Extensive tests are required to ensure that he can survive the physiological and psychological trauma of such acutely demanding and prolonged confinement. Under sealed-cabin conditions we must conduct experimental and research activities to evaluate the effects of claustrophobia, day-and-night cycle changes, personality conflicts, and variations of motivation. We must devise methods to maintain alertness; to overcome the enervating influences of boredom; to anticipate real and imaginary discomforts. We must be able to favorably influence man's reaction to endless hours of hypnotic stimuli or perhaps to endless hours of the absence of stimuli. We must know more of the psychological effects of the breakoff phenomenon or the feeling of being totally detached from mother earth. We must ensure that man can withstand the necessary accelerative and decelerative forces. And we must make ample provision for satisfactory respiratory and metabolic requirements. All this means for space medicine, as it has in years past for aviation medicine, that we must keep men physically capable, mentally clear, and emotionally controlled within this strange and perhaps frightening environment.

It must be remembered that there are no encapsulated areas of medical research. Physiological stress factors encountered in space medicine are related to chronic and acute stress situations of everyday living. There are comparable circumstances between maintaining man's alertness, discrimination, judgment, and will in a space cabin and similar applications on earth such as operating an automobile. Normal standards of physiology that may be affected by the adversities of space are similar to environmental and situational stresses anywhere. Physiological and psychological support and protection methods in space might well serve to increase man's efficiency on earth even to the point of preventing or curing certain diseases and injuries.

Research on all known problems that will be encountered in space flight has been in progress since 1948 with gradual accumulation of valuable data. Momentum for research in space medicine received a substantial, stimulating boost with the advent of orbiting satellites and with the stunning realization that survival of the free world may depend directly on man's ability to successfully operate spacecraft patrolling beyond the earth's atmosphere.

We are now crossing the threshold of space. May travelers to that far country return in safety; but even more important, may their voyages and explorations continue to serve the purposes of peace. The limitless freedom of space must never be used to inflict the nirvana of oblivion.

Headquarters United States Air Force

CHAPTER 2

From Aviation Medicine to Space Medicine

Dr. Hubertus Strughold

The potentialities of human flight are undergoing a radical change. This change has been brought about by the rapid and successful developments in rocketry during and since World War II.

The rocket is a self-contained propulsion device—the only kind known that is independent of an external medium both dynamically and chemically. Dynamically, to attain propulsion it does not require an atmospheric medium to "push against" but rather "pushes against itself." Chemically, it carries its own oxygen or other forms of oxidizers for fuel combustion, in contrast to the jet engine which makes use of atmospheric oxygen in this respect. In case nuclear energy is used, oxygen is not required at all. Furthermore, the powerful thrust of a rocket exceeds by far all other propulsion methods.

These unique features enable a rocket to reach beyond the regions of the atmosphere and operate in space. In fact it is even more efficient in a vacuum. Its natural habitat, therefore, is outside the atmosphere. With regard to its preferred environment, the rocket is a *spacecraft*. In contrast propeller planes and jet planes while "wing supported" and "air supported" can operate only inside the atmosphere within a certain density range. Environmentally they are both aircraft, but the jet is transitional to the rocket.

The altitude ceiling for air-supported craft and air-breathing engines is maximally around 20 miles or about 30 kilometers, the limiting factor being the density of the atmosphere. In contrast the rocket has practically no limitation in altitude. Its vertical operational range is determined exclusively by the thrust. In the realm of rocket flight, therefore, the concept of height above the earth's surface blends into that of "distance" from the earth. The rocket alone has really conquered the third or vertical dimension in flight. It has opened a new frontier to the flyer: the "vertical frontier."

The process of motion along this vertical frontier also reveals the novelty of things to come. Flights in conventional planes are accomplished by the steadily acting power of propulsion. Great variations in the g forces generally do not occur; motion, therefore, is more or less uniform. It lies in the nature of rocket propulsion that fuel expenditure takes place during the first few minutes only, followed by a period of coasting without power or of flight by inertia until the vehicle re-enters the atmosphere. At the beginning and end of rocket flight we encounter high accelerations and decelerations, respectively, resulting in exposure to multiples of g. During the period of coasting the vehicle follows the laws of ballistics and even those of celestial mechanics as formulated in the three laws of planetary motion by Johannes Kepler. The latter means that the vehicle itself behaves like a celestial body following a path which exhibits the characteristics of an orbit (circle, ellipse, and parabola). In such orbits the force of the earth's gravitation is balanced by inertial forces with the result that both craft and passengers become weightless. Thus an environmental factor—weight—which is present everywhere and at all times on the ground and in conventional flights, is eliminated.

The velocities observed in space flight may approach those of meteors. They exceed by far the speeds attainable in atmospheric flights by jet-propelled planes, which may reach about three times the speed of sound. In rocket flight beyond the atmosphere this speed unit expressed in mach numbers is irrelevant. The velocities attainable by rocket propulsion make conceivable an approach to other celestial bodies with a strange environment and perhaps with living organisms. The telescope has brought these celestial bodies closer to us optically, but the rocket has the potentialities of bringing us closer to them physically.

To summarize: First, the environment in rocket-powered flight has the properties not of the atmosphere but largely or completely those of free space. Second, the rocket itself with regard to its motion behaves like a celestial body. And third, other celestial bodies may soon be reachable from the earth. These three facts indicate that we have entered a novel, revolutionary phase in the development of flight, in fact, in the history of man. We are at the *threshold of human space flight*.

Organizing Space Medicine in the Air Force

The near advent of a capability for manned space flight was of extreme importance to the United States Air Force. In anticipation of the medical implications involved in a new branch of technology, now named space technology, Major General Harry G. Armstrong created in February 1949 at Air University's School of Aviation Medicine, Randolph Air Force Base, Texas, a special department for the study of the medical problems encountered in flights beyond the atmosphere. It was named the Department of Space Medicine, with the writer as its chief and Dr. Heinz Haber as astrophysicist.

The fact that this department was founded at an aviation medical institution indicates that space medicine is actually an extension of aviation medicine. It developed from the latter partly in distinctly recognizable steps toward medical space research and partly in an invisible way in experiments which were carried out to meet the requirements of high-performance aircraft but which can today be regarded as belonging, at least to some extent, to the realm of space medicine. These researchers [3 5 27 51] pioneered along the borderlines of a field which came officially into being several years after World War II.*

At about the same time the Department of Space Medicine was founded, preparations for animal studies in rockets began under Brigadier General Edward J. Kendricks and later Colonel Robert H. Blount at the Aero Medical Laboratory at Wright-Patterson Air Force Base, Ohio. The Aero Medical Laboratory had suitable facilities for this type of work at Holloman Air Force Base, New Mexico. In 1952 the research activity at Holloman was made an independent Aero Medical Field Laboratory under Lt. Colonel John P. Stapp with a Space Biology Branch under Major David G. Simons.

Developments Toward Space Medicine

In the following an attempt is made to describe the historical development of space medicine based on those studies and events which show distinctly the trends or steps toward space flight, the

---

* [References cited by number are listed for each chapter in its respective section of the "Reference Notes," pages 259 to 265.]

exploration of space, and travel to other celestial bodies. This article does not claim completeness in detail but rather will give an over-all picture of the transition from aviation medicine to space medicine—where, when, and in what scientific areas it took place. More details are available in references 22, 23, 31, and 44.

But it should be noted that transition does not mean replacement. Aviation or atmospheric flight will always play the dominant role in human flight; and aviation medicine or aeromedical studies will always be required for the health and efficiency of the crew and safety of the passengers, especially in these days of increasing air traffic and of jet service. Space flight will probably always have the characteristics of an operation or an expedition.

As in any pioneer field, general theoretical space-medical considerations preceded the specific experimental approach. Two things had to be determined: first, the actual differences between atmospheric flight and space flight, and second, the height above the earth's surface beyond which atmospheric flight becomes space flight. The answers were found in an analysis of the atmospheric functions for human flight: in the concept of the "functional borders" between atmosphere and space,[9] [42] [52] and in the concept of atmospheric "space equivalence." [46] On the basis of these theoretical considerations, it was recognized that space conditions actually begin as low as 12 miles with regard to certain environmental factors and that practically all space conditions are met above 120 miles. But planes as well as balloons had already penetrated deep into the region of partial space equivalence. Consequently "space-equivalent flight" became the technical term for all flights above 12 miles.

Special experimental research, preceded or accompanied by theoretical analysis, was concentrated upon three major areas:

—the g pattern which included a large range from zero g to multiples of g;

—the study of the biological effect of cosmic rays; and

—the development of a closed ecological system as represented by a cabin to be used in space or even as low as 70,000 to 80,000 feet.

Weightlessness. Considerations of tolerance to zerogravity or weightlessness date back to immediately after World War II. But even during the war occasional observations were made in this respect. In October 1946 a seminar was held at the Aeromedical Center in Heidelberg to discuss "Man under Weightless Conditions." The content of this seminar was published in 1950.[13] At about the same time similar discussions took place at Wright-Patterson Air Force Base.[34]

A solid theoretical basis was laid in a paper entitled "Possible Methods of Producing the Gravity-Free State for Medical Research" prepared by scientists at the USAF School of Aviation Medicine in 1951.[17] [19] Finally actual animal experiments were carried out in rockets by the Wright-Patterson Aero Medical Laboratory at its field facilities at Holloman Air Force Base in 1952.[24] An altitude of 36 miles was reached in these rocket flights, and the state of weightlessness lasted about 3 minutes.

Soon jet planes were used to study human tolerance to weightlessness at Wright-Patterson Air Force Base [4] and by the School of Aviation Medicine at Randolph Air Force Base,[15] [16] as well as by the Aero Medical Field Laboratory at Holloman Air Force Base.[36] The number of parabolic flight maneuvers flown up to the present time at Randolph Field alone is well over four thousand. The duration of the state of weightlessness attained during these parabolic arcs is maximally a little less than one minute. For such a short period we now have a pretty good idea of zero-g tolerance.

These experiments carried out in jet planes represent historically the first phase of the study of human tolerance to weightlessness. The next phase will be experiments in rocket-powered craft of the X-15 type, in Dynasoar, and eventually in vertical rocket flight and orbital flight. It may be added that in 1956 comparative studies of subgravity conditions in swimming pools were carried out at the School of Aviation Medicine and at the Aero Medical Field Laboratory.

Multiple-g forces. The study of increased g forces dates as far back as the middle Thirties. They were carried out on large centrifuges at Wright-Patterson Air Force Base, at the Mayo Clinic,[55] and more recently at the Navy's Medical Laboratory at Johnsville, Pennsylvania. These experiments were required because of the high accelerations during certain maneuvers in atmospheric flight, the necessity of testing anti-g suits, etc. In atmospheric flight maneuvers the g forces seldom exceed 4 g.

During the launching period of a rocket, however, peaks up to

9 g may be experienced, and during atmospheric re-entry even higher values. The g pattern expected during launching was simulated on a human centrifuge in 1955.[32] Valuable results about the tolerability of extremely high g have been obtained by means of experiments on a sled at Holloman Air Force Base since 1950.[40] [41] Because of these many experiments carried out through different means, the physiological effects of increased g are basically well understood today.

Cosmic rays. The problem of biological effects of cosmic rays has been approached theoretically and experimentally. The Navy's School of Aviation Medicine at Pensacola, Florida, concentrated on the theoretical biological evaluation of the cosmic ray data obtained in rockets and started with these studies as early as 1950.[33] The Space Biology Branch at Holloman Air Force Base undertook experimental studies in 1951, partly in cooperation with the School of Aviation Medicine at Randolph Air Force Base. The vehicles used in these experiments were rockets and ultra-high-altitude balloons. So far only minor effects of cosmic rays on mice (grey hairs) have been detected.[35] [36] The ultimate research vehicle will be a returnable biosatellite which permits longer exposure times and the penetration of high-intensity radiation regions, such as have been discovered recently by G. van Allen by means of the Explorer satellites.

The sealed space cabin. One of the most important and vital tasks of space medicine is to keep a man alive in an environment which is distinguished by the absence of an atmosphere. This has to be achieved by the development of a sealed cabin which carries its own atmosphere for the crew.

Such devices have been developed in the form of sealed capsules designed for animal experiments and manned flight in high-altitude balloons at the Space Biology Branch at Holloman.[37] These efforts made possible the record balloon flight of Lt. Colonel David G. Simons to 102,000 feet in August 1957. The Department of Space Medicine developed an experimental sealed chamber at Randolph Air Force Base for laboratory studies,[48] a so-called space cabin simulator, in which in 1957 a 24-hour experiment and early in 1958 a 7-day experiment were successfully performed.

For experiments or flights of days or weeks duration, physical and chemical means are probably the sole method for the regeneration of the cabin's air.[11] [12] [26] For longer periods of time, biological gas exchangers may be more efficient. To cope with this eventual situation, the School of Aviation Medicine sponsored a project to use plants for the regeneration of the air. These studies were started at the Department of Zoology at the University of Texas in 1954 [29] and in a more applied form at the School of Aviation Medicine.[14] In these biological studies in a closed ecological system the recycling of fluid and semisolid body wastes for reutilization has recently been included.

Apart from these main research areas other problems of space medicine have been attacked, such as the physiology of the day-night cycle, vision, psychology of isolation, nutrition, toxicity of rocket fuel, selection of crew,[7] bailout at very high altitudes, etc.[18]

Development of Astrobiology

Closely related to space medicine is a scientific field which deals with the ecological conditions on other planets and with the question of life on these celestial bodies. This field has been called "planetary ecology" or "astrobiology." It is a field not only of interest to the astronaut but also of general human interest. The roots of this study go back to 1877 when G. V. Schiaparelli, astronomer in Milan, Italy, discovered strange features on the surface of Mars which he called "canali." This started the discussion of life on other planets which around 1910 reached its first climax in the publications of Percival Lowell, founder and director of the Astronomical Observatory in Flagstaff, Arizona.*

* [The Italian "canali," by which Schiaparelli meant "channels," designated the network of dark lines resembling, according to Schiaparelli, "the finest thread of spider's web drawn across the disk" of Mars, which he and a number of other competent observers have observed at the dimmest limit of vision. Other competent observers have never seen the "canali," and the markings have not shown on any photographs clearly enough for general acceptance. Professor Lowell, who recorded many successful observations, readily accepted the suggestion the Italian word had in English and was so much impressed by the geometric regularity of the network he himself saw that he proclaimed it an artificial irrigation project, such as might be made visible by bordering vegetation. Many American astronomers have followed Lowell in accepting at least the existence of the markings as real surface features of some kind. Opinion has been advanced that the lines may be cracks in the Martian surface, rays like those on the Moon, or perhaps the vagaries of surface detail transmuted into lines by the observer's straining vision. Concerning life on Mars, most areologists accept the existence of

The recent rapid progress made in space technology and space medicine has had a catalytic effect upon the occupation with astrobiological questions, as is evidenced by a great number of new publications. In contrast to former times when such publications were written exclusively by astronomers, now biologists and medical doctors have entered the field. This is very desirable because astrobiology, as the term indicates, is actually a field common to astronomy and astrophysics on one side, and biology and medicine on the other. Astrobiology started with the question of the possibility of indigenous life on other celestial bodies. This is a matter of general biology. The prospects offered by the construction of space vehicles to approach other celestial bodies and eventually to land there have raised the question of what conditions an astronaut would find there with regard to himself or, in other words, from the standpoint of human physiology. Both aspects have been discussed in recent years in many publications and meetings.

As far as the Air Force is concerned, the School of Aviation Medicine had a project as early as 1947 to study the ecological conditions on other planets. As a result of this project various publications appeared concerning the possibility of life on Mars, such as *The Green and Red Planet*.[43 45] The marriage between astronomy and biology led to new concepts such as that of the "ecosphere" in the solar system.[47] The ecosphere represents a zone in a certain distance range from the sun in which the ecological conditions in space and those on the planets are favorable to space operations and to life. This concept was adopted by a Polish astronomer in 1957 for consideration of the stars found in space up to 17 light years distance from the sun, as he reported to the Congress of the International Astronautical Federation in Barcelona in 1957.

At this point it may be noted that in Russia two books were published under the titles *Astrobotany* (1947) and *Astrobiology* (1953) by G. Tikhof. In these books attention is concentrated upon the optical properties of the green areas on Mars. Recently a book entitled *Astrobiologia,* by F. A. Pereira, appeared in Brazil. Apart

---

broad areas of vegetation, observed as dark green regions between the polar frost caps, in contrast with the red desert that covers five eighths of the surface. This vegetation is considered to be a primitive type, possibly on the order of moss or lichen. Ed.]

from his own contributions the author reviews the "North American School of Thinking" and that of the "Soviet School."

An event which may be considered of historical importance was a symposium on "Problems Common to Astronomy and Biology" held at a joint meeting of the Astronomical Society of the Pacific and the International Mars Committee on 15 June 1957 at Flagstaff, Arizona.[50][54] It was the first symposium of its kind. Mars was the chief topic of the discussions, and the speakers based their reports on the latest spectographic observations, advanced ecological considerations, and space medical achievements. Physiological optics and the use of balloons as astronomical observatories, which require sealed gondolas as developed in space medicine,[39] were among the topics.

The development of transatmospheric astronomical observatories attached to ultra-high-altitude balloons or borne in satellites will mean an important mark in the history of astronomy and astrobiology. As for the latter, the ultimate goal will be an actual approach to other celestial bodies by means of manned space vehicles. We can, of course, simulate to a high degree the environmental conditions on Mars in a chamber and examine the behavior of terrestrial micro-organisms. Studies of this kind in a "Mars chamber" were initiated in 1956 in the SAM Department of Microbiology at Randolph AFB.[25] This experimental approach is interesting not only from the standpoint of astrobiology but also of general biology and philosophy.

Milestones in Space Medicine and Astrobiology

This review of the history of space medicine and astrobiology would not be complete if pertinent meetings and organizations were not included. In November 1948 Major General Harry G. Armstrong held a panel discussion on "The Medical Problems in Space Travel" in which members of the SAM Department of Space Medicine presented papers and six noted scientists from universities and Armed Services institutions participated as discussion speakers.[1] In 1950 a panel discussion on "Space Medicine" was organized by Drs. A. C. Ivy and John P. Marbarger at the University of Illinois.[28] This was the first space medicine meeting which had as one of its participants a rocket pioneer: Wernher von Braun. The others were H. G. Armstrong,[2] H. Haber, Konrad Buettner,[8] Paul Campbell,[10] and the writer.

An important step in the exchange of knowledge on space flight between scientists was the first international symposium on "The Physics and Medicine of the Upper Atmosphere." Forty-four speakers from various countries appeared on the program which was held in San Antonio, Texas, in November 1951. This symposium was organized by Major General Otis O. Benson, Jr., Commandant of the School of Aviation Medicine at Randolph AFB, and Dr. Clayton S. White of the Lovelace Foundation, Albuquerque, New Mexico. A considerable portion of the material presented was devoted to space, space flight, and the medical problems involved. The papers were published in book form.[53] Seven years later, in November 1958, at the end of the Geophysical Year, a Second International Symposium was sponsored by the School of Aviation Medicine under General Benson and organized by the Southwest Research Institute of San Antonio, Texas. The latest findings in the exploration of space by means of research satellites, the latest and future types of rockets, the medical problems in space operations, and the conditions on the moon, Mars, and Venus were discussed by the most prominent physicists, astrophysicists, rocket engineers, and experts in physiology, psychology, and medicine.

In 1950 an organization was created for the specific purpose of promoting space medicine: the Space Medicine Branch of the Aero Medical Association. Organized in Chicago with 20 charter members, it is now ten times its original size. Since 1952 this group has regularly held a panel discussion of the latest developments in this field at the annual meetings of the Aero Medical Association. As a rule these papers are published in the *Journal of Aviation Medicine* (Dr. Robert J. Benford, editor), which has played a pioneer role in the distribution of advanced ideas. Other publications concerning the problems and development of space medicine are listed in the bibliography.[7] [20] [21] [30]

Since 1952 space medical papers also began to appear on the programs of technological societies such as the American Rocket Society, the Institute of Aeromedical Sciences, and the American Astronautical Society. At the annual meeting of the American Rocket Society in Chicago in 1955, for instance, the first paper on the medical problems in satellite flight was given.[49] Since 1956 this Society has had a special Space Flight Committee with several medical doctors as members. Medical problems of space flight were also discussed at the First International Symposium on Health and Travel in 1955 in New York City. A human-factors panel was included in the program of the first Symposium on Astronautics, held in San Diego, California, in March 1957. It was organized by the Consolidated Vultee Aircraft Corporation of San Diego (a division of General Dynamics Corporation) and was sponsored by the Office of Scientific Research of the Air Force, Washington, D. C.

In 1954 space medicine entered the international scene at the annual meeting of the International Astronautical Federation.[46] This organization, founded in 1952, now comprises about twenty-five national member organizations. Actually for several years any meeting dealing with the problems of space flight has been considered incomplete if it did not have space medical topics on its program. The same can be said about the various technical magazines dealing with rockets, space flight, or astronautics. The magazine *Missiles and Rockets,* for instance, started in 1957 with a column on space medicine.

The historical development of space medicine is also reflected in the field of education. For many years courses in aviation medicine for flight surgeons have been held at the School of Aviation Medicine at Randolph AFB, first in the form of primary courses and later also in the form of advanced courses, refresher courses, and review courses. For more than five years space-medical and astrobiological topics have been included in these curricula in order to familiarize the medical students and physicians with problems of the future. Space medicine was also found on the program of two lecture series: one on satellites offered by the Massachusetts Institute of Technology in 1956, and the other on space technology given at the University of California in the spring of 1958.

There is another point worth mentioning. On 5 May 1958 two representatives of space medicine appeared before the special House Select Committee on Astronautics and Space Exploration in Washington, D. C., to testify about the medical aspects and prospects of space flight. Apparently these were considered important for the future military and civilian organization of the national efforts in astronautics. Furthermore the recent creation of a division of bioastronautics of Air Research and Development Command under the direction of Brig. Gen. Don D. Flickinger reflects the increasing role of space medicine in astronautics. And the medical research institutions of the Air Force are expanding their facilities and programs in close cooperation with its Ballistic Missile Division. The "man in space" program of course will be a key project of the recently created National Aeronautics and Space Administration (NASA).

The Renaissance in Aero Medical Research

After World War II it was generally believed that the essential problems involved in human flight had been solved and that medical research was only required to fill some minor gaps. Aviation medicine was considered a matter of routine. But the rocket with its extra-atmospheric capabilities changed this belief, gradually but radically, and we could observe a renaissance in medical and biological research and a distinct movement toward problems related to space. The appearance of artificial satellites in the sky gave this trend a powerful boost. Beyond that it also implied a retroactive justification for the necessity—formerly not generally recognized—of the presatellite pioneer studies, in which the medical institutions of the U.S. Air Force played an early and leading role.

School of Aviation Medicine, USAF *

* The author wishes to express appreciation to Jean Evans, Historian, School of Aviation Medicine, for assistance in historical research during preparation of this chapter.

CHAPTER 3

Basic Factors in Manned Space Operations

Dr. Hubertus Strughold

PART I: PHYSICAL ENVIRONMENT

The physical environment of the space between the celestial bodies in our solar system is radically different from that found on the earth's surface. The decisive difference is the absence of an atmospheric medium. Space is an environment of emptiness, an almost perfect vacuum. To realize the full significance of this fact for human space flight, we need only examine the atmospheric functions for life in general and for manned flight in particular. Then we must ask ourselves what happens when these functions are missing. The linking question between the two is where above the earth's surface do these atmospheric functions come to an end and, consequently, the conditions of space begin. From the answer we will get a clear picture of the physical environment of manned space operations, and how deep this environment reaches down to the earth's surface.

The Atmospheric Environment

The atmosphere as a functional medium for life and for manned flight does not extend as high as its material expansion. The region around 600 miles out, or 1000 kilometers, is generally accepted as the material limit or border of the earth's atmosphere. This estimate is based on the occurrence of collisions between the air particles. Only as far out as such collisions occur can the atmosphere be considered a continuous medium. Above 600 miles the separation (free path) of the air particles has become so spacious that intermolecular collisions are very rare. Instead the air molecules and atoms move out toward space with high kinetic energy imparted by their last collision. The heavier ones follow an elliptic trajectory, fly many miles high—as a kind of microrocket—then fall back into the atmosphere. Others with very high kinetic energy, essentially the light elements hydrogen and helium, may even escape forever into space.

Thus we observe above the 600-mile level a kind of spray zone of free-moving air particles, the so-called "exosphere," for which an extent of about 600 miles is also assumed. Above about 1200 miles, or 2000 kilometers, the exosphere gradually thins out into the near vacuum of space, with a particle density of about one to ten gas particles per cubic centimeter.

The Space Environment

These gas particles in interplanetary space, which are essentially in an ionized state, consist primarily of hydrogen. One cubic meter contains about one million hydrogen particles and very many less particles of oxygen, potassium, sodium, silicon, calcium, etc. Also about 11 million electrons are found in 1 cubic meter, or 11 in 1 cubic centimeter.

This interplanetary gas is only a part of the so-called "interplanetary matter." Other components are dust particles essentially of cometary and meteoric origin, micrometeorites, and meteorites. In addition to this very thinly dispersed matter, interplanetary space is permeated by electromagnetic and corpuscular radiations of both solar and galactic origin. These will be discussed in more detail later.

As mentioned before the significance of this physical environment of space for manned space operations can best be understood by contrasting it with the atmosphere as a functional medium for manned flight. We shall see that these functions of the atmosphere for manned flight do not terminate at the 600-mile material limit. Rather they end at different altitudes and all much lower than 600 miles; some end even within the stratosphere. These various altitude levels are called the "functional borders" between atmosphere and space, or the "functional limits" of the atmosphere. At and above them we find spacelike or space-equivalent conditions with regard to certain functions. The concept of the functional limits of the atmosphere and especially that of space equivalence within the atmosphere permits a determination of where space begins for the flyer.

Density and Free Path of Particles
in Atmosphere and Space

	Sphere	Altitude (miles)	Particle density per cm^3	Free path (centimeters)
				$< \infty$
			1	$> 10^9$
space	free space	1200	10^2	10^9
	exosphere	600	10^6	10^6
atmosphere	ionosphere	50	10^{14}	10^{-1}
	stratosphere	7	10^{18}	10^{-5}
	troposphere	0	10^{19}	10^{-5}

ATMOSPHERIC FUNCTIONS FOR MANNED FLIGHT

The functions of the atmosphere can, by and large, be divided into three principal categories:

- life-sustaining pressure functions
- life-protecting filter functions
- mechanical effects and functions

In the following discussion, these categories will be subdivided in greater detail. Ten of the most important specific functions will be used as a basis for the characterization of atmospheric flight and space flight. The first three concern the life-sustaining pressure functions.

Life-sustaining Pressure Functions

Oxygen. The atmosphere supplies us with oxygen for respiration. In space there is no oxygen. This atmospheric function ends at about 50,000 feet. At first glance this seems strange, because up to 70 miles the atmosphere contains free biatomic oxygen (O_2), the kind we use in respiration. The reason lies in the fact that an internal airbody of about three liters is physiologically interposed between the external atmosphere and our blood, the oxygen-absorbing body fluid. This airbody, the alveolar air, constantly maintains a rather high carbon dioxide pressure of 40 mm of mercury (Hg) and/or water vapor pressure of 47 mm Hg. The combined pressures amount to about 87 mm Hg. As soon as, with increasing altitude, the barometric pressure drops to this level, the influx of oxygen into the lungs from outside becomes impossible, because the alveoli are already occupied to the full barometric pressure of the atmosphere by carbon dioxide and water vapor, both issuing from within the body itself. The air pressure of 87 mm Hg corresponds to an altitude of about 50,000 feet. At this altitude the contribution of the atmosphere to respiration is zero, just as if the breather were surrounded by no oxygen at all, as in space. The pressure level at 50,000 feet is the first of the vitally important functional limits of the atmosphere, or space-equivalent levels within the atmosphere.

Composition of Interplanetary Gas

Particle	Number of particles per cubic meter of interstellar gas	
	according to T. Dunham, Jr.	according to O. Struve
electron	11,000,000	
hydrogen	1,000,000	2,000,000
oxygen		1,000
sodium	107	0.8
potassium	10	
calcium	4.8	0.12
titanium	0.05	
carbon hydride	0.4–3.4	
cyanide radical	0.3–1.8	

Barometric pressure. The atmosphere exerts sufficient pressure upon us to keep our body fluids in the liquid state and to prevent them from passing into the vapor phase. This atmospheric function ceases as soon as the barometric pressure decreases to equal or below the vapor pressure of our body fluids. The water vapor pressure of our body fluids at normal body temperature is about 47 mm Hg. As soon as the barometric pressure decreases to 47 mm Hg or below, our body fluids will "boil." Experiments on warm-blooded animals in a low-pressure chamber, carried out as early as 1935 by Captain H. G. Armstrong,* showed this to be true. This boiling

Medical Problems Encountered with
Decreasing Barometric Pressure

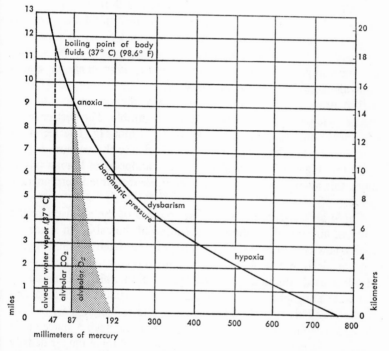

effect is first manifested by the appearance of gas bubbles on the superficial mucous membranes of the mouth and eyes. Later, vapor bubbles appear in the veins, and finally can be seen in the arteries, depending upon the different pressures in these areas of the circula-

* [As Director, Aero Medical Research Laboratory, Wright Field. In the early Thirties then Lieutenant Armstrong had been flight surgeon of the famous 1st Pursuit Group, Army Air Corps. From 1949 to 1954, as major general, he was Surgeon General of the U.S. Air Force.]

tory system. The intrapleural spaces are filled with water vapor—a phenomenon which was called a vaporthorax by F. A. Hitchcock.

There are still a number of questions open in this new field of vacuum pathology. One especially must not be overlooked: the difference between low-pressure, low-temperature boiling as it occurs in the high altitudes and the process of boiling used as a method of preparing food which includes coagulation of the proteins. Recently the term "ebullism," which simply means "bubble formation," has been suggested by J. E. Ward, Jr., for this.

An air pressure of 47 mm Hg is found at 63,000 feet. Above this altitude we lose the vitally important protection of air pressure against profuse unhindered evaporization, just as if we were surrounded by no atmosphere at all, as in space. This is the second and most impressive functional border of the atmosphere, or space-equivalent level within the atmosphere.

The pressure in the vacuum of interplanetary space with one gas particle per cubic centimeter is immeasurable. The best vacuum obtainable on earth is in the order of 10^{-8} mm Hg. The technical vacuum begins with 1 mm Hg. Physiologically the vacuum begins at 47 mm Hg or 63,000 feet. From the standpoint of human physiology this air-pressure condition is equivalent to free interplanetary space.

Cabin pressurization. In the denser zones of the atmosphere the ambient air is used for the pressurization of the cabin. In space we need a new type of cabin, which is pressurized from within, because outside air is not available for compression. It must be a completely closed compartment, a sealed cabin in which a climatically adequate atmosphere for the occupants is artificially created and controlled. This type of cabin has no altitude limits. It is, in fact, *the* space cabin. But it must be emphasized that such a space cabin is required even down to 80,000 feet. At this altitude the air density is only 1/27 of that at sea level. Compressing this thin air to physiologically required levels is beyond the capabilities of present-day compressors. And even if this were possible, the compressed air would attain such a high temperature as to be intolerable for the occupants of the cabin. Therefore, with regard to the necessity of a sealed cabin, space begins at 80,000 feet.

The space-equivalent conditions so far discussed are brought about by the loss of inherent properties of the earth's atmosphere.

With increasing altitude, ingredients of space itself also enter the picture to a greater extent. Finally they create space-equivalent conditions of their own, still within the atmosphere as it is astronomically defined. This group of spacelike conditions is related to the life-protecting filter functions of the atmosphere.

Life-protecting Filter Functions

Cosmic rays. In the lower altitudes we are protected from cosmic rays in their original "space form" and energy by the atmosphere's filtering. In space no such natural protection can be expected.

Cosmic rays in their original form consist of 79 per cent protons, or hydrogen nuclei, the lightest element; 20 per cent alpha particles, or helium nuclei, the second lightest element; and 1 per cent nuclei of heavier (metallic) atoms. These so-called primary cosmic rays possess a very high kinetic energy, which they probably have acquired by accelerations in magnetic fields between the galaxies, star clusters, and cosmic dust clouds.

When these primary cosmic rays enter the atmosphere at a certain density level—about 120,000 feet—they lose their original powerful form and intensity in collisions with air molecules or their atomic nuclei. The collision products, or secondary rays—protons, electrons, mesons, neutrons, etc.—penetrate the lower layers of the atmosphere. They are less powerful than the original primaries, but powerful enough to penetrate several hundred feet of water. So at sea level and in the conventional flight zones we are exposed to only the splinters of these nucleonic bullets from outer space. Above 120,000 feet (in the middle latitudes) the vehicle becomes exposed to the more powerful bombardment of the original cosmic ray particles. Here we are beyond the protecting shield of the atmosphere, as in space. Some variations in cosmic ray exposure will be discussed later.

Ultraviolet radiation. In the lower layers of the atmosphere we are to a great degree protected from the sunburn-producing ultraviolet portion of solar radiation. In space there is no protecting medium.

It is the triatomic oxygen or ozone (O_3), concentrated between 70,000 and 140,000 feet within the atmosphere, that offers a kind of umbrella against ultraviolet radiation by absorbing the larger

Space-Equivalent Levels
of the Atmosphere

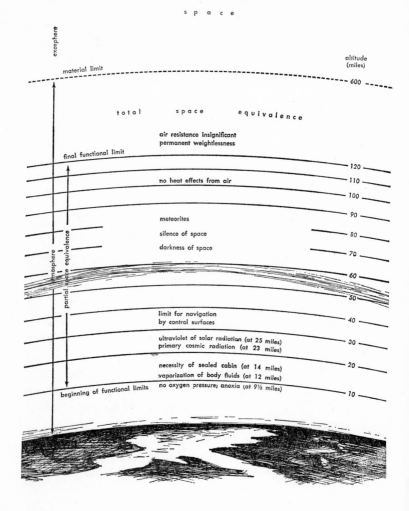

portion of the rays. Beyond 140,000 feet, ultraviolet is found in its full range and intensity as in space.

Visible light. In the denser layers of the atmosphere, visible radiation, or light, is scattered by the air molecules. This scattering produces the so-called skylight, the beautiful blue daylight. Against this bright skylight the stars fade into invisibility. In interplanetary space the particle density is too low for a noticeable scattering effect. In the absence of skylight in space the stars are visible against a dark background at all times, even against a much brighter sun. This strange darkness of space is reached at altitudes of 60 to 80 miles because of the rarefication of the air molecules. This is the transition zone from atmospheric optics to space optics.

Meteors. From ground level we often see meteors in the sky but always at a great distance and great heights. Space is crisscrossed by these pieces of cosmic matter. As soon as meteorites enter the atmosphere, most of them burn out from friction with the air molecules. This takes place at altitudes between 25 and 75 miles. Above this level we are beyond the "meteor safe wall" of the atmosphere, as in space. Variations in this phenomenon are discussed later.

So much for the life-protecting atmospheric filter functions. The absorption of meteorites as a thermodynamic process leads immediately to the mechanical effects and functions of the atmosphere.

Mechanical Effects and Functions

Propagation of sound. A very important mechanical atmospheric function is the propagation of sound. In higher altitudes this property of the air becomes impossible as soon as the free path between the air molecules is in the order of the wave length of sound. The region where this occurs lies between altitudes of 60 and 80 miles. Above this hypoacoustic zone the anacoustic zone or the silence of space begins. There is no sound barrier any more, and the mach number becomes meaningless as in space itself.

Heat. The atmosphere contains, conducts, and transmits heat energy. In space the carrier and transmitter of heat is solar radiation exclusively. In the lower and middle altitudes we must reckon with very high temperatures in the boundary layers around the skin of a very fast flying vehicle, produced by friction with the air molecules. Above 80 to 100 miles altitude, this no longer affects the temperature of the cabin because of decreased heat transfer in air of extremely low density. In this respect this level can also be called the "aerothermodynamic border" of the atmosphere. Above this level there is practically no noticeable thermal interaction between vehicle and environment. The temperature of the cabin's hull is determined exclusively by solar energy, as in interplanetary space.

Support and resistance. The atmosphere provides aerodynamic support for and offers resistance to a fast-moving craft. In space both of these effects are absent. The limit for useful aerodynamic lift and for navigation by means of control surfaces is found as low as thirty miles. Above this line we deal exclusively with ballistics, and navigation by control surfaces has to be replaced by reaction control. Air resistance approaches zero at about 120 miles, even for the fastest-moving vehicle. This is the aerodynamical or, more generally, the mechanical border (H. Haber) between atmosphere and space. When support and resistance by the air vanish, the vehicle and occupants become weightless. This condition in space flight is produced by inertial forces originating in the fast-moving vehicle which, because of their centrifugal direction, counteract the gravitational attraction of the earth. It is, therefore, not a function of the distance from the earth, rather it is the result of the interaction of forces. Weightlessness as it occurs in space flight is therefore a dynamic condition and can be produced everywhere, for short periods of time, even within the atmosphere during ballistic flight maneuvers. But above 120 miles dynamic weightlessness occurs for any length of time.

This analysis of the atmosphere as a functional medium for life and for manned flight is based upon ten atmospheric functions. It reveals the amazing fact that the larger portion of the earth's atmosphere is equivalent to free space. The area in which we encounter one, two, or more but not all factors typical of space must be considered as partially space equivalent. This area begins at 50,000 feet. The area above 120 miles is distinguished by total space equivalence, if we ignore some variations caused by the bulk of the earth itself, its magnetic field, its speed, and its own and reflected radiation.

Summary of Atmospheric Zones

The atmosphere as a material continuum reaches up to 600 miles, but as a functional environment for flight it extends only to 120 miles. Space as a physical environment, with practically all of its space characteristics, reaches down to 120 miles altitude. With some of its physiological effects, space extends down as low as 63,000 or even 50,000 feet. This means that there is a transition zone between atmosphere and space where the functional and physical environments overlap. The well-known classification of the atmosphere in terms of physics must therefore be supplemented by a space-medical one. Based upon the foregoing considerations we can divide the whole atmosphere into four zones:

1. the physiological zone—from sea level to 10,000 feet
2. the physiologically deficient zone—from 10,000 to 50,000 feet
3. the partially space-equivalent zone—from 50,000 feet to 120 miles
4. the totally space-equivalent zone—from 120 miles to about 600 miles.

For the flyer the atmosphere beyond 120 miles is no longer tangible. It is imperceptible. Here it turns into a pseudoatmosphere. The area around the 120-mile level is therefore the *final functional limit of the atmosphere*. Beyond this final functional limit the laws of aerodynamics lose their meaning, and those of celestial mechanisms or astrodynamics become fully effective.

Such is the picture of the physical characteristics of upper atmosphere and of space which we obtain by contrasting them with those found in the lower regions of the atmosphere. These characteristics may be briefly summarized: in space there is no oxygen nor air pressure to keep a man alive, no atmospheric material for the pressurization of the cabin, and no natural protection against meteorites or solar and cosmic radiation. In space we are exposed to the whole range of the electromagnetic radiation spectrum of the sun, from soft X rays of about 10 angstrom in wave length, ultraviolet rays, visible rays, heat rays, and radio waves up to about 10 meters in wave length. We encounter the whole range of cosmic ray particles in their original, primary form and the energy with which they enter our solar system. And there is no material medium in space to support a flying vehicle. But this picture of the physical environment of space would not be complete if we did not consider the variations found in some of its characteristics.

VARIATIONS IN SPACE CHARACTERISTICS

Regional Variations

First, certain regional variations are found in the vicinity of the earth. Space around the earth is considerably different from that found in interplanetary space just as the climate around a house differs somewhat from that found in a nearby open field. The side of a house protects us from wind, rain, or snow, and it offers shadow on a hot, sunny day. Similarly the solid body of the earth protects us on one side from meteorites and cosmic ray particles. Thermal and visible radiation in the vicinity of the earth is strongly influenced by the earth's own and reflected radiation. The regional distribution of ray particles is to a high degree determined by the earth's magnetic field.

Since these rays are charged particles (except the neutrons), they are channeled into the polar regions by the earth's magnetic field, as evidenced by the northern and southern lights (aurora borealis and aurora australis). These displays are caused by light emission from the air molecules and atoms brought into excited states by the bombardment of solar ray particles.

Recently a high-intensity radiation belt consisting of protons and electrons beginning at an altitude of 600 miles above the equator and extending to several earth radii has been discovered by J. van Allen by means of the satellites Explorer I and III. Its location is related to the earth's magnetic field in which the ray particles are stored.

So far we have confined ourselves to the space in the vicinity of the earth and to the area of the earth's orbital distance from the sun. We find regional variations in the properties of space on a much larger scale when considering the whole distance range from Mercury to Jupiter or Pluto. These variations are the result of the differences in solar electromagnetic radiation which follow the inverse-square law in relation to distance from the sun. The differences in the radiation climate of space are enormous and involve all four important sections of the solar electromagnetic spectrum: infrared rays as the main heat rays, visible rays or light, chemically active ultraviolet rays, and X rays.

Heat rays. As is generally known the intensity of the heat-carrying rays (essentially infrared) is measured by the solar constant. This is the amount of heat irradiated upon unit of area per unit of time. At the top of the earth's atmosphere this value is roughly 2 gram-calories per 1 cm^2 per 1 minute. At noon on the earth's surface it is never higher than one half of this value because of heat absorption by atmospheric water vapor and carbon dioxide. At the orbital distance of Venus the solar constant increases to nearly two times its value at the orbital distance of Earth. At the orbital distance of Mercury it increases to nearly 6 times as much. At the distance of Mars it decreases to less than one half, at Jupiter's distance to about 1/25, and at the mean distance of Pluto it drops to 1/1600 of the terrestrial value. These variations in the thermal irradiance from the sun in different parts of the space in our solar system are of tremendous importance with regard to the climatization of the space cabin.

A vehicle designed for an operation into the region of Venus is not fitted for an excursion to Jupiter. And a spacecraft entering the intramercurian space would inevitably run into a kind of solar heat barrier, as symbolized by the legendary flight of Icarus and as actually demonstrated by a real object named Icarus. This Icarus is an asteroid discovered by Walter Baade at Mount Palomar in 1949, about one mile in diameter. It makes a trip around the sun in 409 days. The orbit is so eccentric that at the perihelion the asteroid is only 16.8 million miles from the sun, halfway between Mercury and the sun. At that distance, its surface temperature for a few days must be above 500° C. At its aphelion—in the region between Mars and Jupiter—the surface temperature of Icarus should drop below the freezing point of water.

There are three other asteroids—Hermes, Apollo, and Adonis— which undergo similar but not quite so drastic temperature changes along their eccentric orbits, and which have their perihelion between Venus and Mercury. The most spectacular examples in this respect are, of course, the comets, which—hibernating in the remote regions of Jupiter and Pluto as icy mountains of dirt, frozen water, ammonia, and methane—come to life by exhibiting gigantic tails caused by solar radiation as soon as they approach closer than three astronomical units to the sun.

It must be added that solar thermal radiation has also a decisive influence upon the atmospheric temperatures of the planets.

Light. Another important property of our environment is visible radiation or light. In space the sky is dark everywhere because of the absence of a light-scattering atmospheric medium. The illumination from the sun varies considerably with the distance. Solar illuminance is usually expressed in foot-candles. At noon on a sunny day at middle latitudes at the bottom of the atmosphere, solar illuminance is roughly 10,000 foot-candles. At the top of the atmosphere it is 13,000 foot-candles. This light intensity in space increases to about 26,000 foot-candles at the solar distance of Venus, and to nearly 80,000 foot-candles near Mercury. It decreases to about 6500 foot-candles at the Martian orbit, to about 500 foot-candles at Jupiter's orbit, and to about 8 foot-candles in the remote region of Pluto.

This consideration of the heat rays and the visible rays or light indicates that we observe enormous regional variations in the sun's thermal effectiveness and illuminance within the space of our planetary system.

Ultraviolet and X rays. The same can be said of the ultraviolet part and the X-ray range of the solar spectrum. But even for the orbital region of the earth, considerable gaps exist in our knowledge of these phenomena. These may be bridged eventually by recordings in artificial satellites and interplanetary probes.

It may be added that the chemically very active ultraviolet is held responsible for the different chemical composition of the atmospheres of the inner planets and the outer planets. The former are basically oxygen and/or oxidized atmospheres, the latter are hydrogen atmospheres.

Temporal Variations

The regional differences in the radiation climate in our solar system are not static. Rather they show temporal variations because of variations in the activity of the sun. The latter are frequent and occur in the form of giant flares and eruptions. These phenomena on the sun's surface, associated with sunspots, are characterized by intensified electromagnetic radiations (ultraviolet) and by the ejections of huge amounts of ray particles (electrons, protons). As already mentioned, the latter make themselves noticeable in gigantic polar lights within our atmosphere at altitudes from 600 miles down to about 60 miles. During the period of such solar events, according to Hermann Schaefer, the radiation intensity in the extra-atmospheric polar regions of the earth may reach values considerably higher than during the time of a quiet sun.

It is generally known that the sunspot cycle is of an eleven-year duration. The consideration of this temporal pattern may be important for scheduling space operations.

Also a man in a space vehicle may encounter a surprise when he runs into the path of a disintegrated comet. Such a path is characterized by streams or swarms of macrometeorites, micrometeorites, and dust, all remnants of the perished comet. If the earth crosses one of these paths we observe the spectacle of a meteor shower.

Space as a physical environment is essentially a radiation environment with very thinly dispersed matter. In contrast, the atmosphere is essentially a material environment with attenuated radiation. Emptiness permeated by radiations of a broad intensity range and temporal fluctuations and spiced with meteoric pepper is the environment with which an astronaut is faced unless he is protected. Space medicine, in close cooperation with astronomy and space technology, must and will provide this protection.

PART II: SPACE-MEDICAL CHARACTERISTICS

The successful development in rocketry since the ending of World War II represents an achievement of revolutionary significance in the history of mankind. It has opened wide the gates into space. The conquest of space, however, will take the course of a step-by-step evolution just as did progress from the first simple, manually operated electrostatic machine to the huge electric power plant of today. Paralleling this step-by-step evolution of space flight, the medical problems will become more numerous and complex.

We shall discuss primarily the various stages of manned space operations that are already realized or may be expected in the immediate or remote future. Secondly, we shall briefly outline the increasing complexity of the medical problems associated with the technicological developments in space flight. This will afford a panorama of the grandiose adventure into space as visualized by the space doctor. Too, it may show us where we stand today and what is about to come.

BASES FOR CLASSIFICATION OF SPACE OPERATIONS

A classification of the various kinds of space operations can be based on the properties of the environment, the characteristics of motion, and the destination of the flight.

From Atmosphere to Space

On an earlier page we have seen that at about 10 miles altitude the atmosphere begins to become partially space equivalent. This condition progresses to total space equivalence at about 120 miles, if we ignore some peculiarities found in the vicinity of the earth. This is an important fact, because the lower portion of the partially space-equivalent zone is already the routine zone for high-performance jet planes; and rocket-powered craft, as well as the ultrahigh balloon flights, penetrate in rapid progression higher and higher into these regions. These kinds of space-equivalent flight represent the transitional stage from present-day flight operations to true space operations or astronautics. True space operations are conceivable only above the mechanical border of the atmosphere, i.e., above 120 miles. This region is therefore the dividing line between aeronautics and astronautics. Here we leave behind us the realm of aerodynamics and enter that of celestial mechanics, or the region of Kepler's laws.

Spatiography

To define or classify by categories the possible space operational developments beyond the aerodynamically effective atmosphere, we need a topographical description of extra-atmospheric space—a kind of geography of space or a "spatiography" which subdivides free space into certain areas, using certain "borders" or differences in the environmental properties as demarcations. At first glance such an attempt seems difficult in an environment where emptiness is the rule and where concentration of matter in the form of celestial bodies is the exception. However, there are several possibilities. The simplest procedure is to use the orbits of the moon and planets as topographical demarcation lines, and to speak of cislunar space, translunar space, cis-Martian space, trans-Martian space, and cis-Venusian and trans-Venusian space, as suggested by Krafft Ehricke. Thus cislunar space is the region between the moon's orbit and the earth's orbit. In all these cases, the earth is the point of reference. If the sun is the point of reference, the prefixes "intra" and "extra" are common in astronomy. The intra-Mercurian space, for instance, is the area between the orbit of Mercury and the sun. All these orbits are theoretical topographical lines distinguished by the astronomical fact that they are the paths of celestial bodies. They offer a simple and easily understandable means of subdividing interplanetary space.*

Environmental Conditions of Space

Of practical and vital importance to the astronaut are differences in the environmental conditions of space itself. To begin with, the space in the vicinity of a celestial body is different from free interplanetary space. It shows peculiarities caused by the mere presence of the celestial body, by the optical properties of its surface, and by forces originating from it and extending into space. In the vicinity of the earth, for instance, we are protected from half of the meteorites and cosmic rays by the solid terrestrial body beneath us. The thermal space environment near the earth is strongly influenced by radiation—both the earth's own and that which it reflects. Also the sunlight reflected from the earth's surface and clouds must be taken into account. A special peculiarity in the vicinity of the earth is the regional distribution of solar and cosmic ray particles, which are channeled into the polar regions by the geomagnetic field or stored therein above the equatorial regions forming a high-intensity radiation belt. If we wish to emphasize all these environmental differences of space in the vicinity of the earth, we might call the region around the earth up to several earth radii "circumterrestrial space." Similarly we can also speak of circum-Martian space, circum-Venusian space, and circumlunar space.

Gravity-based Spatiography: Gravispheres

Large spatial areas may also be conveniently designated according to the gravitational forces of celestial bodies. The astronomer

---

* [Ignoring the galactic movement of the sun, which "interplanetary space" may be assumed to accompany *in toto* as a frame of reference.]

is primarily interested in the field concept of these forces and in the mutual gravitational attraction of celestial bodies in order to explain their orbital motions, the occurrence of perturbations, and tidal effects. A space vehicle, however, has practically no gravitational field of its own, its attractive force being in the order of one billionth of one g. In space flight, gravitational attraction is consequently such a one-sided affair that only the gravitational force of the attracting celestial body needs be considered.

The question now arises as to how far into surrounding space this force—or more precisely, the gravitational control of a celestial body over a space vehicle—extends. Here we arrive at an important concept in astronautics, the "sphere of gravitational influence," which may better be defined as the "sphere of predominant gravitational attraction." The earth's sphere of predominant gravitational attraction, as far as its satellite-holding power is concerned, extends about one million miles from the earth's center. Beyond this distance the gravitational attraction of the sun becomes predominant for a space vehicle. After crossing the neutral zone outward from Earth a vehicle would be "captured" by the sun and follow a path around it comparable to the heliocentric orbits of the planets. The earth could continue to exert some influence upon the vehicle's orbit but only in the form of perturbations. Theoretically the earth's gravitational field extends to infinity.

Within the sphere of the earth's predominant gravitational influence the moon exerts a gravitational subsphere of its own, and the balancing line between the two bodies lies at a distance of about 34,000 miles from the moon. The earth and the moon, like the other planets and their satellites, move together in the gravitational confine of the sun. Because of the importance of the spheres of predominant gravitational attraction in astronautics, it might be advisable to call them "gravispheres," in analogy to "atmosphere." The atmosphere is an extension of a planet into its surround in the form of gaseous matter. The gravisphere then is an extension of a planet into its surround in the form of dynamical gravitational forces. Thus we can speak of a terrestrial gravisphere, lunar gravisphere, Martian gravisphere, Venusian gravisphere, etc., and finally, of the giant solar gravisphere which blends far beyond Pluto with the gravitational no man's land between the stars. The spatial extension of the gravispheres of the other planets is, of course, different from that of the terrestrial gravisphere, depending on their gravities and distances from the sun. This subdivision of our solar space is based exclusively on dynamics.

Characteristics of Motion

The dynamical aspect of space leads us logically to the characteristics of motion in space operations. Basically, all space operations consist of three phases: the active (power-on) phase during launching, the passive (power-off) phase of coasting, and the atmospheric re-entry phase.

Coasting: orbital velocities. Here we are concerned only with the coasting phase, because this kind of motion gives space flight a unique characteristic. Above the mechanically effective atmosphere (120 miles), coasting can take place in a closed path or orbit (circular or elliptic) around the earth only if the vehicle has the required velocity. Such velocities—the so-called orbital velocities— are reached when the gravitational (centripetal) attraction of the earth is counterbalanced by the inertial effects of the moving vehicle. The result is the state of weightlessness. Near the earth's surface—if the earth had no atmosphere—the orbital velocity would be 17,668 mph. With increasing altitude the orbital velocity decreases because of diminishing geogravitational attraction. The moon, 240,000 miles away from the earth, has an orbital velocity of 0.7 mi/sec. But it should be emphasized that, in contrast to the decrease of the orbital velocity with altitude, pushing or projecting a vehicle to a higher orbit requires a higher amount of initial energy. Consequently a greater projection velocity is required to attain the higher potential energy of the higher orbit in the gravitational field.

The orbital velocities just explained are examples of the first category of astronautical velocities. This category can also be applied to orbital flights around the moon, around other planets, or around the sun. The orbital velocity of the earth around the sun, for instance, is 18.6 miles per second.

Escape velocities. If the kinetic energy or projection velocity of a vehicle is high enough, the vehicle may leave the earth's sphere of predominant gravitational attraction in an elongated ellipse and enter the area in space where the sun's gravitational attraction prevails. The velocity required for a rocket to cross this balancing border line is called the "velocity of escape." This velocity brings a vehicle into an open hyperbolic path with regard to the earth, but into a closed, circular, or elliptic orbit with regard to the sun—a heliocentric orbit.

Orbital Velocity and Periods of Revolution of Satellites at Varying Altitudes

altitude (miles)	orbital velocity (mph)	period of revolution (minutes)	altitude (kilometers)
1000	15,788	118.5	1600
800	16,116	111.3	1280
600	16,466	104.5	960
500	16,649	101.1	800
400	16,839	97.7	640
300	17,035	94.4	480
200	17,238	91.1	320
120	17,449	87.8	182
near sea level	17,668	84.6	near sea level

The values near sea level are theoretical because of the presence of an atmosphere

Escape Velocity from the Moon and the Planets

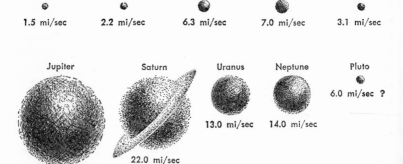

Moon	Mercury	Venus	Earth	Mars
1.5 mi/sec	2.2 mi/sec	6.3 mi/sec	7.0 mi/sec	3.1 mi/sec

Jupiter — 37.0 mi/sec

Saturn — 22.0 mi/sec

Uranus — 13.0 mi/sec

Neptune — 14.0 mi/sec

Pluto — 6.0 mi/sec ?

planets are in order of distance from the sun

The escape velocity from the earth belongs to the second category of astronautical velocities. To escape from the earth into the sun's gravisphere requires a velocity of 25,000 mph or 7 mi/sec. Escape into the moon's gravisphere requires only slightly less. Escape from the moon requires 1.5 mi/sec, from Mars 3.1 mi/sec, from Venus 6.3 mi/sec, and from Jupiter 37 mi/sec. The escape velocity from the earth is the prerequisite for lunar, interplanetary, and planetary space operations. These operations may bring the astronaut into regions of space with ecologically different radiational properties or to other celestial bodies with strange atmospheric environments.

EVOLUTIONARY STAGES OF SPACE OPERATIONS

Space operations may be classified in accord with the properties of the environment, the characteristics of motion and pertinent velocities, and the destination of the flight. The evolution of human flight—as it is today, as it may be tomorrow, or as it might be in a more or less remote future—we may then see in four stages:

1. For the past fifty years we have been in the stage of atmospheric flight. Its characteristics are very well known: propeller and jet propulsion; the lower regions of the atmosphere as the flight zones; pressurized cabins; subsonic and supersonic speeds; generally normal gravitational conditions; distances of geographic dimensions; and flight durations of fractions of a day. Status of the craft: airplane.

2. We have now entered the next stage: space-equivalent flight. The characteristics are: jet and rocket propulsion; the partially space-equivalent regions of the atmosphere; sealed cabins; supersonic and hypersonic speeds; trajectory, suborbital; the gravity pattern—multiples of g, reduced g, and nullified g; operational range of geographic dimensions; flight duration from minutes to several hours. Status of the craft: airplane plus projectile. The craft of the century series and especially those of the X-class—like the Bell X-2, the North American X-15, and the Dynasoar type— are the prototypes belonging to this stage of space-equivalent flight or space-equivalent operations.

3. As soon as it is possible to push a manned vehicle into an orbit with orbital velocity, we will have manned orbital flight or manned satellite flight. The characteristics are: totally space-

equivalent regions of the atmosphere or circumterrestrial space; sealed cabins; orbital velocities in a geocentric orbit or in the earth's gravisphere; the gravity pattern—multiples of g and long durations of nullified g. Status of the vehicle: biosatellite. The smaller research satellites with and without animals in the International Geophysical Year are the first step in the direction of manned satellite operations or circumterrestrial space operations.

4.   The final stage will follow as soon as the attainment of escape velocity makes escape operations possible beyond the gravitational control of the earth. The characteristics of gravispheric escape operations are similar to those of satellite operations except that the vehicle now enters the gravispheres of other celestial bodies and may circumnavigate the moon or other planets, or may even land on them. In this final stage of space operations the vehicle will have attained spacecraft status.

There may be some transitional stages between these four basic stages of space operations, such as satelloid flight, i.e., a powered satellite (as suggested by Krafft Ehricke) for flights in the regions below the mechanical border * of the atmosphere.

This classification gives a realistic perspective of the stage at which we stand today and of the developing possibilities we may expect in the future. The timetable of that development will be determined by space technology, but in any event space medicine must and will be prepared to meet and cope with all these possibilities.

SPECTRUM OF MEDICAL PROBLEMS

The medical problems in space operations are manifold. Some of them are fully encountered in the preliminary stage of space-equivalent flight. They become more and more complex in advanced operations, and the accent of importance may shift from one to another in different space operations.

In the space-equivalent phase of space operations, the regeneration of the cabin's air will offer no problem. Cosmic rays and meteorites are of no concern. The accent may rest on the increased importance of the gravity pattern—acceleration during launching and deceleration during re-entry—and on the landing maneuver.

In manned satellite operations involving hundreds of revolutions,

---

* Concept advanced by Heinz Haber.

the regeneration of the cabin's air by physicochemical means and other climatic measures will demand increased considerations. The same may be said about zerogravity, day-night cycling, and some psychological problems. Cosmic rays and meteorites too may enter the picture. The high-intensity radiation belt above the equatorial regions demands special attention. Return from the orbit will be a problem of primary concern in addition to those already mentioned.

In gravispheric escape operations into heliocentric orbits and via transfer orbits into the gravitational territory of another planet, the time element becomes dominant. In these operations new methods for regeneration of the air by means of natural or artificial photosynthesis may have to replace the chemical type. Recycling of body wastes will be necessary to ease logistics. The long duration of the flight will increasingly pose psychological problems resulting from isolation and confinement. And finally, landing on another planet may open the gates to a new astrobiological world with a strange climate and perhaps with strange flora and fauna. But the astronaut's first concern must be for his survival on his return from this particular celestial body—unless he should find staying there less strenuous than the return trip to that far-distant blue and green planet "Terra" orbiting between Venus and Mars.

School of Aviation Medicine, USAF

CHAPTER 4

Biomedical Aspects of Space Flight

Brigadier General Don Flickinger

Not more than 20-odd years ago there were many who stated categorically that man had reached his tolerance limits in the safe operation of current aircraft. Bioscientists and engineers combined their efforts to prove the fallacy of these predictions, and we may be sure they will again disprove the dire predictions now being voiced on the inhabitability of space for man. This chapter attempts a review of the biomedical problems of manned space flight, particularly those which appear most pertinent to the safety and success of the initial circumterrestrial orbiting missions.*

Metabolic Requirements in Closed Environments

Our past work in oxygen systems and pressurized cabins and cockpits in high-performance aircraft, both military and civilian, has provided us with an excellent basis for the task of developing a complete life-support capsule capable of sustaining a human payload in the vacuum of space with the necessary degree of reliability. Even in this area, however, despite this basis of knowledge and technology, there are many requirements for augmented efforts and new approaches.

Standard information on metabolic requirements is not directly applicable to the space capsule, and new data must be collected on man in an isolated closed environment concerning oxygen consumption, CO_2 production, water loss, and the excretion of metabolic wastes through the skin and expired air. Simulated space chambers at both the Air Force and Navy Schools of Aviation Medicine have been vigorously prosecuting this problem, and the man-carrying capsules of the Air Force's Manhigh balloon flights have provided an excellent and practical means of testing both hypotheses and equipment.

When the metabolic requirements that results thus far have indicated are balanced against the payload available for biomedical needs, we find that our most economic components can maintain a livable capsule atmosphere for two to four days for a single oc-

---

* It should be pointed out that many of the estimates made are ones of personal conjecture and, therefore if proven false under future operational conditions, should not reflect unfavorably upon the large body of dedicated and competent life scientists who are currently engaged in the study and resolution of these problems. Many of our biomedical requirements and tolerance criteria being furnished to the engineers are based upon extrapolations from past experiences, none of which either singly or in combination contained the full spectrum flight stresses. For this reason, therefore, the first few flights will indicate, in a sense, where we erred in the extension of our data. It is, of course, our earnest desire that these errors will not occur in those biomedical parameters which are vital to the safe return of a healthy space explorer.

cupant. Possible state-of-the-art improvements in existing componentry in the form of liquid-oxygen systems capable of functioning in the weightless state with little if any boil-off, a reversible method of scrubbing the carbon dioxide, plus a closed system for water recycling might extend this time to as much as two to four weeks. Beyond that we are faced with the necessity of making a major breakthrough in the form of a completely closed regenerative ecological system. This requirement is truly one of the major challenges which we face in space operations.

At this point we must also consider that our knowledge of space physiology is far from complete, though not too unassuring, as it concerns the effects on man of spending days or weeks at a time in a hypobaric environment equivalent to 25,000 feet altitude breathing 100% oxygen (though at near-normal partial pressure). One could well ask why we do not insist upon a complete duplication of the sea-level environment in the space capsule to begin with and avoid these worries. The answer again depends upon payload in orbit and the off-the-shelf componentry available. An increase from five pounds per square inch to one atmosphere pressure in the capsule requires an increase of three to five times in the weight of the basic structure. And if we ask for a true replica of the composition of sea-level air in our closed environment, we are faced with a requirement for a two-gas demand regulator, with each operation at different partial pressures. This is not yet to be had.

Here consideration quite logically turns towards natural adaptation and acclimatization and to the possible uses of drugs to precondition our space man to live easier and function better in the type of environment which we can afford him. A great amount of excellent work has been done in high-altitude laboratories throughout the world on the problem of adaptation and acclimatization to constant low oxygen pressures. There is no question but that acclimatization does occur. Through certain histochemical changes, the vital organs develop a measurably greater capability for efficient functioning under suboptimal conditions. Whether or not in actual practice the time spent in acquiring this acclimatization, two to three weeks, would be worth the effort in terms of appreciable gains in safety of performance is a matter still open to question.

Certainly, under the best of conditions, the relatively narrow limits in man's ability to adapt to major alterations in his habitual physical environment would lead us to base our hopes upon the future improvements in structures, design, and componentry to provide a completely livable, long-duration environment in space.

At least brief mention should be made of the thermal fluxes to be expected and the possible methods available to maintain adequate thermal balance within the capsule. Many estimates have been made of the temperatures in orbit and during re-entry, and considerable useful data have been accumulated from earth and nose-cone experiments. Upon superficial examination of these estimates we are very easily and quickly lulled into complacency regarding the extent and complexity of the temperature-control problem, yet many of us are extremely chary of writing it off so glibly. We do not really know all that we need to about space-heat relationships, particularly as they concern such measurements as solar loads on a stabilized orbital vehicle, the accurate time-altitude variations of the earth's albedo, and what heat-drains into the space sink can be expected under various conditions. Lacking this necessary information, we have assumed that the major problem will be heat loss rather than heat retention and that the major heat source will be one third man and two thirds his supporting equipment. These heats can be fairly accurately predicted, and in presently contemplated systems are being dealt with by means of a water-ice heat sink. By means of a five-stage heat exchanger this system handles about 1100 BTUs per pound of ice but suffers from excessive weight penalty, appreciable pressure resistance, and relatively high power requirements. A more promising avenue is offered by a recirculating working fluid in contact with the space heat sink, though the inaction of this system during the re-entry phase causes some mild concern.

To sum the heat problem up then, we can say that the present estimates of temperature range during orbit and re-entry are well within long-term comfortable and short-term livable limits. We feel that many additional data need to be collected on orbital and re-entry thermodynamics, after which some high-energy heat engineering must be carried out before completely effective temperature control becomes a reality.

Anthropological Aspects of Capsule Design

The anthropological techniques used in space-cabin design are in all respects almost identical to the techniques used in the design of present aircraft. That is to say, the space cabin must be laid out in such a way that the occupant has the most efficient possible use of his work space. He must be able to reach and recover any items that could stray under zero-g conditions, and these items must be minimized. He must be properly oriented in his cabin with respect to directions of flight and to the earth.

Orientation in a space cabin must be attained for both physiological and psychological reasons. It is of primary importance that the pilot be maintained in the optimum position, or close to it, for taking g during those portions of the flight in which he is enduring massive acceleration loads. This optimum consists of a supine position with a back angle of 20° to 25° to the horizontal, the thighs vertical, and the lower legs 5° above horizontal. For pilot comfort the position of the thighs may be varied 20° without a serious loss of protection. During the orbital phase of the flight it is desirable for psychological reasons that the pilot face towards the direction of flight with his feet towards the earth. This will give him a reference, with his earth-bound experience, to replace his gravity orientation. It is further desirable that he not move more than a few degrees in rotation with respect to his surroundings within the capsule, or severe disorientation will most probably result. On later flights it will be desirable to determine the effects of disorientation in zero-g by deliberately including it, but it had better be avoided for the first few flights at least.

Another anthropological factor which the space-cabin designer must consider is the personal protective equipment of the occupant, such as a pressure suit to protect him against a decompression emergency and provide emergency backup in failure of the life-support system. To cite a specific example of how such equipment will alter the specifications, let us consider the use of the USAF MC-2 full pressure suit. The subject's sitting height is increased 1.5 inches with the addition of the helmet. When the suit is inflated, another 1.3 inches is added to his seated height. His elbow breadth increases 2.8 inches with the donning of the suit and 4.6 inches when the suit is inflated. An absolute minimum hatch size for entry and exit into the capsule is 27 by 17 inches.

One anthropological factor that is not generally understood but is immensely significant to the space-cabin designer is not a characteristic of the new environment in which he will place the pilot but rather is a characteristic of the pilot himself.

In much of the popular literature and in all too many serious proposals the pilot of the first manned satellite is described as a lightweight, short individual. This, it is said, is due to the enormous penalty that must be paid in terms of extra fuel for every pound of pilot weight placed into orbit. Only later when space flight becomes routine, these authors say, will pilots of heroic stature roam the space lanes.

The fact is that the first satellite pilots must be a thoroughly picked group. We must screen our personnel to find those who are experienced observers, who have demonstrated qualities of cool-headedness and resourcefulness in tight situations, who have good intelligence, who can tolerate various extremes of physical punishment, and who are stable, calm, and confident. We must reject those who, although able to give a good account of themselves, do so primarily to prove something to themselves or the world. Then we must narrow this select pool of potential satellite pilots down to those six to ten who are best fit to undertake such a mission.

Let us examine more closely the group of people with whom we would begin our search. We could not search the entire United States Air Force to find our potential satellite crew. Strategic Air Command, Tactical Air Command, and the other operational commands could hardly consent to our pulling off some two hundred of their best pilots for a testing program. The search would doubtless start in Air Research and Development Command itself. Even considering all the test pilots, balloonists, parachutists, flight surgeons, etc., within the Air Research and Development Command, it would take a rash man to estimate a list of much more than a hundred subjects with satellite pilot potential. The elimination of ninety per cent of these for one reason or another would probably be all too easy. Thus it can be seen that satellite crewmen will be at a premium for many years, just as X-15 pilots, Manhigh balloonists, etc., are today.

The problem now begins to take shape. We must select our crewmen on considerations which leave optimum height and weight fairly far down on the list. If we now look at the anthropometric characteristics of the population defined earlier in terms of desirable attributes (and called by the Air Force the "Tigers") we notice a very interesting phenomenon. *The "Tiger" population of the Air Force is significantly larger and heavier than average.*

For comparison with the "normal" height and weight distribution of USAF flying personnel (based on Hertzberg, *et al., Anthropometry of Flying Personnel, 1950*), some 200 "Tigers" were selected from various sources: past and present Air Force record holders, jet fighter aces, past and present rocket plane pilots, special-mission flying personnel, skilled parachutists, balloonists, and test pilots. The taller and heavier man made up a disproportionate amount of the group. It is important to note that extra height tended to be a handicap for most of these men in their jobs, that is, they succeeded in spite of their greater size and not directly because of it.

We find that we can obtain the greatest number of potential subjects for an adjustment in height of two inches if we design our space cabin for the range between so-called 50th and 75th percentile. If we were to restrict our design to the individual in the 5th percentile or below, we would have only two per cent of the "Tiger" population to work with. With a total available population in the neighborhood of one hundred, we couldn't even start a man-in-space program. If we restricted our design to the 25th percentile and below, we would have 17% of the group to select from. Again, this is hardly enough, with any sort of realistic washout rate. It turns out that men of "average" height or less comprise only 35% of the selected sample, and that we must include the 80th-percentile man in our design to have two thirds of the population available.

When we examine the "Tiger" weight distribution in the sample, we see the picture is only slightly better, with the average or lighter than average individual comprising only 39% of the total. Considering the 11 rocket-plane pilots of past, present, and future flights for whom data were available (Armstrong, Bridgeman, Crossfield, Everest, Kincheloe, McKay, Rushworth, Walker, A. White, R. White, and Yeager), only one falls below the 25th percentile range in height (20th percentile) and he is in the 28th percentile in weight. One other falls below the 50th percentile in height, and two fall below in weight. All the rest exceed the standard 50th-percentile man in most critical dimensions. And this is in a profession with a premium on small size, due to extremely cramped cockpits.

All this is not to say that a good average or small man is not as good or better than a good big man. Indeed from the standpoint of the designer, the smaller the man, the better. It is just that the odds are very good that the first men into space will be fairly husky specimens. This is simply another problem for the space-cabin designer which will diminish in seriousness proportionately to the speed of its recognition.

Measurements

Because of the great potential risk and large investment in any manned satellite program, regardless of orbital altitude and duration, biological instrumentation must have high priority in the design of early manned satellites. Only as manned satellites become more reliable and sophisticated, as time in orbit and orbital altitudes increase and as space flight becomes more routine, will the need for thorough biological measurements of the crew diminish.

As we are investigating some totally unknown areas of biology at tremendous expense, we shall wish the maximum amount of biological information per flight, and we shall need information that will be meaningful for future flight. Next, because we are investigating a potentially hazardous area, we will require the maximum amount of usable information on the pilot's actual and potential condition at all times during the flight. This is so that we can terminate the experiment within the time required to ensure safe recovery of our volunteer.

Biological instrumentation falls then into two functional categories: information for the record and safety-of-flight information. Information for the record will be environmental, such as cabin humidity and acceleration; psychological, such as response to tracking and reasoning tests; physiological, such as skin temperature and galvanic skin response; and general, such as visual appearance and recorded comments. Safety-of-flight information consists of environmental data such as cabin pressure, the partial pressures of oxygen and carbon dioxide, cabin air temperature, and oxygen and

THE ADVENTURE OF SPACE

The "Big A" roars, poised at the instant of flight for the black firmament of space. On 18 December 1958 the U.S. Air Force precisely steered its Atlas Intercontinental Ballistic Missile by ground control into orbit round the earth. Eighty-five feet tall and weighing 8600 pounds, the new satellite was as big as a Pullman car. In Air Force research centers the multiplex secrets of putting man safely into space are painstakingly pursued.

The Climb to Altitude

Since the Wright brothers first broke free from the ground in powered flight, the airplane has climbed ever higher into aerospace. The Air Force's P-51, the best fighter of World War II, fought in the 400-mph class at 35,000 feet, higher by 15,000 feet than peak operational altitudes of World War I. Jet and rocket engines then quickly broke through the old speed barriers and reached high for the thinnest edge of sustaining air. ¶ With a liquid-propellant rocket engine that developed a thrust of 6000 pounds, the USAF's experimental X-1 became on 14 October 1947 the first plane to fly faster than the speed of sound (763 miles an hour at sea level). ¶ In 1956 the X-2, powered by a rocket engine of 15,000 pounds thrust, reached an altitude of some 126,000 feet, or just under 24 miles, and a speed exceeding 2000 mph at about 70,000 feet. ¶ Current holder of the world's speed and altitude records for operational aircraft is the new Air Force fighter, the F-104C, with official marks of 1404 mph and 91,243 feet, the very fringe of space. The razor-blade wings of F-104 are so sharp-edged that sheaths are fitted to protect ground crews. ¶ Sustained endurance at space-equivalent altitudes was demonstrated on 19–20 August 1957 by the USAF Manhigh II balloon

P-51

X-1

X-2

F-104

ascent which took Major David Simons in a sealed cabin to 102,000 feet. ¶ Much expert opinion sees the prototype of the manned spacecraft in the rocket aircraft with its capability for aerodynamic control upon re-entry rather than in the ballistic missile. First shown in October 1958, the X-15 is built to attain speeds of over 3600 mph and altitudes above 100 miles. The X-15 will permit manned exploration of problems of aerodynamic heating, stability, and control, and the physiological and psychological effects of hypersonic spaceflight. Launching weight is 31,275 pounds, and the rocket engine is capable of over 50,000 pounds of thrust.

Manhigh II ascent from mine crater

The X-15

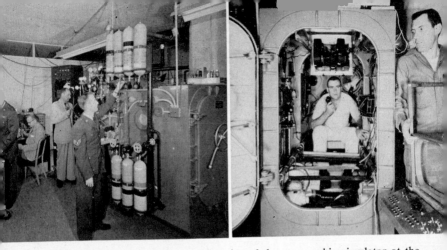

The Space Cabin. Exterior and interior of the space cabin simulator at the School of Aviation Medicine, USAF. Cramped in the 3-by-5-foot interior Airman First Class Donald Farrell duplicated in a week-long "flight" the living experiences, save weightlessness, of confinement during an actual space operation. The ground-control and monitoring stations must be constantly manned during a simulated flight to maintain the gaseous environment, to record physiological and psychological data, and to safeguard the subject's health and well-being. The artist's drawing below displays the complexity of the real space capsule hoisted aloft by the Manhigh II balloon.

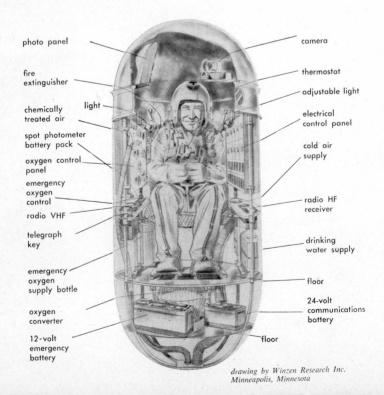

photo panel

fire extinguisher

chemically treated air

light

spot photometer battery pack

oxygen control panel

emergency oxygen control

radio VHF

telegraph key

emergency oxygen supply bottle

oxygen converter

12-volt emergency battery

camera

thermostat

adjustable light

electrical control panel

cold air supply

radio HF receiver

drinking water supply

floor

24-volt communications battery

floor

drawing by Winzen Research Inc.
Minneapolis, Minnesota

Ham dinner at simulated 40,000 feet in a low-pressure chamber. A member of Aero Medical Laboratory's nutrition section prepares to enjoy a spaceman's square meal. His left hand holds aside the hinged port of his facepiece as he inserts the plastic tube containing the food.

Decelerative forces comparable to those of re-entry into the earth's atmosphere are studied with a subject garbed in the XMC-2 full-pressure suit on the platform of the Wright Air Development Center's centrifuge. Problems of body control under changing support are analyzed by standing the subject on an air-bearing, revolving platform.

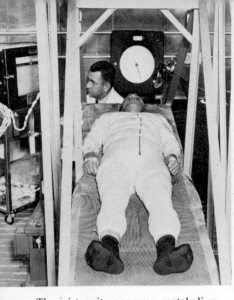

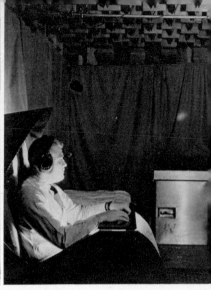

Thermist suit measures metabolism, skin temperature, and body weight during thermal stress tests at the Aero Medical Laboratory. Subject is weighed before and after thermal experiments to measure moisture loss.

Isolation test. Locked in a light-tight, sound-proof chamber, the subject remains as long as he can to study reaction to long periods of complete isolation. Food in refrigerator at background is coded on the packages for identification in the dark.

Thirty-g stop. As the Holloman Air Force Base rocket sled brakes to a crash stop, the test subject is squeezed by pressures of thirty times the pull of gravity at the surface of the earth. A space man will have to survive forces of only 7 to 8 g's at rocket take-off.

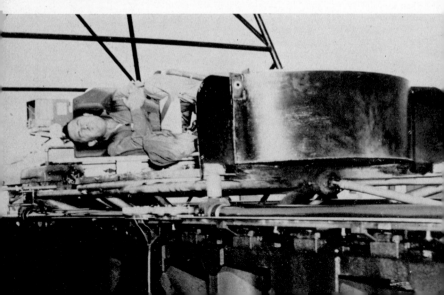

Motion picture scenes of two mice in rotating drum after separation from the Aerobee III. Left, during subgravity the normal mouse (see page 119) floats disorientatedly and the abnormal mouse, with otoliths removed, clings to a hurdle and retains orientation. Right, during parachute descent, at the end of free fall, both mice resume normal activity.

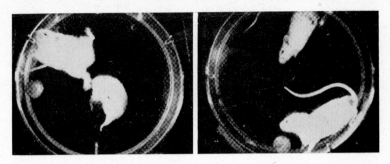

Bubbles, the floating cat. Dr. Siegfried Gerathewohl watches his pet float in some confusion around the cockpit of a School of Aviation Medicine F-94C aircraft during parabolic flight to experience brief periods of weightlessness. Released upside down during the weightless period, Bubbles turned slowly and tumbled out of control. The well-known propensity of cats to land on four feet had disappeared when Bubbles' righting reflex delayed or failed completely.

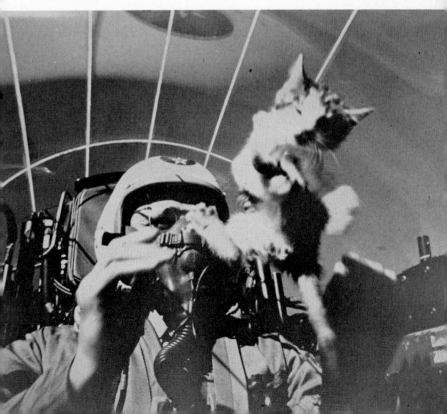

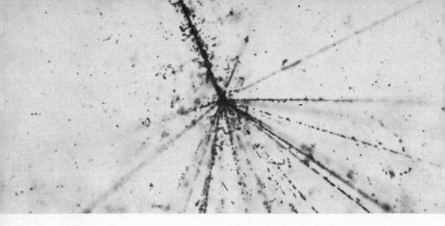

Collision of primary cosmic ray particle with atomic nucleus (see page 136).

Earth's magnetic field as deflector of cosmic ray primaries.

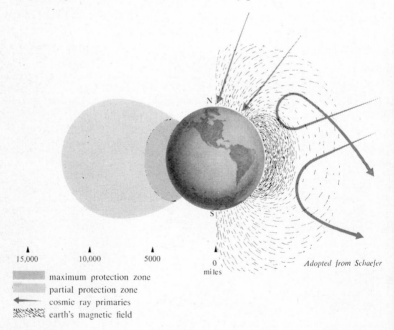

15,000   10,000   5000   0
                                  miles   *Adopted from Schaefer*

maximum protection zone
partial protection zone
cosmic ray primaries
earth's magnetic field

power reserves; physiological data such as electrocardiogram and respiration rate; and general information, such as visual appearance and vocal comments when the subject is over a ground control station.

The safety-of-flight information has priority, of course, and must be telemetered to the ground even if other information does not get through. Once action has been taken to break orbit and re-enter, the priority of this instrumentation automatically drops to that of information for the record, to be recorded and/or telemetered, whichever is more efficient.

For the biological measurements, the physiological instrumentation appears to be the most ready-to-fly. The basic problem lies in base-line wander, trace stabilization, etc., of the nondigital data, such as provided by the electrocardiograph. The environmental instrumentation can be all off-the-shelf equipment, with the exception of the carbon dioxide partial-pressure sensing equipment, which requires some additional development.

Psychological measurements should be made with a maximum of usability and a minimum of interference; that is, any test result must be usable in the widest possible number of space-flight situations, and it should be a valid result for each situation. At the same time the test tasks must not be so universal of correlation and application that they lose significance to the pilot in the dramatic situation of his first orbital flight. Perhaps on later flights the classic psychomotor tests can be applied to measure exact performance increments or decrements, but on the first flight the subject will probably be too interested in monitoring his survival to participate in mission-unrelated tests and his performance level. Thus the psychologist must tax his ingenuity for meaningful tasks, such as an astrogation problem (Where is my orbit? Where am I in my orbit? How long till re-entry?), which contain elements of performance from which he can deduce or extrapolate meaningful data.

The usefulness of vocal and visual communication (2-way and 1-way) and of vocal and visual records of the flight, particularly the critical parts, is obvious. Here the instrumentation consists mainly in the application of various engineering devices to cut down on the most massive of the biological instruments. A two-speed camera with different rates for different phases of the flight is an obvious film-saver. A voice-operated voice recorder is another. Two-way radio communication with satellites presents no major problem. Television presents an interesting band-width and power problem. In order to get a picture of sufficient number of frames per second and lines per frame to be used as a diagnostic and decision-making tool by ground-based medical officers, either a large amount of power must be carried aloft or an extensive and expensive ground station layout must be made. In any event the problem does not appear to be insuperable, and with the passage of time larger and more efficient ground antenna installations will reduce the problem greatly.

Biologic Research in Space Vehicles

When the time comes in the progress of our space technology that we can put vehicles into space where and when we want them and either return or visit them at will, then we will have a space laboratory of inestimable value to the fundamental life scientist. The ability to observe growth and form in tissue cultures and rapidly maturing species in a zerogravity field will of itself alone be worth the expense and effort of the experiment. As Dr. Otto Schmidt has put it: "There is an important philosophy to be established with those in charge of our Space Programs and that is, not only should it be the idea to get biology into outer space, but also to use the outer space for biology."

Some additional animal biosatellite experiments are needed before the first man is sent into orbit. Both large and small subhuman specimens have been recovered from space-probing rockets, but, to my knowledge at least, no orbiting vehicle has been recovered intact, let alone one with viable tissue aboard. Yet there is not much question but that such a recovery will be carried out successfully in the relatively near future. Once accomplished, it could yield the following pertinent information:

1. The animal would provide the necessary viable test bed to determine the efficiency and reliability of our life support system and to validate our estimates of metabolic requirements per unit time.

2. Next, it would provide a biologic standard to calibrate against the actual recorded energy dynamics imposed upon the vehicle during the launch and re-entry phases. During orbit con-

siderable information would be obtained on the efficiency of our heat and humidity control mechanism which is of vital importance to both animal and man alike.

3. Through optimal use of power and telemetry channels, plus ingenious sensing, much could be learned of the effect on the vital systems of the organism in the gravity-free space environment.

4. With careful selection of species and pretraining in various types of operant and respondent tasks, the animal could give us considerable insight into the performance capabilities of a man in orbit.

5. Finally the viable payload would provide a most needed operational test of our search and recovery techniques, which, when it comes time for the human flight, should be well-nigh foolproof. It would indeed be almost the ultimate irony for man to survive all the rigors of the space mission only to lose his life through some unforeseen or untimely event after he had returned in reasonably good condition to the earth.

Biologic Hazards

Of all the biological hazards involved in space operation the exposure of living tissue to ionizing radiations is perhaps the most important and certainly the one with most far-reaching consequences into the future. Man and his biologic predecessors have never lived in an environment containing ionizing radiation as one of its natural constituents, and therefore no biological organism has ever had to adapt itself to such a physical threat in order to survive and procreate itself. Animals and man can neither detect nor protect themselves from significant intensities of ionizing radiations in their environment.

In space operations we must concern ourselves with the radiobiological hazard as emanating from three possible sources: first, those radiations intrinsic to space itself; second, those produced as by-products to the use of nuclear energy as power in the vehicle; and lastly, man-made contamination of space either accidentally through the use of nuclear power units or purposely with nuclear weapons. Whatever the source, the implications on man's future capability to explore and exploit space are of considerable magnitude and complexity.

In the area of space-intrinsic radiations the most urgent need is for additional physical data on the nature and intensities of the radiation fields to be encountered. The reports on the Van Allen phenomena as compiled from Explorer IV measurements suggest that present concepts for manned space exploration may undergo rather drastic changes or at least be carefully re-evaluated with specific consideration of the following points:

1. The necessity for and feasibility of shielding and its influence on capsule design.

2. The possibility of using magnetic deflection for protection against high-energy-charged particulate radiation.

3. The possibility of using these charged particles as a source of power and energy to offset the payload loss imposed by shielding requirements.

The preliminary analysis of the data received from the National Aeronautics and Space Administration–Air Force moon probe Pioneer offers some bit of encouragement as regards the possible depth of the Van Allen layer, though in no way alters the significance of the Explorer findings. Data readouts taken from the omnidirectional integrated ion chamber in the Pioneer show a gradual decrease of radiation intensities from the 10,000-mile to the 60,000-mile level, with the latter figure being approximately one sixth that of the former. No cross correlation or calibration of the measurements from Pioneer is possible as yet with those obtained from Explorer, but it appears that the peak load of intensity would be encountered somewhere below 1.5 earth radii, or under 6,000 miles altitude.

Regardless of this slight encouragement from preliminary Pioneer data, a complete and valid assessment of the total radiobiologic hazard in space must await the acquisition of the following information:

1. Measurements of the flux density and energy distribution of heavy primaries above the earth's atmosphere. The continuation of our balloon flights and high-altitude probes offers the most immediate potential for obtaining these data.

2. The development of a physical means of monitoring primary cosmic-ray hits in biological materials. And specifically in this connection to find a reliable method of locating and identifying primary particle tracks and determining both their angle and depth of penetration. The excellent work started by Dr. Herman Yagoda

at the Air Research and Development Command's Cambridge Research Laboratory on this problem deserves active support and augmentation.

3. Energy spectral measurements of the Van Allen layer with more elaborate pulse scintillator/discriminator combinations than were possible in Explorer IV. Either widely orbiting satellites could be used for this purpose or, as an alternate, backup vehicle, a high-altitude space probe fitted with various cross-sectional threshold detectors. The only problem with the latter is the necessity to recover the payload so that the necessary radiochemical analyses of the detector material may be made in order to extract the data.

4. A determination of the type, quality, and intensity of secondary radiation produced inside the space vehicle, since much of the total radiation dose imposed upon the occupant could emanate from secondaries produced by the interaction of the primaries on the space vehicle itself.

5. The mapping out of a circumterrestrial pattern which would relate intensities of the Van Allen phenomena to altitude, latitude, and time.

Pending the acquisition of this rather formidable amount of physical data, the space bioscientist is far from bereft of useful biological-effects data in making a valuable contribution to the initial man-in-space team effort. The armed services, the Atomic Energy Commission, and the United States Public Health Service have done excellent work in this area over the past fifteen years and have compiled a commendable amount of information on the acute and chronic biologic effects of ionizing radiations.

The Air Force effort centered at the School of Aviation Medicine, USAF, has produced an excellent set of crew tolerance standards which have considerable potential application to the space radiobiologic hazard problem. Data on biologic effects have been carefully compiled and correlated from a study of animal exposures, survivors of Hiroshima and Nagasaki, victims of nuclear accidents, and selected cancer patients under X-ray treatment. It is quite likely that, once the space-radiation intensity measurements are made, a ready answer will be yielded for the very timely and vital question—Man in space, how deeply and for how long?

The problem of the heavy cosmic primaries (nuclei of elements with Z numbers greater than 6) deserves some additional mention despite the fact that its immediate implication in manned space operations has been far overshadowed by the discovery of the Van Allen phenomena. Much of the Air Force effort in delineation of this hazard has been carried out under the direction of Lieutenant Colonel David Simons in the ARDC Aero Medical Field Laboratory at Holloman Air Force Base, New Mexico. In high-altitude balloons both animal and human subjects have been exposed for appreciable durations at altitudes which in terms of the cosmic primaries closely approach space equivalence. Data from these experiments indicate that the terminal portion of a heavy primary particle track (so-called thindown portion) is most injurious to biological tissue because of its extremely high linear energy transfer plus the significant radius of its broad track. Further data indicate that the heavy nuclei responsible for the thindown phenomena are found only at geomagnetic latitudes above 50°. Balloons launched above this latitude can maintain the specimen in continuous exposure to the maximum of biologically significant hits, while in comparison an earth satellite launched in an optimal polar orbit would provide maximum exposure only during 40% of its total orbital period. At the present time and with current quoted rates for the price per pound of payload in orbit this fact gives some comfort to the space radiobiologist.

The possibility of reproducing the mass energies of the significant cosmic primaries in a ground laboratory is a most exciting one, for it would provide us with a real breakthrough in the accurate evaluation of this particular space hazard. The essence of the problem lies in the possibility that a heavy primary striking a vital brain center such as the hypothalamic region could inflict irreversible damage to the human occupant that would result in serious impairment of his functioning and viability.

It is fortunate that an international effort is being vigorously prosecuted toward the objective of heavy primary simulation in ground facilities at Brookhaven National Laboratory, the Radiation Laboratory of the University of California, in Denmark at the University of Aarhus, and at the University of Bonn in Germany. The work of these groups involves the use of high-energy particle beams and low-energy X rays to produce topical neuropathologic brain lesions which can be correlated with demonstrable changes in biologic function and patterns of electrical activity in the brain.

Perhaps through acceleration and increased support to this important program we may have the answer to this particular space-intrinsic biologic hazard by the time our manned space vehicle is ready.

Psychological Hazards

The pioneer man in space will be faced with a complex of psychological factors, the like of which has no past counterpart in human experience. The inherent danger of the mission, its many unknowns as regards his viability and survival would, of themselves alone, comprise a heavy load of stress on his psyche. Yet there are many other stresses to be considered which yield much less to an accurate premission evaluation. Isolation, confinement with its attendant restriction of physical activity, reduced sensory inputs, prolonged weightlessness, disorientation with possible lack of vehicle altitude control—all are major factors of concern in any attempt to select and prepare crewmen with the maximum index of reliability. The majority of our research efforts in this area have a basic objective which might be simply stated as follows: to minimize and counteract such emotional stresses as might impair effective crew performance in space flight.

Much excellent work is being done on this problem by psychologists, psychophysiologists, and psychiatrists the world over. Here only the work going on in Air-Force–ARDC laboratories will be reviewed. This work can be grouped into four general categories:

1. The identification of potential sources of disabling psychic stress within the space-mission regime.

2. The study of performance and behavior under artificial conditions in which these identifiable stresses are simulated with as much accuracy as possible.

3. The attempt to create artificial environments and conditions which will satisfy human psychological needs during actual space missions.

4. The application of valid criteria and standards to the problem of selection, training, and conditioning of space members.

In attempting to identify the potential sources of psychological stress, our workers have exhaustively reviewed the experiences and reported behavior patterns of those individuals who have faced danger, isolation, and exposure under terrestrial conditions. These have included such people as arctic explorers, mountain climbers, deep-sea divers, and shipwrecked sailors. It is indeed interesting that many of the abnormal behavioral patterns reported by and on some of these individuals have been manifest in our subjects under conditions of isolation, confinement, and sensory deprivation simulated with varying degrees of completeness.

The results of these studies thus far completed may be summarized rather generally as follows:

1. Close restriction of physical activity is largely unacceptable. Conversely the ability to flex extremities and neck, shift position, and occasionally assume a fairly erect posture is a basic requirement. Interestingly enough the individual may not take full and continuous advantage of his mobility, but if he knows that he can move if he so wishes, then he is content.

2. A visual reference both internally within the capsule and externally to provide some degree of spatial or geographic orientation plus the ability to control levels of illumination is perhaps next most important.

3. A two-way voice communication with an outside or ground source and preferably with an individual or individuals with whom the subject has previously established a strong identification as regards the objectives and successful outcome of the experiment.

4. Continuous orientation in time with a definite limit or goal set for the duration of the experiment. Without some means of time orientation, the sense of time passage is fairly rapidly lost. This loss becomes more annoying and disconcerting to the subject the longer he remains without an accurate reference. When he attempts to estimate the elapsed time of the experiment, he almost always errs on the short side.

5. The ability to eat, sleep, and carry out assigned psychomotor performance tasks on a schedule or rhythm which reasonably duplicates the subject's normal one in behavior and performance is quite acceptable. Attempts thus far to deviate significantly from his normal psychophysiological rhythm and still maintain the same degree of efficiency in performance have not met with much success.

In choosing subjects for study we have attempted to sample a fairly broad spectrum of personalities and occupations. Medical doctors, engineers, administrators, scientists, standard pilots, Strategic Air Command pilots, test pilots, and Navy frogmen have all been studied, and within each specific group we have had both successes and failures. There seems to be no specific type of personality which uniformly shows a good durability to the artificially imposed psychological stresses. Instead, those subjects who perform well appear to have a good capacity to harmonize internal needs and drives with the external realities of the situation in a mature and flexible manner.

Contrary to some statements of opinion in the popular literature, individuals with neurotic or psychotic tendencies should be most assiduously screened out and eliminated from consideration. The expressed contention that schizoid or other abnormally withdrawn individuals should be chosen for their "presumed" increased tolerance for isolation and sensory deprivation has not proved to be valid in our hands.

Successful subjects demonstrate uniformly a strong motivation towards the achievement of the entire objectives of the experiment but not for purposes of satisfying any personal need for recognition. Volunteers with strong needs to "prove something" to themselves or to test their own personal fantasy of invulnerability are uniformly fairly bad risks. Freedom from impulsivity is another desirable trait, for the spaceman must act economically when action is required yet refrain from purposeless activity when inaction is appropriate to the actual situation. He must be able to tolerate stress situations passively without requiring motor activity to dissipate anxiety.

It is extremely difficult to predict just how long a properly selected, trained, and conditioned individual can remain in space even assuming that most of his psychological needs can be ingeniously engineered into the system. We can never simulate the total situation as it will actually occur, particularly the complete detachment from the earth that could have far greater psychological impact than we now suspect. However if forced to guess, based upon what we know now, we might expect man under ideal conditions to remain in space flight without emotional and behavioral deterioration for a period from 10 to 14 days. For longer periods we have much more to learn about the interplay between emotions, brain mechanisms, and performance.

The Implications of Weightlessness

A good many years before any thought was seriously given to either the feasibility or the value of putting up an artificial earth satellite, Dr. Heinz Haber working with Dr. Strughold in the first laboratory group devoted entirely to a consideration of space-medical problems (at the Air Force School of Aviation Medicine under the command of Major General Harry Armstrong) characterized the state of weightlessness as one of the great mysteries of space, as "the true feel" of space. Many of their original hypotheses on this condition made over ten years ago have been borne out by the numerous investigations conducted since by Henry, Ballinger, von Beckh, and Ward. From the standpoint of the pure bioscientist, the phenomena of weightlessness existing in a space laboratory portend many exciting possibilities to test out theories of geotropism, communication biophysics, basic intracellular energy transformations, and a host of other intriguing experiments which could not be done in any terrestrial laboratory. However, for the space surgeon, concerned as he should be for the in-flight efficiency and safe recovery of his spacecrew, the problem considerably transcends pure academic interest.

Our Air Force experiments studying the phenomena of weightlessness by means of parabolic flight paths flown by various types of aircraft are described by Dr. Gerathewohl in a later chapter. In these experiments we have been unable to study individuals or animals in weightlessness for longer than 80 to 90 seconds. Even with the X-15 research aircraft nearing readiness these time periods for study will not exceed five minutes. It is therefore perhaps easy to understand why most of our scientists working in this field are reluctant to make extrapolations and predictions as to the total significance of this condition when it is imposed upon the individual for durations of from one and a half to twenty-four hours. As in all good healthy scientific groups we have basically two different opinions on the effects of prolonged weightlessness. On the one hand, that it will present no real psychophysiological difficulties to the space traveler and the other, of course, that it will seriously prejudice both his effectiveness, comfort, and even viability.

The physiological parameters significantly affected by exposure to a zero-g field include neurological mechanisms, spatial orientation, motion sickness, the cardiovascular system, the gastrointestinal system, body water elimination, and skeletal muscle activity.

Concern has been voiced among medical investigators over the neurological mechanisms or potential effect of sudden withdrawal of the shower of sensory output from graviceptor transducers of the body. However, there are many other sources of "neurological background noise" which may be ordinarily blocked out by the constant flood of one-g body-positional information pouring into the central nervous system. This sensory output from the integumental surfaces and viscera may substitute for the normal gravity proprioceptive sensor outpourings. Subject training by artificial re-enforcement of skin pressure clues may offer an adequate solution. Deepness and restfulness of sleep under these conditions are presently open to question. Violent nightmares may disturb the rest of the suspended, sleeping astronaut. Drugs may be required to give restful, fatigue-relieving sleep.

Spatial disorientation as a response to the weightless state has been reported several times under both operational and experimental situations in parabolic maneuvers. In virtually all such cases it appears that these incidents resulted from attempts to "free float." Such difficulties are generally obviated when the individual is comfortably restrained with extremities resting against solid objects. However, unrestrained locomotion about a space cabin may cause some degree of disorientation. Cabin design and coloring to indicate "floor" and "ceiling" will assist in maintaining spatial orientation by visual means.

Individual susceptibility to nausea and vomiting or so-called motion sickness under the relatively simple and experimentally reproducibly conditions of ordinary aircraft flight is poorly understood. Any attempt to derive definitive conclusions from the complex motion situation prevailing in the production of parabolic trajectories by jet aircraft is therefore fallacious. Cognizance, however, must be made of the reports by Gerathewohl and others of illness in approximately one third of subjects exposed to such flight conditions. Most, although perhaps not all, of these responses may be explained by the nature of changing acceleration fields upon entry and exit from these maneuvers, the flying experience of the subjects, the "weightless regurgitation phenomenon," etc. The extent to which the weightless state alone influences incidence of sickness will probably remain in doubt until initial manned orbital flights are completed.

It is generally felt that no serious effects on the heart and blood vessels will result from life at zero-g at least during the short duration of the early orbital flights. One interesting fact reported from the Sputnik II experiment was the unusual lag in return to norm rate of the pulse of the canine passenger from the tachycardia induced by rocket boost. Some degree of over-filling of the right heart, shifts of venous pooled blood, and minor changes in electrical and anatomic cardiac axes may occur but there is no reason to believe that cardiovascular instability and/or insufficiency will result. There is certainly more basis for predicting cardiovascular symptomatology in subjects thoroughly "acclimatized" to zero-g when they return to a normal accelerative environment on earth.

Prior to the space age we have never been required to study gastrointestinal functions without the benefit of weight. Obviously the primary physiological problem of handling any sort of foodstuff is to swallow it. Experimental observations of the deglutition mechanism under weightless conditions have indicated that with normal mastication of solids, swallowing of the semiliquid bolus of food offers no difficulty. But bolting of solid foods by the space pilot may have far more serious consequences than under terrestrial conditions. Poorly chewed solids tend to be swallowed with difficulty; indeed these particles may occasionally float over the palate. Therefore the danger of aspiration is real.

The competency of the cardiac sphincter of the stomach under these conditions is dubious. During parabolic jet maneuvers a "weightless regurgitation phenomenon" mentioned earlier has been demonstrated. This consists of the regurgitation of part of the stomach contents when a blow or even pressure is imparted to the abdomen; however this is most often observed after and associated with ingestion of large volumes of fluids. This serves to point out the need for fairly rigid dietary control particularly with respect to fluid volume per feeding.

Many years ago Hoelzel completed a comprehensive study of the passage of inert materials through the intestinal tract in which materials with widely varying densities were surveyed. It was learned that the rate of passage of these materials was largely an inverse function of density. Therefore under a zero-g field, food passage time may be slightly reduced. Considering the length of the intestine and the surface tension of the semiliquid intestinal bolus, the absorption of metabolites appears to offer no problem.

Elimination of body-waste solids and liquids is a function of elasticity of vesicular and visceral tissues, voluntary musculature function, sphincter action, and only to a very slight extent, gravitation. In one study, micturition function was demonstrated in the weightless state with 26 subjects. Fifty-eight per cent of these individuals noted a diminution or total absence of the sense of urgency upon attaining the zero-g state with distended bladders, yet with training, voluntary urination was accomplished.

Studies by Gerathewohl and others of psychomotor performance, particularly eye-hand coordination tasks, indicate that compensation for the loss of upper-extremity weight is rapidly learned. Manipulation of the cockpit controls and environmental components by the space pilot is therefore not anticipated to be a difficult problem. Learning new locomotion techniques will undoubtedly be more difficult because of the relatively greater mass of the lower extremities.

Abortive attempts have been made to study function of single cells while weightless. The lack of weight differentials of cellular constituents may in some measure affect cell metabolism. I might say parenthetically that an attempt to maintain a tissue culture under focus and make photomicrographic movies while unrestrained and weightless in the rear cockpit of a Starfire jet fighter aircraft presents some amusing as well as perplexing problems.

We can already foresee the need for a series of new devices or improvements in currently operational equipment for pilot use in weightless situations. Preliminary work along these lines has already begun to a limited extent at military and civilian research centers. New and original ideas must be incorporated in the design solutions of weightless-conditioning simulators and trainers, recreation, sleeping facilities, human-waste disposal devices, and food dispensers.

Considerable development of ground-based trainers will be required. These may be based on the principles of either air-bearing or magnetically suspended platforms for development of space pilot proficiency in the manual use of small reaction jets. Or radically different designs may be required. Other trainers may be required to increase agility in zerogravity locomotion, e.g., utilizing magnetic shoes in an underwater tank. Teaching of subjective relaxation and sleep with lack of support may become a part of the space pilot's "preflight" training. Other devices will be required which will assist the space crew in gradually learning to accommodate to their new environment, such as graded inertial restraints on extremities capable of giving sensation of varying g, until complete zero-g familiarization has been achieved.

We will require the development of a lightweight, collapsible restraining bed with sufficient differential pressure clues on anterior and posterior body integumental surfaces to give real psychological "top-bottom" information to the individual, even while asleep. Although some degree of restraint is required, the device must permit comfortable and relaxed sleep. Sanitary, lightweight, and esthetically acceptable human-waste receptacles must be developed. Virtually an open field exists in the requirement for design of devices to assist in "free-fall" locomotion for movement inside and outside the space vehicle. Lightly magnetized shoes and gloves, nonprotruding hand holds, and small hand-held reaction guns for extravehicular use are but a few of the fascinating challenges facing the bioastronautical design engineer in the area of human weightless locomotion.

Of course, all hydraulic systems within a spacecraft must be designed for zero-g function; however one of the most critical requirements will be the need for a liquid-oxygen converter. This device must prevent excessive O_2 boil-off, maintain the liquid-gas interface, and function as reliably under high g loading, as well as in the weightless state. A similar requirement for biomedical hardware development may arise for the liquid suspensions of photosynthetic gas exchanges, should these systems prove feasible for flights of long duration.

Finally, serious human engineering consideration must be given to the design of equipment for the storage, heating, and dispensing of both liquid and solid foods. The container-dispenser must be capable of storing large quantities of materials for prolonged periods. It must provide safeguards against bacterial or fungal contamination, spoilage, and accidental spillage. Provisions must be made for placing the dispenser directly into the mouth for introduction of the liquid or solid. The first experimental study of this problem was conducted at the Air Force School of Aviation Medicine, beginning in 1956. Although some difficulty was anticipated in the handling of foodstuffs under zerogravity, we were not entirely prepared for all of the difficulties imposed by the mechanical problems of drinking fluids from open containers.

Headquarters Air Research and Development Command

CHAPTER 5

Biodynamics of Space Flight

Colonel John P. Stapp

It is assumed that scientific and military considerations establish the necessity for space flight. Whether man will be an on-board component in space operations will depend on proof that he is still worth his weight in black boxes under conditions of space flight. In his favor are certain attributes that have defied duplication in nonliving devices: education; rational analysis of information; independent judgment; recognition of error, with correction or overriding thereof; self-maintenance. On the other hand man is afflicted with certain serious limitations and costly requirements, such as emotionality, complex environmental specifications with narrow margins of deviation, cumbersome logistics, obnoxious waste disposal, and inherent limitations with respect to certain factors encountered in space flight.

Man's emotionality has been compared to the problem of signal-to-noise ratio in electronic communications, but is infinitely more variable and unpredictable. Not only the basic elements of his natural environment must be present, but sensitive, reliable, quantitative control of their physical and chemical states must be maintained. His food, water, and oxygen must either be in adequate supply or be recycled where duration of flight prohibits carrying enough. Conversely, he can either detoxify and store his wastes or recycle them in usable form, either potable or edible. Finally, provision must be made for the weight and minimum space requirements of the man himself, for the duration and activities required for the mission.

Presuming that all these grueling obstacles have been overcome and that the human operator is safely enthroned in the capsule, we see new and more formidable handicaps arise, causing him to complain as Hamlet in the words of the ever-prescient Shakespeare: "O God! I could be bounded in a nutshell, and count myself a king of infinite space, were it not that I have bad dreams." Within himself, man's effectiveness is limited by fatigue, isolation, and confinement, which can reduce him to the final absurdity of hallucination or distraction. Unless rest, frequent communication, exercise, and, above all, the self-discipline of trained motivation can renew and maintain his effectiveness, duration limits in terms of these factors must be determined for the anticipated stresses and activities of a space mission.

Assuming that this subjective problem area is under control and that the spaceman is on his way out of the protecting blanket of atmosphere surrounding the earth, we then see other perils that lie in wait. Radiant energy peculiar to the space environment must be either excluded or at least attenuated by shielding, or else predetermined time limits must be set on exposure. As he goes into orbit one novel experience that defies ground-level simulation and that hitherto has been tasted but not definitely tried by man awaits his indulgence. This new experience is weightlessness. Single exposures of less than a minute in jets flying a precise, shallow, outside loop have achieved a combination of inertial force and descent rate that offsets gravitational force, leaving the man suspended in a continuous free fall. Pleasure, fright, sensory and reflex disturbance, relief from the burdens of the flesh, bring to mind once more the fortuitously appropriate Hamlet: "O! that this too too solid flesh would melt,—Thaw and resolve itself into a dew"—except that dew, too, has its difficulties in zerogravity. Food and drink must be captive in containers from which they can be propelled directly into the mouth and must have a consistency that allows easy chewing and swallowing. Contractions of the stomach normal to digestion may propel food back against the palate, causing reflex vomiting. Should it become prudent or essential to restore gravity, it can be simulated by a radial component of acceleration induced by slowly rotating the space capsule.

One factor remains which cannot be either avoided or excluded. This factor is accelerative force. By trading off magnitude against duration, by presenting his body to it in the most favorable orientation, man can modulate the exposure to accelerative or decelerative force so as to make it endurable at relatively high degrees. Accelerative force will be encountered in attaining orbital or escape velocity; decelerative force in re-entry and in recovery. Should emergency require abrupt abandonment of the flight, deceleration and perhaps even windblast may become problems to be surmounted.

Research on the biological effects of mechanical force is called biodynamics. It has to do with the effect on living tissues of accelerations, decelerations, impacts, windblast, and abrupt pressure changes. Limits for human tolerance to impacts and decelerations have been investigated from the standpoint of aircraft crash forces,[11][12][13] automobile crash forces,[14][15][16] escape from aircraft by seat ejection,[9] and supersonic windblast encountered in high-velocity escape.[12][13]

Assuming that orbital velocity is approximately 16,000 knots and that escape velocity is about 22,000 knots, it would require a constant acceleration of 13.8 g for 1 minute to attain orbital velocity and 19.2 g for 1 minute to reach escape velocity. These terms may also be expressed as 828 g/seconds for orbital velocity and 1152 g/seconds for escape velocity. This means that any time-g combination giving one of these two products will attain the corresponding velocity. In actuality no space-missile engine operates with constant acceleration. The decrease in mass burned off as fuel and the decrease in atmospheric resistance with altitude result in a constant increase in acceleration up to burnout. It is conceivable that a single stage of propulsion could thrust continuously to the desired velocity, but most of the currently available propulsion systems require two to four stages to attain space-flight velocities. This introduces the problem of burnout and the abrupt cutoff of acceleration between stages.

Human reactions to both continuous and intermittent accelerations for durations needed to reach escape velocity have been investigated on the human centrifuge [1] [4] [5] [8] and are currently under study at the Aero Medical Laboratory, Wright Air Development Center, and at the Navy Aviation Medical Acceleration Laboratory, Johnsville, Pennsylvania.

In aircraft flight the low order of magnitude and duration of accelerative force that can be endured along the long axis of the body in either direction while undergoing turning maneuvers are a familiar fact. Much greater magnitude and duration of accelerative force can be tolerated when applied at right angles to the long axis of the body. Human volunteers on the centrifuge in a semirecumbent position with the force applied front to back tolerated 10 g of sustained acceleration for up to 2 minutes and 20 seconds, and did not black out until 12 g was reached. Preston-Thomas[8] found that a number of his subjects could perform finger-controlled guidance functions while undergoing 8 g in this position.

Intermittent accelerations duplicating three-stage space-missile propulsion configurations have been applied to human volunteers, totaling eight minutes with coasting simulated between first and second peaks and between second and third peaks. Approximately three minutes of slow increment to 8 g was applied for the first peak, with 5.6 g for each of the two succeeding peaks. Human volunteers adjusted promptly and adequately to intermittent exposures. Data will be available when the experiments of Hessburg, Hyatt, Bondurant, *et al.,* are published.

Deceleration patterns expected for re-entry have also been reproduced on the Wright Air Development Center centrifuge. Three g was well tolerated by several subjects in the semisupine transverse configuration with force applied from front to back for up to one hour. Four g could not be endured quite that long.

An investigation of lethal and injurious time-g exposures in the semisupine transverse position, duplicating high-g re-entry configurations, is in progress on the Johnsville Navy centrifuge as a joint effort of the Navy and the Air Force Aero Medical Field Laboratory at Holloman AFB, the latter providing the animals and some technical support. Anesthetized animal subjects exposed to

38.5 g for 7 seconds were essentially uninjured. The same exposure for 20 seconds produced minimal injury within reversible limits to heart and lungs. Exposure of 38.5 g for 60 seconds approached irreversible injury and lethal limits. Data will be available when these experiments are completed and the results published. Obviously, prolonged exposure to comparatively low decelerative force will be better for re-entry.

Earlier investigations on tolerance to abrupt deceleration by Stapp,[12] [13] Bierman,[2] and De Haven[3] are applicable to parachute-opening shock and ground impact encountered in the recovery

Deceleration Tests on Humans

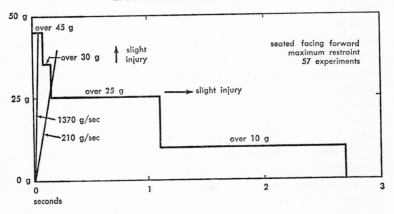

phase of space flight. Abrupt, transversely applied decelerative force of 40 g lasting less than .5 seconds can be tolerated without injury. This provides an ample margin for drogue recovery of a manned capsule. Following re-entry into the aerodynamic atmosphere, the problem becomes identical with that for aircraft bailout.

Injurious and lethal limits for exposure to decelerative force lasting less than .30 seconds have been determined by rocket-sled experiments with anesthetized animal subjects. The conditions simulated would be equivalent to partial failure of a parachute with violent impact terminating a rapid descent in a capsule. Five thousand feet of the Holloman Air Force Base research track was used for these experiments. A 5-second, 8-g acceleration of the sled attained a velocity slightly above the speed of sound. Immediately after rocket burnout the sled and occupant underwent deceleration by a water-inertia brake that dragged a scoop under the sled through a trough between the rails, picking up water and throwing it through a 90-degree arc. Application of 135 g or more at 5000 g per second or higher rate of onset, with a total duration of .35 seconds or less, produced persistent injury in the form of hemorrhagic spots in the heart and lungs and transient physiological dysfunction. This was equivalent to 7 tons of force applied in 27 thousandths of a second. With the subject in the same orientation, forward-facing with force applied from back to front during deceleration, 237 g at 11,500 g per second rate of onset during .35 seconds proved fatal within four hours. This was equivalent to applying 11 tons of force in 27 milliseconds for the same duration. With the subject facing aft so that transverse force was applied from front to back, moderately severe, nonlethal injury resulted from exposure to 242 g at 16,500 g per second rate of onset. This means that a properly restrained subject suspended within a capsule in the aft-facing, semisupine, transverse orientation should survive an 80-knot impact of the capsule in a hard landing on average soil, provided the capsule did not fail, crushing in on him. Forces would be in the order of half the injurious exposure for animals.

The feasibility of ejection from an X-15 type rocket-powered research vehicle or even escape from a space capsule would depend on tolerance to the effects of windblast as well as to heat of atmospheric friction and high decelerations. The 21,500-foot rocket-sled research track at the Naval Ordnance Testing Station, China Lake, California, has been used in a continuing series of experiments to determine the effect of 4000 pounds per square foot of windblast on anesthetized animal subjects. This is a joint project with the Holloman Air Force Base Aero Medical Field Laboratory.

In the three experiments accomplished to date the anesthetized animal subject was fully exposed to ram air while mounted on a seat near the prow of the sled, with no obstruction from the feet up. In the most recent experiment the subject was protected by a coverall of 13-ounce dacron sailcloth and a windproof fiberglass helmet which completely enclosed the head and was secured to the headrest. A peak force of 4000 pounds per square foot can be withstood for .8 seconds. During peak velocity, stagnation temperatures registering 320° Fahrenheit and noise of 165 decibels were measured at head level. Skin exposed to this heat and windblast combination was seared through and dehydrated to half thickness, as though by very intense sunburn. This exposure would require a maximum velocity of 1150 knots, or 1.7 mach at 2300 feet altitude for the prevailing temperature and air density. The exposure is survivable, provided helmet, garment, and restraints function according to plan. A more complete report will be available when the experiments are completed and published by Stapp, Mosely, *et al.*

From these findings the dependence of manned space flight on biodynamic research becomes evident. Newton's three laws of motion cannot be repealed, nor can their predicted effects be excluded by any known material for making space capsules. However, the results of experiments show generous margins of safety for all human limits in terms of biodynamic factors, for solving the problems of manned space flight. Escape from a capsule throughout a significant percentage of the trajectory of a space missile seems feasible.

Wright Air Development Center

CHAPTER 6

The Engineered Environment of the Space Vehicle

Dr. Hans G. Clamann

A decade ago a "space vehicle" would have meant to most people a vehicle capable of carrying man to a far-distant interplanetary destination. At that time the term "space" was almost exclusively used by astronomers with reference to distances of interplanetary magnitude.

In the meantime man with his airplane has conquered higher

and higher altitudes. With increasing altitude, for about each 53,000 feet, the atmospheric pressure decreases to a tenth of its previous value. So does the density. This decrease in density means fewer molecules of air per unit of volume and consequently less oxygen, despite a constant 21 per cent of the volume.

Both the power plant of an airplane and the passengers need oxygen to sustain "life." If the air becomes too thin to provide enough oxygen, either compression to higher density without adding oxygen or addition of oxygen to the noncompressed air may correct the deficiency. The enormous quantities of air at sufficient pressure needed to supply oxygen for the thousands of horses of an airplane engine dictate the use of powerful high-speed compressors. Man, less powerful with barely one tenth of a horsepower for continuous physical work, is relatively modest in oxygen consumption. But man lacks the structural strength of an engine; his weak chest muscles will not allow pressurization of the lungs by much more than five per cent of atmospheric pressure. Therefore pressurization has to be extended to the whole cabin, which now constitutes a pressurized cabin. In contrast to an engine, where pressurization serves only the purpose of oxygen supply, a pressurized cabin has to be ventilated for removal of carbon dioxide, water vapor, odors, and possible traces of noxious gases (for instance, carbon monoxide). The two latter factors increase ventilation requirements almost tenfold.

The other possibility, of breathing oxygen-enriched air, to maintain man at altitudes above 10,000 feet may just be mentioned. Its main advantage lies in the protection it affords against "bends" at altitudes above 25,000 feet and, in combination with partially pressurized cabins, against failure of pressurization, against rapid decompression, and in preparedness for bailout.

Above 80,000 feet, where the atmospheric pressure has fallen to three and a half per cent of normal, air compressors become increasingly bulky, heavy, and power-consuming if they are to provide both a high pressure ratio and a large mass flow. And this does not count the problem of high temperatures caused by the high pressure ratio.

Therefore both the power plants and passengers of aircraft flying above such altitudes have to rely completely on oxygen supply rather than upon pressurization. The reciprocating engine and the jet are replaced by the rocket, carrying its own fuel and oxidizer. Instead of the pressurized cabin, a completely sealed cabin separates the passengers from the outside rarefied atmosphere or vacuum. Oxygen supply and means for removal of carbon dioxide, water vapor, etc., have to be carried along.

Since the sealed cabin constitutes the only means to keep man alive from 80,000 feet and outward to any realm of space, it is well justified to say that for man "space" begins at 80,000 feet and to call any craft cruising at such altitudes a spacecraft. With reference to oxygen supply alone, even lower altitudes may be called "space-equivalent." This situation has been explained in detail by Dr. Strughold in Chapter 3.

Actually man needs protection besides the need for oxygen. Even on earth, without protective clothing, housing, and heating and cooling systems he would be restricted to a rather small geographical area. For full physical performance and even more for full mental performance, he has always needed an "engineered environment." In modern aircraft, especially military aircraft under operational conditions, and likewise in future space vehicles, fast sensory reactions, alertness, and good judgment are paramount. Thus the so-called "comfort conditions" with respect to all environmental factors are no longer a luxury but a necessity. As an example certain studies on radio operators may be mentioned. These studies showed that errors in receiving radio code increased eighty per cent above normal after the first hour when the operator was exposed to a room temperature of 98° F, compared to a normal of 78° F. Even excessively loud noises have been shown to decrease mental performance.

THE SEALED CABIN

The predominant factor of the sealed cabin seems to be the confined environment. Studies on confined environment are generally regarded as an outcome of the space age. Actually such studies on man and animals had been carried out long before the idea of a sealed cabin came close to practical applicability. For instance as early as 1870 the French physiologist and father of aviation medicine, Paul Bert, put sparrows in sealed glass jars of various sizes filled with normal air or various air-oxygen mixtures to study the effects on their survival.

It has been known for a long time that the ratio or quotient between the volume of exhaled carbon dioxide and the volume of consumed oxygen, the so-called Respiratory Quotient (RQ), is, on the average, close to 0.85. In other words, referring to volume, about fifteen per cent more oxygen is absorbed from a surrounding atmosphere than is replaced by exhaled carbon dioxide. Thus a pressure drop is produced in a confined space, provided there is no interference by changes in temperature and humidity. If temperature and humidity are kept constant and carbon dioxide is completely absorbed, the pressure drop in this case provides a simple means of monitoring the proper oxygen supply in a sealed cabin.

In a sealed cabin of 50 cubic feet occupied by one man at rest, without any oxygen supply or absorption of carbon dioxide or water vapor, the oxygen percentage will drop after 4 hours to about 14 per cent, corresponding to 10,000 feet equivalent altitude, while the carbon dioxide concentration will rise to 6 per cent. Complete water vapor saturation, or 100 per cent humidity, will be obtained within the first quarter of an hour. This example demonstrates that the rise in carbon dioxide concentration is the decisive factor for survival under such conditions.

While there is little doubt as to the lowest permissible concentration of oxygen, in the order of 12 per cent for the unacclimatized man, there is less agreement on the highest permissible concentration of carbon dioxide. The main reason is probably the neglect of the time factor. Two human subjects spent three days in a sealed cabin in an atmosphere of 3 per cent carbon dioxide with apparent signs of acclimatization. Animals were kept for two weeks in a sealed cabin while the carbon dioxide rose to 11 per cent. They lost their appetite, but recovered rapidly when they were brought back to normal conditions. These examples show the influence of long exposure time on acclimatization to carbon dioxide concentrations. Eleven per cent carbon dioxide would be intolerable during acute exposure. For the human, carbon dioxide concentrations up to one per cent may still be regarded as maximum. Theoretically acclimatization to low oxygen and acclimatization to high carbon dioxide concentration may not be compatible with each other. While acclimatization to either low oxygen or high carbon dioxide partial pressure would aid in tolerating emergency situations in a sealed cabin, such acclimatization would not help to decrease either oxygen consumption or production of carbon dioxide. Such decrease alone would be decisive in reducing weight of oxygen and of carbon dioxide absorbents.

Physiologically, normal atmospheric pressure and composition of gases would be most desirable. From the viewpoint of the design engineer, a lower than normal pressure may be preferable for two reasons. First, a pressure differential of less than 14.7 pounds per square inch (psi), as it would exist between the vacuum of space and the interior of the cabin, may be required for structural reasons. Second, if uncontrollable leakage of cabin air should occur, the best situation to minimize such leakage would be a pressure differential as small as possible.

In conclusion, the discussion of these general problems of the sealed cabin indicates the predominant influence of the time factor, or, in other words, the influence of the duration of an excursion into space upon the construction and equipment of a space cabin. For short flights (in magnitude of hours or several days), many problems are not very different from those of ordinary high-altitude flights in space-equivalent conditions.

Special Problems

... Man as Energy Converter

Before entering a detailed discussion on the supply problems of sealed cabins, we need a closer look at our primary energy converter: man. In principle, man like other living beings obtains the various forms of energy necessary to sustain life—for instance, all muscular work—by converting chemical substances of high energy into those of lower energy. As an example, carbohydrates and fats are converted to water and carbon dioxide. Such conversions are called "metabolic conversions" and the total process "metabolism." A kind of standard man has been created and his metabolic conversions are quantitatively shown for the state of rest with occasional light muscular activity, as in the case of a pilot in flight.

It is well known that in man the daily metabolic turnover undergoes considerable fluctuation. Especially the oxygen consumption may vary between anything from 360 liters per day at complete body rest (sleep) to more than five times as much at heavy muscular work. Next to muscular work, eating and the subsequent processes of digestion exert a powerful stimulation upon metabolism, as does environmental temperature.

For a pilot of an airplane a consumption of 535 liters of oxygen per day has been reported. While it is impossible to arrive at a single figure for oxygen consumption without showing correspondingly accurate figures on all the factors mentioned above, an oxygen consumption of 603 liters per day has been tentatively set for our standard man, assuming that the activity of a "space pilot" may be close to that of his counterpart in the troposphere. In reality the pilot of a large spacecraft with more room and occasion for muscular exercise may consume considerably more oxygen. In any case, for determining fairly accurate figures on oxygen consumption a previous complete duplication of all conditions that may occur in the cabin of a spacecraft has to be arranged and tested. Such duplication can be performed in special sealed cabins, so-called "space simulators," in a ground laboratory.

One interesting question that is unanswered at the present time is whether or not the state of weightlessness will cause a relative decrease in oxygen consumption, since there are no "weights" to be lifted, such as the weight of the body and its parts. Of course there are still "masses" to be accelerated and decelerated.

All the factors of metabolism are closely interlinked. The data shown in the chart are calculated for an assumed average man of about 154 pounds body weight. Again, while these values may fluctuate, over a length of time they remain fairly constant. Especially the mass of all input substances must equal exactly the output mass, since the body mass of a healthy adult remains practically constant and no substance can vanish. The only "loss" consists of heat energy (2830 kilogram-calories per day).

Consequently all the water consumed on the intake side has to reappear quantitatively at the output, whether as part of the urine, feces, perspiration, or exhaled water vapor. But added to this output is the water produced metabolically by the oxidation of food. With the diet chosen for our standard man, the metabolic water surplus will amount to about 10 per cent of the total water turnover. The percentage of metabolic water depends on the type of food. Fat, for instance, would produce more metabolic water than carbohydrates or proteins.

This example of a single metabolic factor (water balance)

demonstrates how closely biological problems and problems of the engineered environment are interlinked. To keep the weight and space requirements of equipment to a minimum, it is necessary to consider carefully all the factors involved in maintaining a proper balance. An increase of fat in the diet with its high caloric value would save weight on the food supply, but it would also increase the amount of oxygen and water absorbents needed. In any case the amount of water in a space cabin will constantly increase with time.

Daily Metabolic Turnover

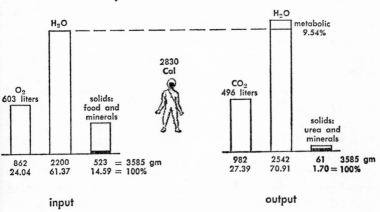

This quantitative portrayal of man's metabolic conversions assumes an average man weighing 154 pounds with a respiratory quotient of 0.82. His assumed diet consists of proteins (80 grams), carbohydrates (270 grams), and fat (150 grams).

. . . Supply Problems

Basically, for a self-sustaining ecological system as constituted by the sealed cabin, everything needed to support life has to be stored before departure of a spacecraft. With increasing duration of a flight into space, the necessary storage will increase correspondingly. To minimize the mass of storage, it is desirable to develop as absorbers for carbon dioxide and water materials which can be used again. Such "regeneration" can be carried out for some absorbers by heating. The ideal process would be the complete "recycling" of the metabolic waste products back to food: carbon dioxide and water back to sugar and starch, nitrogen compounds (for instance urea in the urine) back to proteins.

An ideal prototype in this respect is the spacecraft on which we spend our whole life—our own earth. Because of its gravity, the earth can afford to have its atmosphere on the outside, thus killing four problem-birds with one stone: leakage, solar radiation, cosmic radiation, and meteorites. There is also a perfect recycling process between oxygen and carbon dioxide, which is based upon photosynthesis, as well as one for nitrogen and water.

While such ideal conditions are beyond the possibility of even the largest spacecraft, regenerating and recycling processes have been taken into consideration.

Oxygen. The three main sources of oxygen available at present are: compressed gaseous oxygen, liquid oxygen, and chemical compounds that liberate oxygen. Gaseous oxygen has the advantage of the best and most complete flow control. Contained in metal cylinders, it has the disadvantage of a high dead weight of between 80 and 90 per cent. Considerably smaller dead weight may possibly be achieved by the development of containers based upon synthetic resin material.

Liquid-oxygen converters have a much better dead-weight ratio compared to cylinders filled with compressed gaseous oxygen: only 50 to 60 per cent of their poundage is lost to dead weight. The main problem with them is to avoid evaporation. Normally only good thermal insulation can prevent excessive losses. In a spacecraft with controlled position toward the sun, the cold "shadow side" may support thermal insulation by minimizing the temperature gradient. If the rate of evaporative losses is smaller than the rate of requirement for gaseous oxygen, this would not be harmful for a sealed cabin, in contrast to a normal airplane where free gaseous oxygen is not retained. Special precaution would have to be taken to prevent liquid oxygen from entering the evaporator during the state of weightlessness.

Oxygen supply from chemical sources, such as hydrogen peroxide (H_2O_2), sodium chlorate ($NaClO_3$), sodium superoxide (Na_2O_2), and other superoxides, has two disadvantages: oxygen release cannot be controlled, and there is explosive hazard in the possibility of contact with organic material. In the state of weightlessness a drifting of organic particles is likely to occur at any time. As to the dead-weight factor, chlorate candles, for instance, must be listed between gaseous and liquid-oxygen systems.

To represent the multipurpose processes, potassium superoxide (KO_2) may serve as an example of an oxygen producer that at the same time acts as a carbon dioxide absorber. According to the equation

$$4\,KO_2 + 2\,H_2O = 4\,KOH + 3\,O_2$$
$$4\,KOH + 2\,CO_2 = 2\,K_2CO_3 + 2\,H_2O$$

water vapor causes liberation of oxygen and formation of potassium hydroxide, which in turn absorbs carbon dioxide and liberates water. As a net result, three gram molecules (moles) of oxygen correspond to two moles of carbon dioxide, and the RQ of this

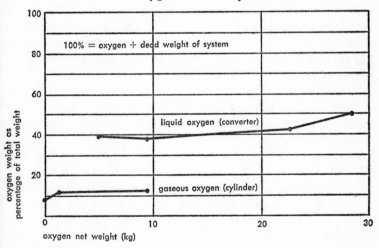

Comparative Weight of Oxygen in Two Systems

system is 2/3 or 0.67. This ratio reveals a problem common to most multipurpose and recycling processes: carbon dioxide and oxygen exchange between man and chemical is not in complete, controllable balance. Here an excess of oxygen is produced if all the carbon dioxide is absorbed, or if only enough oxygen is released, not all of the carbon dioxide will be absorbed. As far as water is concerned, theoretically the same amount is consumed as is produced. Actually some water may be retained as solvent for the potassium carbonate. Such and other secondary processes are also typical for all chemical compounds, whether they are producers or absorbers. Together with physical factors (active area, diffusion processes) they may considerably alter the expected efficiency of a system.

Photosynthesis as a regenerative process, with its possibility of unchanging dead weight regardless of the length of time, makes very attractive the use of green plants for production of oxygen by the uptake of carbon dioxide, water, and light energy. With their high amount of chlorophyll, algae seem especially well suited. In the photosynthetic process, for each mole of carbon dioxide and water one mole of oxygen is generated. This would result in a RQ = 1. But in algae such as *Chlorella,* where the dry substance consists of 50 per cent protein, we have to assume other synthetic processes indirectly related to photosynthesis. Therefore theoretically a lower RQ should be expected. Indeed RQs of 0.9 to 0.7 have been found, depending on the feeding of the algae with either nitrates or urea. Thus a certain regulation of the RQ close to man's RQ of 0.82 seems possible, maybe at the expense of optimum oxygen production.

Chlorella algae are most effective in a one-per-cent suspension in water. For the production of 600 liters of oxygen per day, 2.3 kilograms of wet algae in 230 liters or 8.1 cubic feet of water are necessary. Actually this much oxygen is produced only in a rapidly growing algae solution. Growing at a compound-interest rate, one kilogram of algae would increase to 2.6 kilograms in one day. In any case a certain amount of algae has to be removed at intervals. How far this "harvest" with its high protein content can be utilized for inclusion in the nitrogen cycle of man or algae remains to be studied in the future. The nitrogen cycle is the exchange of nitrogen between man and plant: plants convert urea or nitrates into protein, man digests protein and excretes its nitrogen content as urea.

A comparison may be made between the weight of a liquid-oxygen system sufficient to sustain life of one person for 180 days and the weight of a tank of algae 8.1 cubic feet in volume. The former weighs about 800 pounds and the latter about 500 pounds. In the liquid-oxygen system, the oxygen decreases from 360 pounds at start to zero, leaving only the dead weight of the converter (440 pounds) at the end of 180 days. The weight of the algae suspension remains constant, notwithstanding the increase of the weight of the algae proper at simple rate or compound-interest rate growth. The accessories needed for the algae system (tanks, pumps, light system, etc.) have been omitted because their weight is very hard to estimate at the present time. But even on this basis of comparison, the weights of the two systems do not approach the same magnitude before 150 days. With accessories added, a comparison favoring the algae system may require a considerably extended time.

As a last possibility to produce oxygen, electrolysis of water may be mentioned. With the use of high-current-density systems—a process of electrolysis using electrodes of relatively small area with electric currents of high amperage—about 40 pounds of equipment would be required to produce 600 liters of oxygen per day. The utilization or removal of hydrogen and the provision of adequate electric power (by solar energy?) are some additional problems of such systems, not to mention the potential explosive hazard of free hydrogen.

Carbon dioxide, water, waste. The conventional absorbers for carbon dioxide belong to the class of the alkaline metal hydroxides. Such absorbers are sodium and potassium hydroxide, baralyme (a mixture of calcium hydroxide and barium hydroxide), and soda lime (a mixture of calcium hydroxide and caustic soda or sodium hydroxide [NaOH]). About three units of weight are required for the absorption of one unit of weight of carbon dioxide. Lithium hydroxide, on the other hand, requires about one and a half units. Also it retains full reactivity almost down to the freezing point of water. Temperature and humidity exert an influence on most of the absorbents.

Size of the granules, bed height, and velocity of the ventilated air are other parameters which have to be considered for development of an effective absorptive system. It has to be emphasized that the exact quantitative behavior of a system cannot accurately be predicted. Only experimental testing can yield performance characteristics.

Other methods of carbon dioxide removal are based upon the high solubility of carbon dioxide in certain liquids. Under high pressure in a special container, correspondingly large amounts of carbon dioxide go into solution. Thereafter, release of pressure liberates the carbon dioxide which is vented to the outside. Such methods, as used in submarines, are not feasible for space vehicles because of weight and bulk. Another method open for future development may be the "freeze out" method. Here, upon the application of temperatures below the freezing point of water, water solidifies (freezes to ice) and at much lower temperatures, even carbon dioxide solidifies (dry ice) and can be removed as such.

It has to be mentioned that the alkaline metal hydroxides, such as sodium hydroxide, produce one mole of water (18 grams) for each mole of carbon dioxide (44 grams) absorbed. Part of this water is retained by the absorbents but the rest evaporates and has to be removed by the water absorbents.

Common absorbers for water are the oxides of calcium and barium. They require about ten units of weight for one unit of water. The absorptive quality of silica gel is strongly influenced by the relative humidity: the weight requirement falls from 10 to 7 units between 10 and 30 per cent relative humidity at 80° F. Silica gel is capable of regeneration by heat. So is Anhydrone (magnesium perchlorate) which requires—except lithium chloride—the smallest amount in weight (2 to 3 units of weight per unit of water). A disadvantage is the possible explosive hazard if in contact with high concentrations of organic vapors at high temperature.

The previously mentioned absorbents remove water that is in the form of vapor. But a greater amount of water is produced in urine and in feces. Not much has been done to tackle this problem. Urine can be distilled, feces dried. For short flights removal of water does not constitute a serious problem; waste can be stored.

Can water or solid waste be expelled from a spacecraft? Expulsion would mean a certain loss of cabin atmosphere. Any expelled solid material would constitute artificial "meteorites" which might endanger other spacecraft. The loss of mass as such would not alter the course of a spacecraft when it cruises after burnout of the rocket in a purely inertial orbit. Only the momentum (mass × velocity) of the ejected material would have an influence on the craft's course in proportion to the momentum of the craft. To prevent this influence it would be necessary to expel waste material at two opposite points symmetrical to the craft's axis simultaneously in equal quantities.

Based upon the previous discussion, the weight of material necessary to sustain one man one day in a sealed cabin could be presented as follows:

Oxygen	862 grams	Lithium hydroxide to absorb	
Water	2200 "	496 liters of carbon dioxide	1330 grams
Food (dry)	523 "	Anhydrone to absorb 800	
Total supply:	3585 grams	grams of water	2400 "
Total absorbents:	3730 grams	Total absorbents:	3730 grams
Total:	7315 grams or 16 pounds		

This weight does not include the weight of containers, blower ducts, etc., which will remain constant for a given period. As an average figure, a weight of fifteen to twenty pounds has been calculated by engineers for an absorber blower and circulation blower, including the power supply of half a horsepower per occupant of a space cabin, provided the cabin pressure does not deviate much from the normal value. Special attention has to be directed toward the arrangement of the absorptive material with respect to weightlessness to avoid drifting of material and to secure proper airflow.

No figures can be presented for storage of inert gases in cases where a constant leakage of a "sealed" cabin would be unavoidable.

Temperature. The temperature of an aircraft or of a sealed cabin within such craft is determined by the difference in heat gain and heat loss. The heat gain is composed of several sources; the heat loss is effected by the usual channels of heat transfer:

> *Heat gain*
>> External sources—aerodynamic heating, solar radiation
>> Internal sources—rocket motor (or other propulsion), auxiliary equipment, passengers
>
> *Heat loss*   conduction (heat transfer through a substance as such), convection (heat transfer by moving substance), radiation, evaporation

For space vehicles which start from the ground, aerodynamic heating by friction during the first phase of their flight seems to be of lesser importance. In passing through the denser layer of the atmosphere shortly after start, the speed of the vehicle is still not high enough to generate much heat by friction. With increasing speed the vehicle soon leaves the atmosphere, thus eliminating friction. During orbital flight the heat balance is completely determined by radiation. With the sun as practically the only outer source of heat energy, it should be possible to maintain a suitable cabin temperature within the area between the orbits of Mars and Venus by varying the area of highly reflective surfaces toward the sun and surfaces of high emissivity (black) in the opposite direction. This requires that the spacecraft maintain a stable position with reference to the sun. For manned satellites orbiting at such distance and speed that time within the earth's shadow does not exceed several hours, protection against heat loss should not be serious.

The most important problem for all space vehicles destined for return to earth is the re-entry into the atmosphere of the earth, reducing a speed of thousands of miles per hour to a tolerable landing speed. At supersonic speed the movement (kinetic energy) of the air molecules is decelerated—mainly on the leading edges—and then converted to heat. If the air molecules come to a complete standstill, the temperature reached by the air is called "stagnation temperature" (T_s). The relation between T_s and the mach number M (1 M equals the speed of sound) has been described by a simplified equation:

$$T_s = 90 \times M^2 \text{ (degrees Fahrenheit)}$$

So at a speed of 3 mach, $90 \times 9 = 810°$ F would be reached.

But temperature must not be confused with heat, which always can be expressed in units of energy. As an example a small gas burner of high temperature may need a considerably longer time to heat a pot of water to the boiling point than a large wood stove of much lower temperature. The stagnation temperature is only one factor. Heat transfer from air to the skin of the vehicle and heat conduction from the skin through the intermediate material to the wall of the cabin is another factor. Time is a third factor. It has been considered whether a fast, steep dive or a slow, long-lasting glide would produce the smallest amount of heat. As a protection for the cabin it has been proposed to sacrifice some material to melting and evaporating, while the cabin remains in the "shadow" of a mach angle cone by means of a suitable shape of he vehicle. Engineers seem recently to have more confidence of achieving tolerable temperature conditions within a cabin during he re-entry phase.

Sometimes one will find a statement that fifty per cent of man's heat exchange is performed by radiation. This is true only if the wall temperature of a room is cooler than the temperature of the skin or clothing. Man's most powerful means of temperature regulation rests with evaporation of water. Each milliliter or gram of water evaporated at a skin temperature of $25°$ C carries away 582 gram calories or about 2.25 British thermal units (BTU). This figure demonstrates the importance of keeping the cabin air dry, of making perspiration possible if high temperatures cannot be avoided. The Air Force has had considerable success in developing a heat-reflectent, ventilated suit. As important as studies of heat tolerance under extreme conditions are, it should always be remembered that the upkeep of normal temperature-humidity conditions is the basis for full mental and physical performance.

Heat production of man is about equivalent to that of a 100-watt electric light bulb, 470 BTU per hour. This amount is probably negligible compared to heat production by auxiliary equipment, for which definite values may be given only in concrete cases.

Heat production of the propulsion mechanism is, in the case of the rocket motor, enormous. Since the blast of a chemical rocket carries most of the heat away from the vehicle itself and lasts only a short time, it does not constitute a problem at present.

Rapid decompression. One of the most discussed accident potentials in space travel is the puncture of the hull by a meteorite. Depending on the size of the hole, volume of the cabin, and pressure differential between cabin atmosphere and outside space, the cabin air will leak out more or less rapidly. In contrast to general opinion, the total decompression time increases with decreasing outside pressure and theoretically becomes infinite with an outside vacuum, as exists in space. Also in contrast to the general opinion, in case of a finite counterpressure the speed of the outrushing air reaches its highest value—the speed of sound—at a pressure ratio of about 1.9 and does not further increase. The greatest danger of a rapid decompression to extremely low pressure is the onset of acute hypoxia, with vaporization bubbles in the body fluids above 53,000 feet. In present-day military airplanes the pilot is protected by a pressure suit. For short flights in orbiting vehicles a pressure suit may also be used. But there is another problem. Cruising in an orbit makes bailout useless, since after bailout the pilot himself would remain in the orbit. Therefore cabins have been designed which can be operated independently from the main vehicle.

In large spacecraft on long flights the passengers cannot wear space suits all the time. Here also the possibility for plugging a leak is much better. But the loss of cabin air may be so severe that the flight cannot be completed. In this case the best solution seems to be to use a "fleet" of spacecraft on such flights instead of just one. This would permit the passengers of a crippled vehicle to board another vehicle of the fleet.

The creation of a suitable environment in a sealed cabin, then, is a complex problem to be solved by the close cooperation of engineers and biologists. Much has been done; more remains to be done. Ups and downs will occur during further development. But this is natural and no reason for pessimism. The science of applied celestial mechanics is here to stay.

School of Aviation Medicine, USAF

CHAPTER 7

Human Performance in Space

Dr. George T. Hauty

From the first Wright-delivered airplane to the X-15 in 50 years represents technological advancement of sometimes unappreciated magnitude. Less dramatic and consequently even less appreciated has been the concomitant evolution of human functions required by manned weapon systems. In earlier flight these functions entailed the high level of psychomotor ability required, for example, in the coordinated manipulation of stick, rudder bar, and throttle. At present, advances in mechanical, hydraulic, and electronic supplementary systems have reduced these functions essentially to those of information processing and decision making. In considering the obvious further advance in supplementary systems, particularly electronic, it seems plausible that man may eventually invent himself out of those systems designed for space operations. But plausibility in this case cannot be regarded as more than a superficial derivative for several reasons:

First, the very best electronically synthesized approximation of man's ability to process information and make decisions will have a mass at least a thousand times that of man.

Second, this degree of approximation falls far short of the levels of resolution and extent of variability inherent in man's capacity for differentiation and decision.

Finally, since an electronic synthesization of these functions will not possess man's ruggedness and environmental tolerances, sufficient reliability will not be obtained. It is these and several other comparative characteristics which doubtless gave rise to the appropriate observation that "nowhere else can you obtain a self-maintaining computer with built-in judgment which can be mass produced by unskilled labor."

By necessity, then, man will be incorporated as an integral component in systems designed for extended space operations. Together with the other principal components he will be subjected to extensive and systematic testing for reliability determinations. The need for such testing is occasioned not so much by a lack of information on human limitations as by the lack of information on the interactions of these inherent limitations with the conditions man will experience in space. Since these interactions are somewhat unique, a brief discussion of the presently obvious conditions peculiar to a closed ecological system in space and of certain relevant human limitations will serve to indicate what man's performance will have to tolerate.

Confinement

Throughout the development of the submarine the Navy has had sufficient experience with the problem of confinement to be able to mitigate its deleterious effects by a variety of means. Nevertheless the atomic-powered submarine so greatly extended the capability to remain submerged that the problem of confinement and its indirect effects upon morale and proficiency was reopened for study. Extensive and systematic investigations were conducted prior to the commissioning of the *Nautilus*. In one the crew remained "submerged" for 43 days. The resulting habitability improvements and human engineering refinements are clearly evident to anyone who has had the opportunity of visiting the *Nautilus*.

Many of the Navy's general findings and recommended courses of action on the problem of confinement may be extrapolated to space travel. Yet critical differences do exist, and these require further investigation. In a closed ecological system on extended space operations, the crew will be much smaller, restriction of mobility far greater, and the duration of confinement considerably longer. What the joint effects of all these factors may be requires very little speculation. The direct effects of confinement—irritability and hostility—and boredom and fatigue could be intensified to detrimental levels.

The 7-day simulated space flight. In a recent study at the School of Aviation Medicine, USAF, a carefully selected subject was confined within the SAM space cabin simulator for seven days. This experiment was preceded by a two-week period of briefing and short training runs to give the subject a valid and comprehensive basis for estimating his behavior in his unique situation and, accordingly, for predicting his success in completing the simulated space flight.

The daily log maintained by the subject is particularly revealing of the progressive degradation of his good spirits that characterized the beginning of his flight, the gradual increase in irritability, and the seemingly abrupt onset of frank hostility. This progression is illustrated by his reactions to an equipment malfunction. When the television camera that had been trained on the subject became inoperative on the third day, the subject recorded this reaction:

... can't help notice [in the mirror-like glass face of the TV monitor] the tiny one-half inch square peephole opening and closing rather frequently. Guess they're checking me visually in lieu of TV monitoring.

On the sixth day he recorded this comment:

... HA! Just caught someone peeping thru the peephole in the porthole covering. What a ridiculous situation. People sneaking around and peeping thru tiny holes at me!

Again, on the third day, he entered this note in the log upon receiving the command signal to reapply his electrocardiograph (EKG) electrodes:

... signaled back that I would accomplish same after finishing what I was presently doing. Such inconsiderate people. When through I got busy and reapplied the left shoulder electrode. Right shoulder electrode appears to be functioning properly. Got the OK signal on the EKG electrodes from ground crews.

On the seventh day a command signal to reapply the EKG electrodes provoked this entry:

... HA! I knew it. Got the change electrodes signal. It never fails, — 17 — hours left in this abortion and now they want me to change electrodes. Got a good mind to tell them — — — — . I only yank out about 99,000 hairs from my back and shoulders every time I remove that — adhesive tape. — —, might as well get started on it —. 1650— finished with reapplying the EKG electrodes. Nice and raw back there on both shoulders like beefsteak. Oh, well, maybe I'll get disability out of this—one per cent. That'll be all I'll get. — — won't even give me hazardous duty pay for this "ride." Chintzy slobs!

It is significant that during the latter stages of the flight it was the subject's hostility which became a matter of increasing concern to the investigators. In fact it reached the point of becoming the single conceivable reason for a premature termination of the flight. No less extreme were the manifestations of boredom and fatigue, generated in part by the conditions of confinement. During the first two days the subject developed a highly efficient system of work, housekeeping, eating, toiletry, recreation, and sleep. As time continued, this system was gradually reduced to the minimal essential effort required for working, eating, and sleeping. The cumulative effects of boredom and fatigue upon operator proficiency were equally severe.

Detachment

Throughout the duration of an extended flight in space, man will also be subjected to the effects of a condition which, like zerogravity, is not only quite unusual but also capable of compromising the integrity of his performance. This condition may be termed "detachment." It concerns that particular state of isolation in which man is separated or detached from his accustomed behavioral environment by physical or psychological distances of inordinate extent.

Again, as in the case of zerogravity, a complete and valid discussion of the effects of detachment upon human performance cannot be presented until after man has sustained himself in space. Nevertheless some pertinent information is available which does permit one to infer the probable effects over an extended period of time.

In 1934 Admiral Byrd elected to remain alone at an advance base in the Antarctic during the six-month winter night. In 1952 Dr. Bombard sailed alone for the 65 days it took him to cross the Atlantic. These two remarkable men, both dedicated scientists, experienced what perhaps is the closest approximation to the degree of detachment characteristic of space travel. They reported their initial impressions in a lucid manner. Admiral Byrd wrote in a philosophical vein:

> It was a queer business. I felt as though I had been plumped upon another planet or into another geologic horizon of which man had no knowledge or memory. And yet, I thought at the time it was very good for me; I was learning what the philosophers have long been harping on—that man can live profoundly without masses of things—there were moments when I felt more alive than at any other time in my life. Freed from materialistic distractions, my senses sharpened in new directions, and the random or commonplace affairs of the sky and the earth and the spirit, which ordinarily I would have ignored if I had noticed them at all, became exciting and portentous.

The feeling of exhilaration expressed by Byrd is also reported by some pilots in connection with the "breakaway" phenomenon.

But evidence of such exhilaration is completely lacking in Dr. Bombard's comments:

It seemed sometimes as if the immense and absolute solitude of the ocean's expanse were concentrated right on top of me, as if my beating heart were the center of gravity of a mass which was at the same time nothingness. The day I dropped the tow off Las Palmas I thought that solitude was something I would be able to master, once I had become accustomed to its presence. I had been too presumptuous. It was not something I had carried with me; it could not be measured by the confines of myself or the boat. It was a vast presence which engulfed me. Its spell could not be broken, any more than the horizon was finite. And if from time to time I talked aloud in order to hear my own voice, I felt even more alone, a hostage to silence.

In due time the effects of detachment, its constant nothingness, were manifested by acute depression. Byrd reported a disturbed state:

Something—I don't know what—is getting me down—[this] would not seem important if I could only put my finger on the trouble, but I can't find any single thing to account for the mood. Yet, it has been there; and tonight, for the first time, I must admit that the problem of keeping my mind on an even keel is a serious one. . . .

To combat their acute depression, both men realized the necessity of maintaining an extremely high level of mental and physical activity and of completely controlling these activities by rigid routine. In this way each man felt that it was he who was in control of himself and the environment, and not the environment in control of him. Byrd described the value of his self-imposed regimen:

It brought me an extraordinary sense of command over myself and simultaneously freighted my simplest doings with significances. Without that or an equivalent, the days would have been without purpose; and without purpose they would have [ended] indeed, as such days always end, in disintegration.

The effort made by both men to counteract depression was remarkable. Nevertheless depression appears to have been a continuing state, interrupted by occasional moments of anxiety, fear, and irrationality. Bombard reported mounting fears:

Although it might be supposed that my senses had become deadened, my fears increased. I had been at sea for twenty days, always with the realization that one wave might finish me. The fact that the boat had at no time been in mortal danger made no difference. I was to remain at the mercy of that single wave until the last day of the voyage.

And he was aware of a growing irrationality:

To add to the turmoil in my head, I became very superstitious about small things, the inevitable accompaniment of solitude. If I could not find my pipe the moment I looked for it, I considered it a bad omen. The little doll mascot which my friends had given me on leaving the Canaries, began to acquire a tangible personality. I used to look at her and start a conversation, first of all in monosyllables, then whole sentences, describing exactly the next thing I was going to do. I did not wait for a reply, it was not yet a dialogue, although that would come.

From what has been presented, one assumption appears obvious. The detachment to be encountered in extended space operations, with its direct effects of depression, anxiety, and fear, can be expected to be deleterious to the well-being of the human component. Of greater importance is the fact that such detachment, in conjunction with confinement, sleep deprivation, and the nature of the functions required of the human component may lead to sensory deprivation. This in turn causes irrationality and other forms of mental aberrations. This condition will be treated separately, and thereby artificially, but only for ease of discussion.

Sensory Deprivation

To appreciate fully the significance of this condition and its probable effects upon human proficiency, it is necessary to understand something of its etiology, as it is illuminated by recent investigations. Bexton and his associates undertook the study of a question relating to a highly interesting line of current thought. Recent neurophysiological studies have suggested that a given sensory excitation impinges upon the brain by way of two different neural pathways and upon reaching the brain exercises two different functions. One of these, a specific function, is to evoke a specific behavior. The other, a nonspecific function, is to elicit an increase in the diffuse and indiscriminate cortical activity which might be thought of as a continuous background activity. What is so significant about these two functions is the apparent dependence of the specific function upon the nonspecific function. In fact it is speculated that this continuous cortical background activity—induced by the normally incessant sensory input during the period of wakefulness—is responsible for the normal efficiency of brain function. The question then becomes, what happens when the brain is deprived, in substantial part at least, of normal sensory input?

The Bexton-Heron-Scott study. To obtain an answer, male volunteers were confined to a cubicle for 48 hours under conditions that had the effect of greatly reducing the visual, auditory, tactile, and proprioceptive stimulation normally experienced. Deterioration of emotional and cognitive processes was evidenced by increase in irritability and by inability to engage in complex productive thought. The most striking effects were the intellectual aberrations or disturbances. These consisted of hallucinations and illusions of differing levels of complexity. For example, one subject reported seeing ". . . a procession of squirrels with sacks over their shoulders marching purposefully across a snow field. . . ." Even more extreme and perhaps more appropriate was the report of a subject who saw a miniature rocket craft discharging pellets that kept striking his arm. At first the subjects were amused by these phenomena but later on would complain that their vividness interfered with their sleep. Apparently, then, depriving the brain of its normal total sensory input does not induce cortical rest or a coma-like state. Instead the efficiency of this system becomes seriously impaired.

The Mendelson-Foley study. In a second study Mendelson and Foley observed the behavior of patients with poliomyelitis who were confined in a tank-type respirator. Following an initial period of from 25 to 48 hours in the respirator, these patients began to experience hallucinations and illusions. These images were as well organized and vivid as those experienced by the subjects of the Bexton, *et al.*, study. They could not be attributed to the physical disease because the authors reported none of the accompanying symptoms of febrile, anoxic, toxic, or metabolic derangement. Instead the aberrations were attributed to the unique sensory conditions.

Comparison of these conditions with those of the Bexton study reveals similarity and a critical difference. Similarity is given by the fact that confinement to a tank-type respirator does deprive the patient of normal sensory input, though not to the extreme degree achieved in Bexton's study. This difference in degree of deprivation is not the critical difference. Confinement to this type of respirator also imposes upon the patient a most dominant, persistent, and repetitive auditory stimulus—the rhythmic sound of the motor and bellows. On the basis of other experimental results, it does seem probable that this prolonged exposure to a dominant repetitive sensory event did contribute significantly to the disturbances of normal brain function and to the consequent aberrant manifestations.

The Hauty-Payne study. In a third study Hauty and Payne committed highly motivated volunteer subjects to 30 consecutive hours of work at a complex perceptual motor task. The essential nature of this task was to require constant monitoring of an instrument panel and appropriate control of discrete events. With the exception of 20-minute breaks for food and relief, which were given at regular mealtimes, the subjects remained confined to their cockpits and were not permitted to sleep. Following 12 to 15 hours of work and continuing up to the end of the 30-hour work period, all subjects, surprisingly enough, reported having experienced disturbances similar to those mentioned in the two preceding studies. Their hallucinations and illusions ranged from simple and poorly defined phenomena such as "the instrument panel kept melting and dripping to the floor" to well-organized aberrations such as "on several occasions the bank indicator showed a hippopotamus smiling at me." Needless to say, these disturbances exerted quite an adverse effect upon proficiency. One subject, in fact, had to spend a good deal of his time brushing away the little men that kept swinging on and thereby obscuring the airspeed indicator.

In comparing the sensory conditions of this particular study with those of the two studies already discussed, one is struck by the fact that the subjects were not physically deprived of normal sensory input. This was adequately provided by the technicians who were always present during the 30-hour period, by the normal activity going on in the rest of the building, and by the proximity of the laboratory to a very busy flight line.

What then did occasion these disturbances?

The most obvious answer is the work situation, or rather what was required of the subject. This subject was highly motivated to achieve and maintain the highest proficiency score possible. To do so, he had to confine his complete attention to a rather small perceptual field of work. In concentrating his attention to such an extreme degree and for such a long period of time, it seems most probable that the subject in effect deprived himself of the ambient or extraneous sensory events which otherwise would have served to stimulate him. In addition to this likely possibility is the recognized fact that the functions required of the subject, despite their complexity, were highly repetitious in nature. In fact, as time continued, repetition became so dominantly oppressive that many of the subjects grew highly irritated at their inability to think of some undetectable way to throw a monkey wrench into the programing system.

The implication provided by the foregoing studies is clear. In space travel the human operator will be subjected to the three essential environmental conditions that make for sensory deprivation: the reduced sensory environment of detachment, the restrictions on self-initiated stimulation due to confinement, and probably highly repetitious work. Unless the dangers inherent in these conditions are recognized and counteracted by appropriate measures, the human could become the most aberrant component.

Other Conditions

There are several other conditions peculiar to a closed ecological system in space which can be expected to affect human performance adversely. Weightlessness, which is treated in another chapter, is one such condition. Another is habitability. Because of the extreme restrictions on weight and therefore on allowable occupant space, habitability promises to be a substantial problem for the medical scientists and for the design and human-factors engineers. For example, in the seven-day simulated space-flight experiment the approach to the problem of food and the mechanics of its storage, reconstitution, and preparation proved definitely successful with respect to the fulfillment of nutritional requirements, the relative absence of gastric disturbances, the acceptability of the food, and the consequent maintenance of morale. Considerably less successful was the treatment of solid biologic waste and its generation of odor, which became increasingly disturbing to the subject. Still another condition, particularly serious, is occasioned by changes in the levels of essential gases. As is well known, even moderate increases in carbon dioxide and decreases in oxygen relative to accustomed levels will bring about impairment of human proficiency. Such impairment has been experimentally shown to become progressively greater the longer the operator is committed to his task.

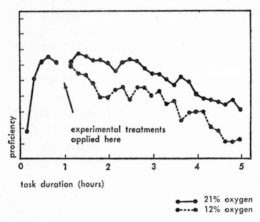

Two trained groups performed a complex 4-hour operator task, breathing different nitrogen-oxygen mixtures. One group got 21 per cent oxygen, the other 12 per cent. Low-grade hypoxia in the latter group increased the degradation of proficiency that normally is the result of fatigue.

proficiency

experimental treatments applied here

task duration (hours)

●——● 21% oxygen
●----● 12% oxygen

INHERENT LIMITATIONS OF THE HUMAN OPERATOR

A moment's reflection will reveal many human limitations which, in conjunction with the environmental conditions already discussed, will act to determine the well-being and proficiency of an operator or crew committed to long-term space operations. Of these, two are not only uniquely relevant but also unlikely to be sufficiently nullified by the techniques of selection, training, and counteraction: the physiological day-night cycle, and fatigue.

Physiological Day-Night Cycle

The first of these two limitations is occasioned by a phenomenon common to all higher forms of biologic life, the physiological day-night cycle, which is most overtly manifested by the alternate phases of sleep and wakefulness. For the essential points to be made it is not necessary to stray into the theories that have been proposed to explain the etiology of this diurnal rhythm. Mention need only be made of, first, the astronomical schedule of events responsible for the periodic variations in illumination, temperature, and other environmental factors and, second, the normal regimen of purposeful or productive activity necessary for sustaining life. Both of these external factors, particularly the latter in the case of man, act to synchronize the physiologic day-night cycle with our daily schedules of work, rest, and sleep.

Physiological manifestations of this cycle are evidenced by all systems and functions which regulate or contribute to the metabolism of the human organism. The temporal course of these manifestations is perhaps best illustrated by body temperature. Depending upon the given individual's daily schedule of activity, the plotting of hourly readings for a 24-hour period reveals a monophasic cycle with maximum temperature occurring during the regular period of wakefulness and minimum during normal sleep hours.

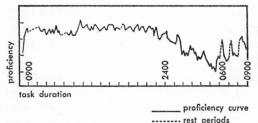

Highly motivated subjects performed a 24-hour operator task. Proficiency declined from 2400 to 0600, then rose—but not to the level of preceding day.

_____ proficiency curve
-------- rest periods

The psychological manifestations of this cycle are more commonly known because of our own personal experiences of having to work for prolonged periods of time or during periods normally devoted to sleep. When highly motivated volunteers are required to perform an exacting task demanding vigilance and judgment for 24 consecutive hours under controlled conditions and when their proficiency is objectively and quantitatively assessed and plotted, a curve is obtained that looks very much like the aforementioned temperature curve. In both cases the sharpest onset of decline and the lowest point of decline coincide with the usual times of retiring and arising.

Most of today's civilian and military requirements are compatible with the physiologic day-night cycle. Hence, barring frank emergency, this limitation receives little consideration insofar as the reliability of the human component is concerned. In extended space flight this metabolic cycle and the consequent periodicity of proficiency will require considerable attention for three reasons. First, it appears that we are committed to this diurnal rhythm; that is, it can be shifted, reversed, lengthened, and shortened to some extent but neither broken nor eliminated. Second, since the space vehicle itself will be a celestial body revolving around the rotating earth or passing to other celestial bodies in the gravitational field of the sun, there will be none of the common referents of the natural sequence of day and night. Consequently a day-night cycle must be simulated within the closed ecological system housing the crew. It must be an effective simulation, i.e., fully synchronized with the work and sleep schedules of the crew members. Third, this synchronization must be maintained for periods of at least several days or weeks.

Such an achievement is faced with certain difficulties. Weight restrictions surely preclude spacious conditions that facilitate sleep. Consider also the unphysiologic nature of zerogravity; specifically, how do the processes and functions responsible for inducing and maintaining sleep adapt to zerogravity? A related question, also unanswerable at the present, is raised by the following consideration: Let us assume, first, that wakefulness and productive activity are maintained by the total sensory input impinging upon and processed by the organism and, second, that under zerogravity, total sensory input is substantially less than under normal conditions. How will this reduction in input modify the ratio of work to sleep; specifically, will the ratio be greater or less than what is normally characteristic of a proficient operator? Finally we come to the indisputable fact that the degree to which a simulated day-night cycle will be synchronized with work-sleep schedules is dependent upon what the system requires of the human component—the nature of the functions, the load these impose, and the temporal distribution of this load. When work-sleep schedules are not synchronized with the accustomed physiological day-night cycle, fatigue is engendered. This becomes cumulative. The final result is a drastic deterioration of proficiency.

Fatigue

The fatigue which is our concern is not the traditional fatigue associated with foot-pounds of expended energy. Instead it is the fatigue associated with the depreciative effects of sleep deprivation or prolonged commitment to a skilled or semiskilled task upon the subsequent inclination or ability to continue that task. Manifestations of these depreciative effects consist of decrement in proficiency such as impaired judgment, slower decision time, and decline in alertness; increased variability of proficiency; degradation of attitudes and feelings; and various metabolic changes.

With the increasing complexity and duration of conventional flight, skill or operator fatigue—as it may be called—has been subjected to extensive investigation. The principal findings are revealing.

In the case of relatively simple tasks requiring the detection of a single sensory event such as a radar or auditory signal, it has been generally found that detection proficiency will begin to decline after about half an hour. At the end of two hours it will have deteriorated to levels that may be operationally unacceptable.

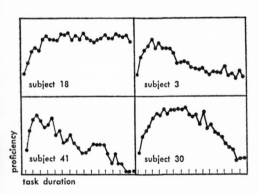

Any discussion of a general "fatigue" curve should not obscure individual variation. To illustrate, these proficiency curves of 4 different subjects who were committed to an operator task during 4 consecutive hours clearly indicate the wide degree of variation among individuals in their susceptibility to fatigue.

Initial levels of detection proficiency could be raised or lowered depending upon stimulus definition, stimulus duration, stimulus frequency, and instructions. Nevertheless the general form of the proficiency curve over an extended time remains essentially the same as that just described. The implication of this for crews committed to similar task requirements in space operations is obvious and requires proper countermeasures.

In the case of skilled tasks, such as pilotry, which involves complexly integrated display and control systems, fatigue is manifested in several different ways. These include:

1. Increase in the range of indifference. Early in the work period the operator permits the indicators to make only a slight departure from the limits of tolerated error before executing corrective action. As work continues, progressively greater departures from null are tolerated. The operator's standard of performance becomes lower the longer he works, and this may occur with or without his awareness.

2. Loss in timing. In monitoring a collectivity of events and successfully integrating the corrective action indicated, the skilled operator must be able to program his corrective responses efficiently prior to their execution. As he becomes fatigued, the less able he is to program efficiently. The operator may well execute the correct response, but unfortunately at the wrong time.

3. Disintegration of the perceptual field of work. In most display systems the indicators requiring the most frequent attention are generally located in the center, while those requiring the least attention are at the margins of the display. At the beginning of work the operator's attention encompasses the entire field of work through peripheral vision and efficient scanning habits. As work continues, progressively less of the field is monitored regularly. Finally only the center indicators receive regular attention and the marginally located indicators apparently are ignored.

4. Dissociation of corrective responses. With disintegration of the perceptual field of work, it is inevitable that the operator also loses his ability to respond in an integrated manner. Eventually he responds to the different indicators as if they were separate instead of linked components.

5. Loss of proficiency under fixation–block-confusion. Finally as fatigue becomes acute the operator experiences the sequential occurrence of fixation–block-confusion. He suddenly realizes that he is monitoring only one particular indicator. When this occurs, he freezes or blocks and is powerless to take any necessary action. This blocking is of short duration—one or more seconds. But then it is followed by a state of momentary confusion, which can be so

extreme that the operator does not know which control is associated with which indicators. Confusion too is of short duration. With its termination the operator resumes his previous method of scanning and attains his immediately previous level of proficiency.

Also obtained in these investigations were these additional points of practical importance:

• It has been repeatedly found that the effects of operator fatigue are cumulative, that is, the deleterious effects of prolonged commitment to a task are not completely dissipated by a normal period of sleep. Should the operator again resume work, he gives every indication of being completely rested. But as work continues, the onset of proficiency deterioration occurs sooner than during the previous work period and progresses at a greater rate.

• As fatigue increases, so does the operator's irritability. Aside from degrading the operator's feeling of well-being, irritability—in the extreme case—also endangers the operator and the system in which he functions. For example, the force with which the operator manipulates his controls often exceeds the limits of the action required and the tolerances of the controls themselves.

• The most dangerous aspect of fatigue is the low order of correspondence between the fatigued operator's actual level of proficiency and what he believes it to be. That is to say, the operator is aware of his fatigue—general tiredness, boredom, and vague discomforts—but he is not aware of what has happened to his proficiency. Despite the fact that his proficiency may have deteriorated to unacceptable levels, he may believe—he may even argue with considerable vehemence—that his proficiency has not changed at all. And fortified with this belief, he elects to continue working. Attesting to the danger of such a decision is the number of fatal automobile accidents that occur late at night and early in the morning.

In space flight, fatigue will be a problem just as in the case of conventional flight. It will probably be even more critical because of the interactive effects of the conditions and limitations which we have discussed. This probability is supported by the proficiency curves obtained during the aforementioned seven-day simulated space flight. The character of these curves indicates that the subject would have been in serious trouble had he been in actual flight.

MITIGATION OF DEGRADATIVE EFFECTS

What has been presented thus far would seem to argue against man's inclusion as a functioning component in a space-vehicle system. At the very least the task of predicting the reliability of a human component would appear to be a difficult, if not grim, undertaking. The intention implicit in this chapter is to foster such an inference. And this is done to direct attention to the fact that in adidtion to the problems of propellants, guidance systems, and astrophysics there are equally critical human problems that urgently need research. With the completion of this research, valid predictions of reliability will be ensured, and measures will have been assessed for their efficacy in attenuating the effects which otherwise would be of substantial detriment. Such measures which are presently indicated include pre-exposure training, programing of functions, improved information displays, and the use of drugs.

Pre-exposure Training

By committing candidates who have been selected on the basis of relevant physical and psychological standards to a simulation of the joint conditions of confinement and detachment, three practical purposes will be served:

First, those candidates who fail to make an acceptable adjustment to these conditions can be eliminated from further consideration. In this way, selection—which actually will be a continuing process—will have been further refined.

Second, those candidates who do adjust satisfactorily will be subjected to additional exposure under systematically manipulated conditions. With sufficient exposure and appropriate indoctrination, these candidates will have adapted to the conditions of confinement and detachment at least to the point where their direct effects can be tolerated.

Finally, the objective assessment of the behavioral effects of these conditions can be expected to provide additional information concerning the etiology and mitigation of irritability, hostility, depression, and fear.

Programing of Functions

The area requiring the greatest research effort is the programing of functions required of the human component in synchrony with metabolic diurnal cycles. As a specific illustration we might consider the following not-too-unrealistic situation. Let us suppose we are told that the technical capability to send one man on a flight to the moon and back will be available shortly; that the flight will require eight days; and that to maximize chances of a successful mission, the human operator will have to function intermittently and at top proficiency for as long as he is able on each of these eight days. Now let us suppose that we are then asked: How many hours of each of these days will the operator be able to function at acceptable levels of proficiency and how will these working hours have to be distributed? Since these appear to be exceedingly simple questions, one is surprised to learn that the answers are simply unavailable at present. The reason is that, like most simply stated unanswerable questions, these particular questions protrude like the iceberg's tip from a formidable complex of basic, long-term physiological and psychological problems. The principal physiological problem, man's commitment to a physiological day-night cycle, has already been discussed at length. Of relevant interest is a finding from the seven-day simulated space flight.

During this simulated flight the subject, who regularly retires at 2400 and arises at 0630, was subjected to a drastic revision of his accustomed day-night cycle. He was committed to a four-hours-on–four-hours-off duty schedule for the entire flight. During the four-hour on-duty period he was required to perform tasks believed to be similar in nature and load to those required of the operator during actual space flight. During his four-hour off-duty time he was free to devote his time to such recreational activity, sleep, etc., as the cabin permitted.

As was predicted, the subject's level of proficiency declined progressively for the first four days because of the deprivation of sleep and the consequent accumulation of fatigue. This in turn is attributable to the difficulty normally experienced in adjusting to a new and considerably different day-night cycle. It was expected, as time continued, that a satisfactory adjustment would be achieved and that this would be reflected by an arrestment of proficiency decline and then a gradual increase in proficiency. During the final three days proficiency decline was arrested and some increment in proficiency was noted. Still the level of proficiency during the last three work periods fell far short of the subject's initial levels. In large part, as could be inferred from the subject's log, this was because of his incomplete adjustment to his new schedule. What would have happened had the simulated flight been longer is a matter for speculation.

From the data obtained from this single subject it is impossible to generalize to a population of equally capable men. Many more simulated flights will have to be made before it can be concluded whether the work-sleep schedule which was used is an appropriate schedule. If found to be generally inappropriate, other schedules will have to be tested. In conjunction with this line of investigation it will also be necessary to explore the advantages to be gained from pre-exposure adaptation. That is, for periods of from two to

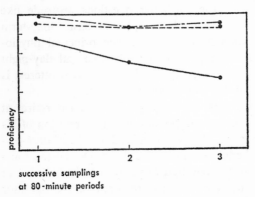

Comparison of the two uppermost curves with the lowermost curve reveals the extent to which optimal work-rest ratios will attenuate the decline in proficiency resulting from a less-than-optimal work-rest ratio.

four weeks prior to the simulated flight, subjects will be committed to the very same schedule of work and sleep that will be required during the flight itself. Another related line of investigation concerns the programing of work within a given on-duty period. It can be predicted, and has been experimentally shown repeatedly, that the ratio of work to rest is of critical importance in the production or attenuation of fatigue.

To summarize, the area of programing will require greater exploration of the modifiability of metabolic diurnal rhythms and,

r a given period of extended flight, the determination of those
atios and schedules of work and sleep which will ensure continuity
f optimal proficiency. With this information the design engineer
ill be better able to program functions with such compatibility as
> attenuate substantially those manifestations of metabolic rhythms
nd fatigue which otherwise would limit human performance.

formation Displays

The presentation of information required by the operator of a
anned system represents an extensive area of continuous research
nd development. As a result of this research substantial gains
ave been made in the reliability and speed with which relevant
nformation can be received and processed. Such gains in turn are
videnced by increased proficiency. A profound increase in pro-
ciency will sometimes come from a seemingly slight or insignifi-
ant modification of an information display. This can be illustrated
riefly by the results of several studies:

• In one study two experimental groups and one control group
f subjects were required to monitor an information display made
p of several conventional aircraft indicators and to control for
eir driftings from null positions. One experimental group was
rovided with supplementary information given by a single visual
ignal which was activated by the departure of any one of the
adicators from null. The other experimental group was provided
ith a supplementary auditory signal. The proficiency of the former
xperimental group was nearly twice as great as that of the control
r standard group. The proficiency of the experimental group pro-
ided with the supplementary auditory signal was even greater.
he superiority of the auditory over the visual signal might be
ttributed to the reduction in visual load effected by enlisting the
dditional input channel of hearing.

• In a subsequent study, the effectiveness of the single supple-
entary visual signal was compared with the effectiveness of a
ultiple supplementary visual system, that is, a visual signal for
ach of the different indicators. This latter group was provided with
upplementary information which not only indicated that one or
ore indicators had departed from null but in addition identified
he specific indicators requiring corrective action. It was found
hat the gain in proficiency resulting from the multiple system was

approximately double the gain of a single supplementary informational signal. These relative gains were not short-lived but sustained throughout prolonged work.

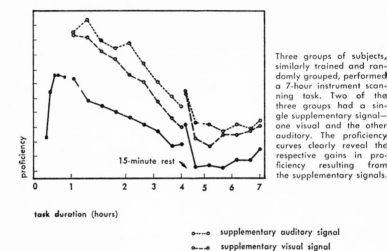

Three groups of subjects, similarly trained and randomly grouped, performed a 7-hour instrument scanning task. Two of the three groups had a single supplementary signal—one visual and the other auditory. The proficiency curves clearly reveal the respective gains in proficiency resulting from the supplementary signals.

o----o   supplementary auditory signal

o---o   supplementary visual signal

o——o   instrument scanning

Why was the multiple system superior? It is most probable that its specificity of supplemental information was the determining factor. This factor also may have accounted for the sustentation of superiority, although perhaps not entirely, because of the possible pertinence of an interesting line of theoretical speculation. In the general discussion of sensory deprivation, it will be recalled that subjects who were committed to a 30-consecutive-hour work period began to experience mental aberrations following 12 to 15 hours of work. These aberrations were attributed to the possibility that, in effect, these subjects had deprived themselves of the ambient sensory events which otherwise would have stimulated them. The question is, How did this happen? Possibly the focusing of attention on a constant patterning of stimulation has as its consequence the progressive adaptation of the operator to his ambient or background sensory events, however normal or excessive these may be. In short, because of adaptation the effective level of background sensory input will be gradually reduced. Since it is this sensory input which is so essential to efficient cortical function, it follows that sufficient reduction of input would be accompanied by obvious manifestations. In the early stages these would be evidenced by decline in alertness and a consequent deterioration of operator proficiency. In the later stages, when reduction is of extreme degree, manifestations are equally extreme in the form of outright hallu-cinatory behavior. As was pointed out, the preceding is at present no more than a theoretical explanation.

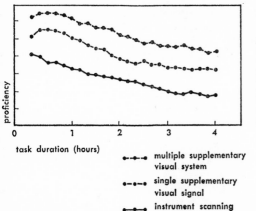

After identical training, three groups performed a 4-hour operator task. The gain in proficiency from a multiple supplementary visual system was rough-ly twice the gain result-ing from a single sup-plementary visual signal.

task duration (hours)

•—•—• multiple supplementary visual system

•—•—• single supplementary visual signal

•—•—• instrument scanning

If this theory is empirically supported, means will exist for the attenuation of fatigue-induced proficiency decline—and for the counteraction of sensory deprivation. These means will be informa-tion display systems designed not only for the presentation of nec-essary information but also for the sustentation of normal levels of sensory input.

Drugs

A discussion of the possibilities inherent in the use of drugs for the maintenance of well-being and proficiency would far exceed the space allotted this entire article. For brevity and a clear-cut illus-tration of certain of these possibilities, only one drug—d-ampheta-mine, or Dexedrine as it is more commonly called—will be dis-cussed. This particular analeptic preparation was selected because of its distinctiveness in having been subjected to extensive system-atic investigations on young, healthy, normal men.

The first question explored concerned the extent to which this preparation would postpone the onset of fatigue and the consequent deterioration of proficiency. It was found that a standard dosage (5 mg) had the property of sustaining initial levels of proficiency for from four to seven hours of prolonged work. This was accom-

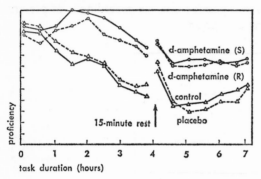

Following task training, d-amphetamine dosages were given to 2 of 4 groups required to perform a 7-hour operator task. The drug had considerable effect in sustaining proficiency. The effects of a single dosage (S) appear to be fully as efficacious as the effects of repetitive dosages (R).

plished with no discernible evidence of an increase in physiological costs, which is in keeping with electrophysiological studies that have indicated the effects of d-amphetamine to be confined to those subcortical systems considered to be the physiological correlates of alertness. Finally, with the dissipation of analeptic effects there was no evidence of a letdown effect, that is, a refractorylike state due to depletion of energy and manifested in such a case by abrupt loss of proficiency.

The second question concerned the extent to which this preparation would restore proficiency that had already deteriorated as a consequence of prolonged work. In a study designed to answer this question, a standard dosage of the drug was administered following 24 consecutive hours of work. The result was a sharp increase in proficiency. During the six remaining hours of work following this experimental treatment, proficiency was restored to the levels of the preceding day. The proficiency level of the subjects receiving a placebo preparation was approximately one half that of their initial levels of the preceding day.

The third question concerned the possibility of side effects, such as irrationality of judgment, lowered frustration thresholds, etc., which have been popularly ascribed to this and other analeptic preparations. In view of the practical consequences of such side effects, objective and systematic assessment was made. Only negative results were obtained. This indicates that if side effects are occasioned by a standard dosage of d-amphetamine, they are of such a low level as to be undetectable.

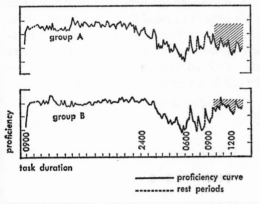

Groups A and B performed a 30-hour operator task. At 0900 of the second day group A was given a placebo capsule and group B received 5 mg of d-amphetamine. Comparison of the shaded areas reveals the extent to which d-amphetamine restored proficiency that had been degraded by prolonged, continuous work.

This description of the experiments with d-amphetamine may seem to take the form of a testimonial for this drug. Such is hardly the intention. The purpose, as stated initially, was merely to demonstrate in a specific context the benefits that might be gained from the pharmacological support of human capability.

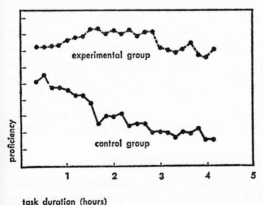

Two groups performed a 4-hour operator task. Only the experimental group had the advantages provided by 3 entirely different techniques—drugs and feedback systems—designed to increase and sustain proficiency. The comparative proficiency curves show the combined effectiveness of the techniques.

The potentialities to be realized from man's inclusion as an integral component in a space system are difficult to predict at the present time. The reason is that certain of the conditions peculiar to extended space operations—such as confinement, detachment, weightlessness, and required functions—will exact a profound modification of man's biological and psychological intolerances. The extent to which these can be modified will depend in large part upon those measures which act either to extend these intolerances or to attenuate the deleterious effects of the modifications required. Present relevant information affirms, first, the efficacy of such measures and—most significantly—their additive function, and second, the gains to be obtained by continued research.

School of Aviation Medicine, USAF

CHAPTER 8

Weightlessness

Dr. Siegfried J. Gerathewohl

Of all the strange conditions that men will encounter in sustained rocket flight the strangest is the state of zerogravity, in which there is no sensation of weight. Psychologically it is the most fascinating problem of space flight because it has no parallel in human experience on the ground or in most conventional flying. The investigation of this condition is difficult, since it can be produced only in circumstances approximating those of actual flight in space. Moreover there will not be a real substitute for the absence of gravitational force in space operations even if human ingenuity is strained to its limits.

THE BACKGROUND OF WEIGHTLESSNESS

Weightlessness is a new concept in the thinking of physicists, physiologists, and psychologists, born in the air battles of World

War II. When the Allied formations that were bombing Germany acquired fighter escorts, the German fighter pilots developed a new type of firing pass on the heavily guarded enemy. The attacking fighters penetrated the Allied defense from high altitudes, made their pass at the bombers from below after a violent pullup, and then evaded the massive firepower of the bomber elements by another dive. During this maneuver the pilot first produced high "positive g," from the arresting of his downward motion as he pulled up from his dive. "Negative g" and weightlessness were produced during the pushover into the second dive. These gyrations frequently caused disturbances of vision.

Startled by this unusual ordeal and the resulting gunnery misses associated with it, the fighter pilots reported their experiences to Dr. Heinz von Diringshofen, a German professor of aviation medicine in Berlin. He made some flights himself and experienced a weakening in the legs and insecure control movements during the weightless state. After he had become accustomed to the maneuver, he enjoyed it as a pleasant flying experience.

On first impression it might seem that weightlessness would be a very simple and pleasant experience—rather like floating through the air as we do sometimes in dreams or like drifting on the surface of a pool of water. But this is not necessarily the case. On earth we are never free from weight. The dream condition is only a wish fulfillment which in itself recognizes the lasting yoke of weight. The swimmer afloat in the pool is also subjected to the force of gravity though buoyed up by the liquid support. Even men and birds in flight have weight although their aerodynamic properties enable the air to support them as if they were on the solid surface of the earth.

Actual weightlessness can be experienced only when the force of gravity is absent or is counterbalanced by an opposite force. The first case refers to a body outside the earth's gravisphere. The second can happen inside the earth's gravisphere. In either case, but for different reasons, no gravitational pull acts on the body's organs. The result is a condition that can seriously affect the flyer's well-being and his operational performance. It may deeply affect the autonomic nervous functions (those automatically or unconsciously controlling heartbeat; respiration; digestion, bowel, and bladder function; touch; sight; balance; orientation). Ultimately it may produce a severe sensation of succumbence and an absolute incapacity to act.

Speculations about the effects of weightlessness have been far from unequivocal. Just after the Second World War Drs. O. Gauer and H. Haber noted the rapid advance of rocketry and drew some hypothetical conclusions about the effects of zerogravity and weightlessness on the flyer's mind and body.* They postulated that the brain receives its information on the position, direction, and support of the body from four perceptual mechanisms: pressure on the nerves and organs, muscle tone, posture, and the labyrinth of the

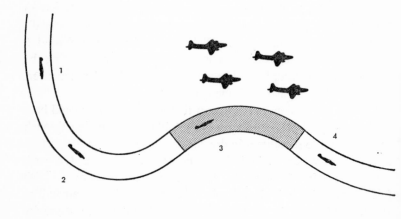

| 1. Attacking maneuver starts with steep dive | 2. Start of pull up for underside attack on bombers | 3. Period in which weightlessness occurs | 4. Final dive to evade bombers' fire |

inner ear. These mechanisms indicate changes in acceleration and position by exerting pressure on their sensory cells. It was theorized that the first three of these mechanisms would cease to function properly in the weightless state. Also that the otoliths, the sensory organs in the ear which normally aid orientation, might send signals to the brain that would actually confuse the space traveler.

* Although the terms *zerogravity* and *weightlessness* designate the same condition, *zerogravity* is used here to refer to the physical state and *weightlessness* to the psychophysiologic experience of the individual.

These prospects—and there was even a prediction of death due o failure of the circulatory system—convinced the authorities of he United States Air Force that some means should be found to tudy weightlessness experimentally. These experiments will be liscussed after the principles involved in gravity and subgravity 'esearch have been defined.

Table I: Sense Modalities and Organs, Their Stimulation and Response to Subgravity

	Mechanoreceptors[1]				Photoreceptors[4]
	Specific Gravireceptors[2]	Nonspecific Gravireceptors[3]			
	Exteroceptors[5]	Proprioceptors[6]		Tangoreceptors[7]	Exteroceptors
	motion and position sense	muscle sense	posture sense	pressure sense	optical sense
Sense organ	otoliths	muscle spindles[8]	Vater-Pacini corpuscles[9]	nervous plexuses & Meissner corpuscles[10]	eyes
Normal stimulus	acceleration and weight	tension & weight	tension	pressure & weight	light
Effect of subgravity	decreased weight and displacement of otoliths	decreased weight & tension of muscles	no effect	decreased pressure at contact points of body with support	no effect
Effect of zerogravity	lack of weight and displacement of otoliths	lack of physical stress	no effect	lack of pressure at contact points of body with support	no effect
Sensory input during zerogravity	no or zerogravity stimulation	no stimulation	no effect	no stimulation	no effect
Sensory output during zerogravity	no or zerogravity signal	no signal	no effect	no signal	no effect
Sensation during zerogravity	no gravitational vertical	stress-free sensation	no effect	stress-free sensation	no effect
Psychophysiologic result	loss of vertical orientation without visual reference	disturbance of muscular coordination	no effect	loss of tactile orientation	no effect when visual cues available

[1]Nerve endings and receptor organs stimulated by differences of pressure (such as those of touch and hearing).

[2]Nerve endings and receptor organs with the specific function of responding to stimuli having a gravitational source.

[3]Nerve endings and receptor organs which do not have the sole function of registering gravitational forces on the body but which provide similar information to the brain.

[4]A nervous end-organ or receptor sensitive to light.

[5]Sensory nerve terminals stimulated by the immediate external environment (such as those in the skin).

[6]Sensory nerve terminals which give information concerning movements and position of the body. They occur chiefly in the muscles, tendons, and inner ear.

[7]A sense organ that responds only to physical contact (such as touch).

[8]Bundles of fine muscular fibers enclosed in a sheath of connective tissue.

[9]Sense corpuscles, the largest of the end-organs of the skin, scattered throughout the tissues beneath the skin, as in the pulp of the fingers and along the course of nerves.

[10]Sense corpuscles (of touch) in the tips of the fingers and toes, in the skin over the lips, etc.

Physical Concepts

To understand the problems of physics involved in subgravity and zerogravity research and to appreciate the use of modern aircraft for producing weightlessness, some basic principles of mechanics and dynamics must be discussed.

Concepts of gravity. The force of gravity decreases in inverse proportion to the square of the distance from the earth's center. At a height of 4000 miles above the surface, or twice the earth's radius above the earth's center, it is only one fourth of what it is on the ground; at 8000 miles it is one ninth, and so on. At a distance of 36,000 miles it is reduced to a mere one one-hundredth. But the near-gravity-free state at this distance is a static condition, valid only for a fully supported body.

A vehicle in flight may also approach and attain a zerogravity condition. In "horizontal" flight, for example, the airplane actually follows a curved path because of the pull of the earth's gravity. In certain instances of higher supersonic velocities, centrifugal tendencies begin to counteract the earth's gravitational force to an increasingly noticeable degree as the inertial force in the line of flight resists the centripetal pull of the earth. In other instances the inertial force may reinforce the gravitational pull. When the forces are in balance, the condition of zerogravity or weightlessness is experienced by the crew of the aircraft.

Concepts of weight. These examples show that we have to deal with several concepts and kinds of weight. First of all, the term *weight* refers to the attractive force exerted between the earth and bodies near it. The weight of a body is a force acting on the body, not a description or an indication of the quantity of matter in the body, which is its *mass*. Weight in this sense is identical to heaviness and simply means that a given mass is subject to a given force of gravitation. But in dynamic instances of motion such as flying, additional forces besides the force of gravity enter into the phenomenon of "weight" and must be added to or subtracted from the force of gravity. These forces are, again, the forces of inertia characteristic of a mass in motion (velocity). Suppose a mass is supported, as a stone on a table; then the reactive upward push of the table equates the weight of the mass, the downward pull of gravity on the stone. Similarly "weight" of a moving mass may be defined as the resultant force exerted on the body in reaction to the forces of gravity and inertia. "Weight" is therefore dependent upon the dynamic conditions to which the body is subjected.

Quantification of the principle of weight can be accomplished by providing a conveniently defined unit of force. The best-known procedure consists of measuring the weight of an unknown mass against the known weight of a standard mass by means of a balance. For cases of locomotion, particularly in aeronautics and astronautics, this form of measurement is too restricted. So we turn to the general theory of relativity, which states that heaviness and inertia are merely different aspects of the same basic phenomenon. According to Newtonian mechanics the force applied to a body (mass) may be determined as proportional to the acceleration imparted to the body; that is, *force* is equal to the product of the *mass* and its *acceleration, $F = ma$*. The force of gravitation is thus measured most conveniently and practically in terms of acceleration, using the acceleration of gravity at the earth's surface, $g = 32.17$ ft/sec^2, as a unit. When an object is at rest the forces of inertia are absent, so the object is in the "normal state of gravity," expressed as $g = 1$.

Concepts of weightlessness. Allowed to fall freely, a body is subjected to a downward acceleration of 1 g. In this case the force of its inertia counterbalances the force of gravity at each point on the downward path, thus putting the body in a state of zerogravity. Actually the body is pulled down by the gravitational force and therefore is not "agravic," but it is unsupported and therefore without weight. If the body is subjected to a downward acceleration of less than 1 g, the force of inertia is subtracted from the gravitational force. In this case the body is in a state of subgravity.

Another case of weightlessness is provided when a body moves in a so-called Keplerian trajectory. This is the kind of arc whose most familiar examples are the orbits of celestial bodies and of artificial satellites. Actually the free-fall situation is nothing but one extreme case of such a trajectory when the initial velocity is zero and the acceleration equals 1 g directed toward the center of the earth. If an object above the surface of the earth is accelerated away from its center, it moves along a conic section. The kind of trajectory produced depends upon the energy (force) applied and consequently the velocity attained. For small velocities such as those achievable by aircraft, the trajectory is a very elongated ellipse with one focal point at the center of the earth. The small section near its apex, emerging from the surface of the earth, can well be represented by a parabola. If a velocity between 18,000 and 25,000 mph is reached, the body revolves around the earth as a satellite in a circular or elliptical orbit. The body is then completely weightless in relation to the earth, and so is any part, or inhabitant, of it relative to the moving system. This means an inhabitant is not appressed to the floor or sides of the vehicle. This condition may also be thought of as falling freely through space but in a curving path that never brings it downward to the center of the mass that holds it in its established orbit. If a velocity over 25,000 mph is attained, the object will escape from the earth. In both cases a continuous state of weightlessness or lack of appression prevails.

Table II: Characteristics of Optimal Keplerian Trajectory*

Vehicle	Velocity at entry or maximum speed after burnout (mph)	Height of trajectory (mi)	Angle of climb (deg)	Duration of weightlessness (min)
T-33A	370	.49	55	.47
F-94C	450	1	63½	.6
F-104B	650	4	75½	1
X-15	3,600	82	85	5.5
Boost glider	10,000	200	90	10
Meteor Junior	18,000	500	90	infinite

*The figures given in this table are approximations only.

WAYS OF PRODUCING WEIGHTLESSNESS

The simplest means to produce the state of weightlessness would appear to be the vertical free-fall. But a speed of fall is soon reached at which strong frictional forces from the air restore the body's weight. To produce an appreciable period of weightlessness, it would be necessary to drop the object from a very high altitude. The difficulties involved in preparing and recovering such an experimental object—say, a manned capsule—are rather prohibitive.

Another means proposed to produce weightlessness is the eleva-

or. By moving an elevator up and down after an initial acceleration
one can produce a state of subgravity, but the durations obtainable
are relatively short, even in long-shaft elevators. The same is even
more true in specially built towers or pipes which have also been
proposed and used for studies of weightlessness.

Only the aircraft seems to be practical means, because of its
availability, safety, and the longer periods and various amounts of
reduced gravity that can be produced. Moreover the situation obtained in flight is more realistic than that obtained in any other way.
Thus it can serve as a training condition at the same time it is
employed for research.

The flight maneuver to produce weightlessness requires the elimination of all accelerations except the one caused by gravitation,
which constantly acts downward at a magnitude of approximately
1 g. The pilot can accomplish this elimination by flying his plane
through a specialized pushover, in which he must hold the needle
of his accelerometer precisely at the zero mark of the indicator. A
pushover is a vertical planar maneuver in which the angle of climb
changes continuously from a plus to a minus value. The indicated
airspeed decreases uniformly from an initial value at the start of
the maneuver to a minimum at the top of the curve and then increases back to or exceeds the initial value. Thus the aircraft moves
at considerable speeds. A power output ranging from an appreciable fraction to full power must be maintained to overcome
drag, although no lift is required. This holds for the upward as well
as for the downward leg of the maneuver.

In 1951 it was concluded that brief periods of subgravity and
zerogravity could be obtained by flying a parabola within the earth's
atmosphere. Several prominent test pilots, including Lt. Col.
"Chuck" Yeager, Bill Bridgeman, and Scott Crossfield, made flights
in modern fighter aircraft following Keplerian trajectories. They
either enjoyed the weird situation or experienced befuddlement, a
feeling of falling and disorientation, and a tendency to overshoot.
The results of these flights were inconclusive in many respects.

In 1955 and 1956 various experiments on the effects of virtual
weightlessness were conducted at the School of Aviation Medicine,
USAF. The aircraft used was either a Lockheed T-33A or—since
the spring of 1956—a Lockheed F-94C Starfire. After preliminary
flight tests it was found that the best working altitude for both air-

craft was between 17,000 and 25,000 feet. This height usually lacked turbulence and clouds and provided a safety margin in the event of an emergency.

Two different flight patterns were employed. The first consisted of four individual parabolas, which started at an altitude of about 21,000 feet with the T-33 and at about 23,000 feet with the F-94. After a shallow dive to 17,000 feet the pilot pulled the aircraft up smoothly so that an acting force of 1.5 g was not exceeded. He

F-94C Zerogravity Flight Pattern

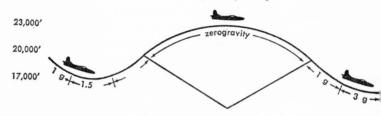

T-33 Zerogravity Flight Pattern

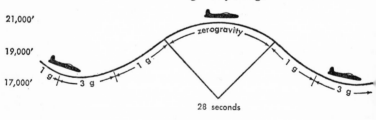

28 seconds

then put the aircraft into a 60-degree climb at full throttle and initiated the pushover, using the inertial effect to counteract the gravitational pull of the earth. By utilizing his thrust to overcome drag, he kept the airplane on its Keplerian course until the pullout, which was started early enough to prevent the aircraft from passing its mach limit and the aforementioned acceleration. The subjective experience of the increased weight during pullout thus was slight. In some cases it was not even noticed because of the large radius and slow rate of change of acceleration.

The second flight pattern consisted of three parabolas in a row. At 20,000 feet a sharp dive was started and the aircraft nosed down at an angle of about 65 degrees. Then the plane was pulled up rather abruptly, resulting in a 3-g acceleration. With the higher climbing speed available a longer parabolic arc was obtained. Recovery at 17,000 feet provided the necessary speed for the up-swing into the next parabola. In this maneuver the individual was subjected to a sequence of relatively high and sharp increases of weight and longer periods of virtual weightlessness than in the other type of maneuver.

The average time of weightlessness was 25 and 35 seconds, respectively. In one attempt with the F-94 the additional power of the afterburner was used. This produced the longest time of virtual weightlessness recorded in experimental flights, namely 42 seconds. The most important factors which determine the characteristics of the Keplerian maneuver make it evident that longer periods of weightlessness can be produced by the utilization of thrust and acceleration. By and large the duration of the weightless state is approximately proportional to the maximum speed that the aircraft can achieve at the beginning of the maneuver. This is conditioned by the fact that individual pilots vary in skill in obtaining maximum durations and that minute accelerative forces are present during about half of the subgravity period.

WEIGHTLESSNESS IN SPACE FLIGHT

Powered flights at the border of space have already taken place in various experimental aircraft, and use of the rocket craft for operations outside the atmosphere is at hand. The first step into space with manned vehicles will most probably consist of extending the periods of unpowered glides of the rocket aircraft after burn-out, and thus weightlessness, from a few to several minutes. In fact converted intermediate-range ballistic missiles could be used to probe into the unknown of prolonged weightless flights.

The second phase in the development of human space flight may attain long-distance flights at supersonic and hypersonic speeds through regions of the upper atmosphere. These are flights on a global scale and can be called global space flights. With regard to motion dynamics the vehicles will again be a crossbreed of aircraft and missile. Powered for only about two minutes, they will climb to great altitudes, from which they glide to their destinations around the globe. After an initial acceleration of 3 or 4 g acting for several minutes, a state of reduced gravity will be maintained for the rest of the flight. Since these planes are still equipped with wings, they skim the upper layers of the atmosphere, and the traveler never becomes really weightless because the glider is not following the path required for such effect.

The third step into space may be the use of multiple-stage rockets to carry men several hundred miles above the surface of the earth to remain in orbit for a definite period of time and return to the earth, re-entering the atmosphere nearly tangentially, decelerating, and gliding in for a landing. Vehicles that thus achieve orbit may be special-purpose satellites and be manned and equipped for operational duties, such as search and surveillance or the relaying of scientific and meteorological data. Relatively high and prolonged accelerations are needed to attain orbital distance and orbital velocity. They may range from 3 g for 10 minutes to 10 g for approximately 2 minutes. After the last burnout the rocket and its crew are weightless. They will not receive their weight back until they land or slip back into the atmosphere.

The final step in the conquest of space will be the exploration of other planets and excursions into outer space. To reach escape velocity, accelerations of about the same magnitude and time pattern are required as were specified in the preceding paragraph. But while the crew of an artificial satellite may have to endure the weightless state for days or weeks, the space traveler must live in it for even longer periods of time.* While a trip to the moon would take several days, journeys to our neighboring planets would require much longer. Unless fuel is abundant, the spacecraft must undertake an orbital transfer course similar to that of a comet around the sun. Normal traveling time for such an earth-to-Mars trip is about 260 days and for a round trip to Venus about two years. Such interplanetary voyages would require that men live in an artificial environment for long periods of time.

One problem confronting them would be that of permanent weightlessness of long duration. As was the case during orbital exposure, zerogravity is no longer a temporary experience. It

* [Unless a means of restoring a degree of apparent gravity can be provided, as by constant acceleration or by rotating the spacecraft.]

becomes the prevailing psychophysiologic state in which the individual must live, work, sleep, eat, drink, eliminate, etc. The questions to be asked at this point concern not only his tolerance to weightlessness. Of greater significance is his ability to adapt himself psychologically and physiologically to this condition and to readjust himself to the normal gravitational state upon his return to earth. It is in this connection that the physiological effects of zerogravity—such as on circulation, digestion, and muscular functions—are of primary importance. These questions will only be decided by launching a manned artificial satellite into orbit and by using such a biosatellite as an experimental laboratory.

WEIGHTLESSNESS EXPERIMENTATION

Experiments with Animals

In 1951 a group of scientists headed by Dr. James P. Henry of the Aero Medical Laboratory at the Air Research and Development Command's Wright Air Development Center started the first experiments on animals during rocket flight. An instrumented capsule was developed for the nose cone of the V-2 and Aerobee rockets, and laboratory animals were placed inside this miniature laboratory. The capsule also contained instruments for telemetering heart rate, blood pressure, and respiration to a ground station. Several of the flights were successful. The capsule gave adequate protection, and its temperature and pressure did not change significantly. The electrocardiogram, breathing pattern, and blood pressure of the lightly anesthetized animals were undisturbed by accelerations and subgravity states during the free cruise at 200,000 to 400,000 feet in the ionosphere.

Later a very simple psychological test was included in the Aerobee experiments. The object was to find out how an unrestrained animal would behave during the two-minute near-weightless state and after the deployment of the recovery system. A special motion-picture camera photographed the activities of two white mice placed in the two compartments of a drum mounted with its axle across the long axis of the rocket and rotated at a rate of four revolutions per minute.

One compartment was equipped with a small hurdle over which the mouse had to jump in order to remain on the bottom of the drum. The mouse had undergone the removal of the labyrinths of the ear with their directional otoliths; the other mouse in the unobstructed compartment was normal. During weightlessness the normal mouse was confused while floating freely in the compartment. The labyrinthectomized mouse was less disturbed. Having no otoliths, he received no clues either true or false. This did not disturb him because their prior removal had accustomed him to a lack of orientation. When the parachute opened, arresting free fall and imposing a steady descent, both mice resumed their normal walking and jumping activity, keeping in pace with the turning drum.

Another series of experiments was performed by Dr. H. J. A. von Beckh at the National Institute of Aeronautics in Buenos Aires, Argentina. He placed several South American water turtles, including one with damaged labyrinths, in an aquarium. He fed them during states of subgravity produced by dives in a fast two-seater fighter aircraft. One difficulty was that the water, with the turtles in it, would rise and float above the bowl, and several times it was necessary to lift the tank and fit it back around the water. But as Von Beckh had expected, the turtle that had been deprived of his otoliths was able to snap his food without trouble, whereas the normal turtles were slow and missed the bait. After about twenty or thirty attempts they too began to regain their normal coordination.

Recently this author conducted experiments on the labyrinthine righting reflex of the cat during parabolic flight trajectories in the T-33 aircraft. The objective of this test was to find out if the cat would right itself when held upside down during weightlessness and how this condition would affect the reflex behavior of the animal. Under ordinary conditions if a cat is held upside down and then released, it turns in a flash into the normal posture so that it always lands on its feet. This reflex functions under both visual and blindfold conditions. How would it function in the gravity-free state?

An analysis of the motion pictures taken in the air shows that the animal retained its reflex functions as long as minute accelerations were present. If the cat was really weightless, the reflex was delayed or failed completely. Then the animal was confused and panicky and tumbled, or righted itself in the wrong direction. The available visual cues did not essentially affect this reflex pattern. When the resultant of the forces involved (gravity and inertia) was zero, the otoliths were not stimulated at all. This caused complete disorientation. The animals were still bewildered after the weird experience was over.

Table III: Animal and Human Responses During Periods of Weightlessness of Different Durations

Short Duration		Moderate Duration
Animal experiments in rockets and aircraft	**Human experiments in aircraft, subgravity devices, and water**	**Animal experiment in Sputnik II**
no significant cardiovascular, pulmonary, and respiratory changes	disorientation without visual reference	no significant changes of physiological functions during six days of weightlessness
no pathologic aftereffects	disturbance of neuromuscular co-ordination	
disorientation and panic during exposure, change of reflex pattern	prolonged blackout and delayed motor responses during post-acceleration weightlessness	**Human experiments**
orientation through minimum otolith stimulation, visual and tactile clues, and learning	motion-sickness symptoms ("space sickness")	no information available on human functions and behavior
	mental set for falling	
	oculo-agravic illusions in the dark	
	but	
	majority of subjects feel elated, tolerate changing accelerations and subgravity, adapt and compensate during exposure, move more easily than normal, and learn to perform as under 1 g conditions	

The entire series of experiments indicates that the stresses imposed by rocket ascents and the condition of virtual weightlessness are well within the range of tolerance of the animals used. This conclusion is in accordance with the semiofficial reports released on the Russian dog in Sputnik II that she survived her six days' exposure to complete weightlessness without ill effects. With this amount of experimental confirmation of animal reactions, future work can be directed more toward the investigation of man's performance during weightlessness. Of course the development of higher performance rockets and research satellites favors the testing of new and miniaturized equipment in which the use of animals seems to be indicated. This also holds for long-time exposure and performance control through continuous telemetering and television display. But we should not place too much emphasis and significance on behavioral studies of animals during weightlessness, because they may not truly reflect the adaptability of men to this condition.

Experiments with Humans

Experiments on human subjects were begun as early as those on animals. In the summer of 1951 Dr. Ballinger of the Aero Medical Laboratory performed a series of physiological tests in a modified F-80E. His subjects were given 15- to 20-second periods of subgravity during parabolic trajectories. The men, firmly strapped in place, were able to maintain their sense of orientation. Blood pressure, heart rate, and respiration did not show significant alterations. Head-shaking had no adverse effects either. But had the subjects been unrestrained and without visual reference, disorientation might have been extreme.

Disturbances of motor coordination, first reported by test pilots, were also studied by Von Beckh. His subjects were required to draw crosses in seven small squares arranged diagonally across a sheet of paper attached to the instrument panel of the experimental airplane. The tests were made during the subgravity dives, sometimes with the eyes open and sometimes with them closed. In the subgravity state they had difficulties in drawing. When their eyes were shut, they lost their sense of orientation and drew the crosses in anything but a diagonal line. But, as with the turtles, after a number of flights their results improved.

Von Beckh has demonstrated another effect of weightlessness previously mentioned. He had the pilot pull out of the dive abruptly, then rise on the ascending arc of the parabola. In this maneuver, after about 6.5 units of g, he found that the blackout lasted longer, his responses were delayed, and he felt as if he were flying upside down.

Systematic experiments involving a large number of volunteers were then made at the School of Aviation Medicine, USAF. At first eye-hand coordination was studied in a T-33A during parabolic flight maneuvers. The test consisted of aiming and hitting a target attached at arm's length to the panel in the rear part of the cockpit. By and large the men in subgravity hit too high because of the changed input-output ratio of the elevating muscles. This finding was confirmed by Professor Lomonaco in Rome, Italy, who tested his subjects with a tapping problem in his subgravity tower.

n both types of experiments the men adjusted to the situation after epeated performances in a state of weightlessness.

Man's ability to orient himself depends upon a variety of factors. 'n conflict situations such as during weightlessness, the eye becomes he only reliable organ. But will it remain reliable or may it be leceived by illusions? There definitely are such occurrences in the gravity-free state, and one, the so-called oculo-agravic illusion, was nvestigated by USAF scientists. A luminous target as well as a visual after-image, observed in the dark, seemed to move and to be displaced upward during the states of subgravity and zerogravity obtained in F-94C aircraft. If the normal gravitational condition was restored or acceleration increased, the targets seemed to move below the horizon. Such illusory perceptions can cause confusion, and disorientation may be expected to recur when operating in such an unusual environment.

Another attempt to study orientation during weightlessness has been made by immersing men in water. Since the body and the fluid have about the same density or specific weight, the body, though supported, is in a kind of weightlessness relative to the surrounding medium. It had been voiced before that skin divers lose their orientation at some depth if visual cues are lost. Some recent studies under controlled conditions seem to confirm this conclusion. Simulation of the sensation of weightlessness in the swimming pool has yielded information on the function of the gravireceptors.

Thus far no experiment has been conducted which clearly isolates the altered stimulus–sensation relationship during subgravity. Even in flights in the T-33 and F-94 zerogravity was obtainable for only a few seconds. Subgravity prevails for the rest of the parabola, and various types of acceleration occur during the experimental flight pattern. As the result of human exposures to subgravity conditions lasting 20 to 30 seconds, it is generally agreed that minimal disturbance of coordination and orientation is experienced as long as the subject retains tactile and visual references. But even so the responses are highly individualistic. This is particularly true for human tolerance to weightlessness.

To date almost one hundred men have participated in experiments on weightlessness conducted at the Aero Medical Field Laboratory, Holloman AFB, and at the School of Aviation Medicine, Randolph AFB. A group of 47 individuals was studied by scientists of the latter organization with regard to their egocentric experiences. All were physically qualified for jet flying and were highly motivated for the adventure. Seventeen were either Air Force pilots or had at least some flying training; only nine had no jet experience prior to the experiment; and all had flown at least once in conventional aircraft.

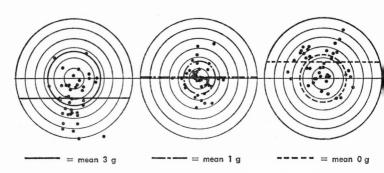

——— = mean 3 g   —·—·— = mean 1 g   — — — = mean 0 g

An eye-hand coordination test was administered first at ground level (1 g) in the cockpit of a T-33A aircraft. The subject tries to hit with a stylus a bull's-eye located 3 feet away. The same experiment was then repeated during increased (3 g) acceleration and during weightlessness (0 g) while flying parabolic maneuvers. Above, the results of a group of subjects show the trend to hit too low during increased g-forces, and too high during the weightless condition. Right, diagram of test results. The hit accuracy for the weightlessness curve shows steady improvement during the six trial attempts.

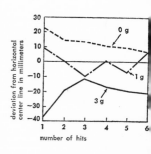

Subjective symptoms prior to flight consisted mostly of a moderate apprehension and mild tension or nervousness. While the experienced jet flyers were generally found to be free of symptoms, some of the neophytes showed signs of mild fear before take-off and during first exposure to weightlessness. These symptoms were occasionally followed by autonomic disturbances in the latter phase of the flight. In some cases subjects were apprehensive because of their proneness to motion sickness and anticipated discomfort during the parabolas.

Practically all subjects reported sensations of floating or slowly drifting during lack of appression. About half of these felt very comfortable and reported no unusual sensations of motion other than a slight elation associated with the feeling of exhilaration and pleasantness. Several others rather vividly described sensations of

Table IV: Responses of 47 Human Subjects to Short Periods of Virtual Weightlessness

Group	No. of subjects	Attitude prior to flight	Psychological reactions	Physiological symptoms	Autonomic disturbances
I	22	normal, or slightly apprehensive	sensation of rest or slow floating; feeling of well-being, comfort, pleasure, relaxation, enjoyment, and exhilaration; same experience during repeated exposure; euphoric or enthusiastic responses	tingling and "light" sensation at abdomen; slight disorientation with eyes closed; slight giddiness; slight hyperventilation; slightly hyperactive patellar reflex	none
II	11	normal, or slightly apprehensive	sensation of floating or tumbling forward and backward; sensation of falling or lift during transition; sensation of standing on head, or being suspended in an inverted position; mildly elating situation, neither unduly pleasant nor exactly comfortable	slightly disoriented with eyes open, enhanced with eyes closed; hyperventilation, mildly dizzy and slightly nauseated; hot or cold feeling, increased perspiration; tired and sleepy after flight	none, or moderate degree of vertigo and nausea attributed to changes of acceleration and weight
III	14	normal, or slightly apprehensive; occasionally fear and acute anxiety	sensation of floating, drifting, or tumbling, sensation of falling forward or rolling over; "light" or "heavy" feeling in head or stomach; stomach seems to move upward; elated in the beginning with progressing discomfort	generalized motion-sickness syndrome including sweating, dry throat, increased salivation; feeling of cold or hot	vertigo and nausea; vomiting during flight

falling, tumbling, rolling over, or being suspended in mid-air in an inverted position. About one third of the subjects experienced discomfort, nausea, and severe attacks of motion sickness.

There is some evidence from our findings that flying experience and conditioning affect tolerance to weightlessness. Also that pilots of jet aircraft may be best suited for operations under conditions of reduced weight. About one third of the volunteers developed troublesome symptoms that reflected unfavorably upon their attitude, motivation, and performance. The evidence indicates the necessity of carefully selecting future rocket flyers, of properly conditioning crews and passengers of vehicles exposed to weightlessness, and of protecting them against its effects.

CARE OF THE SPACE FLYER

With respect to weightlessness there are three main areas of research and programing in the Air Force: the medical, the psychological, and the operational.

The Medical Aspect of Weightlessness

The first concerns the general medical aspect of well-being of the weightless individual and the intactness of his physiological functions. The reasons for the undesirable responses observed are still unknown, and so are the remedies to be employed. We know for certain that our unhappy test subjects were under a heavy strain. In some cases this was removed by repeated exposure and in others it was enhanced. More studies must be conducted on human tolerance, training, and possible remedy by medication.

Strain. As the human body is mainly elastic and semirigid in structure, the concept of stress as used in elasticity theory may be applied to explain the distressing effects of altered weight. Since weight can be the mechanical cause of stress, its increase will tend to induce strain, its decrease to reduce strain. We know that the organism is under a severe strain, for example, during the take-off. It is physically stress-free in the appressionless state because no forces whatever act on the body. This may be the reason why most individuals feel elated during the weightless condition.

The relation between weight and strain does not seem to be that simple. Even considering the fact that the undesirable symptoms may be brought about by the whole flight pattern, weightlessness seems to play the dominant role in their development. Weightlessness can be experienced as stressful by individuals who are unaccustomed or hypersensitive to unnormal gravireceptoric signals. The reason for this may be that normally the zero point of psychological stress corresponds to the 1-g situation. This is a situation of considerable physical stress, whereas the zero point of mechanical stress corresponds to the gravity-free condition. A flight-line study of stress conducted by the Department of Pathology of the School of Aviation Medicine at Randolph AFB, using variations of 17-hydroxycorticosteroids and blood eosinophils as an index, showed that almost all subjects tested experienced the parabolic flights as a stress situation.

Further studies of the basic physiologic functions are needed in this area against possible hazards to spacecrews through weightless periods of long duration. Although we have no indication that there would be any difference in cardiovascular and respiratory processes during periods such as those found in a satellite, even small irregularities may indirectly lead to psychosomatic disturbance.

Eating and drinking. The question of the space flyer's well-being involves eating and drinking, digestion, and elimination during weightlessness. On the basis of his study of flights, involving over 200 parabolas, Dr. Ward of SAM's Department of Space Medicine confirmed the necessity of using special food and drink containers and pointed to the potential hazards of aspiration while eating and drinking during weightlessness. Foods of different specific weights are digested at different rates, and this may require appropriate measures for adequate nutrition. Similarly the elimination of waste products must be considered from the standpoint of mass alterations within the spacecraft and of how it can be accomplished to the benefit of the crew.

Sleep. The next problem is relaxation and sleep. Although the majority of our subjects felt relaxed and comfortable, nothing is known about the easiness of sleep. Since under normal conditions the posture of rest is associated with a shift in weight distribution within our body, it may be easier to fall asleep in a satellite. On the other hand the deprivation of gravireceptoric input may have different effect upon our nervous system during sleep than during the conscious control of the environment. The lack of cutaneous stimulation—body contact with the chair or bed during sleep—may give rise to a feeling of insecurity and to wild dreams. A substitute for this stimulation might be a large-area body harness made of foam rubber or similar elastic fabrics, which will gently press the body and provide natural rest.

Movement. A third problem is how man will be able to walk and move in the gravity-free state. For the time being this is not an important problem because the space flyer will be fastened to his seat for safety reasons. In a larger artificial satellite handrails and suction-type shoes will be mandatory. In addition it seems necessary to study how men can turn, walk, and work in an unsupported state where a minor shift of equilibrium through voluntary and involuntary motion can cause the body to float or tumble.

Table V: Areas of Research on
Weightlessness in the Air Force

Technical Aspect	*Human Aspect*	*Operational Aspect*
Means	**General research problems**	**General requirements**
free-fall elevator conventional aircraft boost-glide vehicles research rockets biosatellites	general medical implications physiological implications neurological implications psychophysiologic implications sensory implications	general activities scientific activities military operations subgravity flight zerogravity cruises
Special problems	**Specific research problems**	**Specific performances**

producing subgravity
  states
producing zerogravity
demonstrating weightless-
  ness
sensing and indicating
  devices
automatic guidance systems
telemetering and recording
  of data
processing of data
miniaturization of equip-
  ment
construction of specialized
  equipment
simulators of weightlessness
training devices
emergency and protective
  equipment
	general health and well-being
	nutrition, digestion, and
	  elimination
	stress, fatigue, rest, and sleep
	reaction performance
	neuromuscular coordination
	general intelligence
	alertness and attention
	orientation
	sense organs and sense
	  modalities involved
	sensory input-output ratio
	sensory thresholds
	proprioception
	gravireceptors of the body
	tolerance to subgravity
	tolerance to changed accelera-
	  tion pattern
	adjustment and learning
	readjustment to normal
	  gravitational conditions
		piloting of aircraft in sub-
		  and zerogravity
		piloting of rocket craft in
		  sub- and zerogravity
		communication
		search and surveillance
		warfare
		construction of space
		  platform
		crew and passenger
		  comfort
		emergency procedures
		rendezvous
		escort of space station
		recovery of separated
		  personnel
		re-entry problems

The Psychological Aspect of Weightlessness

The second area of research concerns the psychological aspect of weightlessness. In theory motion sickness and vertigo can be interpreted in terms of the information-handling capacity of the brain—that is, the effort expended by the individual to maintain his frame of reference—rather than in terms of physiological stimulation. Several of our subjects described sensations of motion and position very different from the actual weightless situation. The occurrence of perceptual illusions of the oculo-agravic type must also be mentioned in this connection. It seems that some of the unusual and disturbing experiences may be produced by the sensory peculiarities and the final breakdown of the egocentric frame of orientation.

In a similar way Lt. Col. Simons introduced the concept of "mental set for falling" into the picture of motion sensitivity during space flight. It seems that some individuals may develop such a set more easily than others, whereas others compensate for unusual sensory information, or lack of any, by means of rationalization. As one of our subjects put it: "I am weightless; hence I cannot fall." If we assume that the psychologic factors associated with weightlessness are subject to learning, we may conclude that the person will adjust better as he improves his ability to remain oriented. We do not know whether visual orientation will be stable under all circumstances or whether the eye function itself will be disturbed. There is evidence that visual acuity may be unaffected. Nevertheless we should investigate the performance of operational tasks like the adjustment of crosshairs and aiming or tuning procedures requiring vernier acuity, steadiness, and accuracy. Such tasks may be required during reconnaissance, communication, and combat actions in a satellite or rocket glider.

Further investigation must aim at the determination of the egocentric threshold of weightlessness. We still do not know the amounts of acceleration necessary for an individual to have the sensation of weight or weightlessness. The practical implications concern pros and cons of the application of an artificial acceleration or "quasi gravity" for the comfort of the space flyer if this should prove necessary in case of prolonged exposure to the gravity-free state. This substitute has been proposed again and again, but it should be avoided if possible. While a slight acceleration of a large space station will have certain advantages, the Coriolis force (deflecting forces on a moving object caused by the earth's rotation) operating on a small spacecraft will be considerable. They cause greater discomfort than benefit to the crew. How can orientation and navigation be maintained in a continuously spinning body? These are complications that the designer wants to avoid. Every additional device and load is a greater nuisance in a spacecraft than in any conventional airplane. If on the other hand a platform is to be rotated slowly, we should know the amount of quasi gravity desired.

By and large the problems encountered during weightlessness point primarily to neurophysiologic and psychologic factors. It is planned to study these factors through more personal experience in flight and more basic research. The latter includes morphological changes of cell and tissue structure, afferent fiber response in the labyrinth of the ear, muscle tone and eye movements, and other neurologic and psychophysiologic processes associated with weightlessness. The program has expanded since the advent of space medicine research, and it will expand further with the increasing significance of space operations for the Air Force.

The Operational Aspect of Weightlessness

The third area concerns the engineering problems, the hardware and its operation. The problem of producing longer periods of weightlessness for future medical research can be approached in the near future by alternative compromises. One is to use current and future aircraft, including the experimental types. The other is to convert available and future boost vehicles of the intercontinental ballistic missile type to manned research vehicles. Since they all would be single-seated, the occupant cannot be pilot and pure subject at the same time unless an automatic guidance and recovery system is provided. These features should also be so constructed that they can be controlled by hand if an emergency arises. It is generally agreed that automatic programing and guidance would yield a more accurate zerogravity flight profile. Also various degrees of subgravity can be produced by these means. The application of missile control and guidance systems to zerogravity problems will be an important step toward increased research capability.

Instrumentation. Closely related to this problem is the construction of accurate sensing and recording devices, including indicators to the pilot. Considerably longer periods of absolute zerogravity are anticipated in future experimental flights. It has been demonstrated in the past that residual accelerations of small magnitude can cause significant difference in orientation responses. At present attempts are being made to develop sensitive and reliable accelerographs for subgravity studies. Only if more accurate instruments are available can we conduct more sophisticated experiments.

Since visual reference is the most valuable means of orientation in zerogravity, its functioning must be ensured under all circumstances. Without sight there is no longer "up" and "down," and this eventually may cause confusion. Actually as long as visual orientation is maintained, the loss of the gravitational vertical is not alarming because the cockpit of a space vehicle will be so designed that the canopy, instrument panels, and table tops will always point upward. This directional orientation, though valid in relation to the spacecraft only, will still be convenient and practical. It will sustain that frame of reference to which all creatures on earth are accustomed. Everything within the vehicle must be kept as simple, unambiguous, and natural as possible.

This holds as well for the pilot's instruments and controls. He has to perform under rather changed conditions anyway. More than in any other type of flying the pilot will be told from the ground what to do. Outside the atmosphere, control input and feedback are absent or qualitatively different. The monitoring and firing of swivel-mounted steering rockets have nothing in common with conventional flying. The pilot will mostly monitor servomotors and ignition systems. There is no "feel of the pants" during zerogravity. Gliding through space will be an automatic, push-button affair and a rather inhuman type of locomotion. Only when plunging back into the atmosphere will the pilot's flying skill be required.

Conditioning and training. This brings us to the last problem—the conditioning and training of the future space flyer. Elaborate personal-propulsion devices and air-jet trainers are being suggested to train the men for weightlessness. They are based on the assumption that in this state a man must use a rocket gun and all kinds of body twists in order to move along or change position. It is also contemplated to expose him to accelerations of several g to study his coordination during changes of acceleration, and to submerge him in water and let him regain his orientation.

These conditions simulate very crudely the subgravity condition because the man is still supported by a solid or liquid medium. The amount of transfer from the training to the actual situation can only be guessed. There is a good possibility that the "kinesthetically gifted" individuals may show better training results than the less talented ones, but this does not indicate their better tolerance to weightlessness and long periods of physical inactivity. We know that a man will fall to his death if he loses his balance at the rim of the Grand Canyon. But in teaching a man how to cope with this danger we do not teach him how to whirl around in the air. Instead we provide him with means of preventing the accident and tell him how to use them. This principle must also be applied to weightlessness. A rope with which the subject can pull himself, and appropriate harness, handrails, fixtures, and suction-type shoes that prevent him from floating will most probably do the trick. The training must aim at the skillful utilization of such safety devices.

Finally care must be taken to provide for the readaptation of the weightless man to the normal condition of gravity. We do not expect too much difficulty because this process should even be easier than the adaptation to weightlessness. For readjustment studies the use of the human centrifuge seems appropriate. It can serve to expose a man to an increased acceleration of, say, 2 g for longer periods of time and then bring him back to normality.

Weightlessness is not the sole problem during space flight. Changes of acceleration must also be considered. We know today that protected personnel can tolerate the accelerative pattern of a rocket ascent, and that the majority of flying personnel enjoy the exposure to the subgravity state in our controlled experiments. We have reason to believe that even longer periods of absolute weightlessness can be tolerated if the crew is properly conditioned and equipped.

School of Aviation Medicine, USAF

CHAPTER 9

Observations in High-Altitude, Sealed-Cabin Balloon Flight

Lieutenant Colonel David G. Simons

In Chapter 3 Dr. Strughold has shown how flight at 100,000 feet is equivalent in many ways to flight in free space. Facing the problems of existence at this altitude provides an opportunity to gain a keen insight into many of the human-factor problems that are becoming critically important as the tempo of progress toward manned space flight steadily increases.

Weightlessness is the only major factor requiring extensive investigation for manned space flight which cannot be studied, at least to some degree, with balloon techniques. During the past five years the critically important question of the effects of exposure to heavy primary cosmic radiation has been effectively studied, using balloon-borne sealed cabins.

The first part of this chapter will consider the biological effects of heavy cosmic ray primaries, emphasizing the results to date of exposure of biological materials and animals. The second part will review flight experiences and observations made on the first two Manhigh flights.

ANIMAL FLIGHTS AND RELATED EXPERIMENTATION

Preceded by a few preliminary flights, the first serious attempt to expose animals to altitudes above 90,000 feet to evaluate biological effects of heavy cosmic ray primary radiation was started at the Aero Medical Field Laboratory, Holloman Air Force Base, in August 1951. During the next two and one half years, thirty-nine flights were launched from Holloman Air Force Base and from northern launch sites. Many of these flights suffered serious difficulties because of the lack of experience with sealed-cabin techniques at very high altitudes and the necessity for developing twenty-four-hour balloon tracking and recovery techniques. Although the primary purpose of these flights was to evaluate the effects of heavy radiation primaries on biological specimens, most of the effort had to be directed toward solving the problems of conducting the experiments. By the end of this period satisfactory techniques had been established or their principles proved. Meanwhile the work of Dr. Hermann J. Schaefer at the Naval School of Aviation Medicine, Pensacola, Florida, had established clearly the theoretical nature and hazard of heavy cosmic ray primaries in terms of tissue exposure.

Cosmic Radiation Problem

What are primary cosmic rays? Physicists have obtained much information about the nature of primary cosmic particles, using nuclear emulsions or track plates, which are similar to photographic film but are several times as thick and designed specifically for recording the tracks of ionizing particles. Nuclear track-plate emulsions flown to high altitudes on balloons and rockets have shown that incoming cosmic radiation is not radiation as we ordinarily think of it but consists of very-high-energy nuclear particles. These individual atomic nuclei are completely ionized, i.e., have no orbital electrons. They carry a maximum positive charge, such as carbon 6, iron 26. Cosmic radiation consists of nuclei of the elements from hydrogen through the heavier elements up to iron, but rarely beyond. Nuclei of the two lightest elements, hydrogen and helium, comprise approximately 96% of the total charge spectrum, while the nuclei of the medium and heavy elements comprise the remaining 4%. In general the heavier particles occur with decreasing frequency, following roughly the distribution of cosmic abundance. To date, the relative abundance of the heavy component with respect to energy is not so well established and appears to vary considerably with time.

All the primary cosmic ray nuclei have been accelerated to high velocities (energies) approaching the speed of light. Most of them arrive at the top of the atmosphere with speed corresponding to a minimum cutoff energy or an acceleration of one billion electron volts (Bev) per nucleon. In general, nuclei of progressively higher energy are observed in decreasing abundance. The minimum-energy heavy nuclei (carbon through iron) are considered to be of greatest biological interest. The shift in the low-energy cutoff correlates inversely with changes in the eleven-year sunspot cycle. This changes exposure to the low-energy heavy primary by as much as 100%.[8]

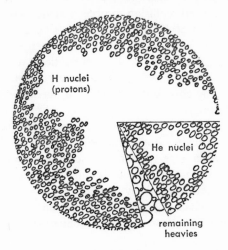

Low-energy primary cosmic ray particles hurtle in all directions through space in the vicinity of the earth's orbit. When they approach close to the earth they are absorbed by the earth's atmosphere. Many are first deflected from equatorial regions by the earth's magnetic field because of each primary nucleus's charged condition. From altitudes that can be attained by balloons and up to satellite orbits within 1000 miles of the earth, there is nearly complete shielding from low-energy primaries through the first 50° of geomagnetic latitude. All latitudes are exposed to medium- and high-energy primary particles which penetrate the magnetic field to the atmosphere. Most of them are converted to secondary cosmic radiation. Poleward of 55° geomagnetic latitude there is essentially no magnetic protection from primaries. (See photo section.)

Within the atmosphere many of the low-energy particles are stopped above 80,000 feet by ionization. The energy of the atomic nucleus is expended in ionizing the air through which it passed. This event is called a thindown because of the tapered appearance of the track in nuclear emulsions. The remaining low-energy particles and essentially all high-energy ones eventually collide directly with atomic nuclei of the traversed material. Each collision results in mutual disintegration and is called a star because of its stellate appearance in nuclear emulsions (see photo section). For heavier primary particles this collision process occurs when they have reached 100,000 to 80,000 feet. The resulting energetic nuclear debris of protons, neutrons, mesons, etc., comprises secondary cosmic radiation. For biological considerations, only secondary radiation occurs below 75,000 feet. It is responsible for the total ionization of air by cosmic rays reaching a maximum value in the 75,000-foot region.

The scatter of nuclear debris from a star represents a scatter of ionization that quickly dilutes the original concentrated path of ionization through a large volume of absorbing material. The effect of this scattered ionization on cells is comparable to nuclear radiation and has been extensively studied. The secondary cosmic radiation dose produced by stars[9][16] is less than half the generally accepted permissible dose of 0.3 roentgen-equivalent-physical (rep) per week.

By contrast the intense track of ionization characterizing a heavy primary particle just before it reaches thindown produces a unique microbeam. To date no method has been devised to reproduce the length, width, and intensity of ionization occurring in this prethindown portion of heavy cosmic particle tracks. These events occur within a small fraction of a millisecond.

To establish a basis for estimating the biological effects of cosmic ray primaries at various altitudes, Schaefer[10] assumed that whenever a particle produced more than 10,000 ion pairs per micron of path length in tissue (i.p./μ_T) corresponding to the radiation intensity produced by a radium alpha particle, it would be biologically damaging. He therefore defined a traversal by any particle reaching this intensity of radiation as a prethindown "hit." His calculations indicate that a carbon atom can produce 10^4 i.p./μ_T for a distance of 900 microns; an iron nucleus produces 10^4 i.p./μ_T along nearly 10,000 microns (1 cm) of its path length.

Calculations of radial spread of ionization by Schaefer[9] indicate that the radius depends as much upon the residual kinetic energy of the particle as on its atomic number. Peak radiation intensity of the order of 50,000 roentgens (r) can occur within the central one-micron diameter of a prethindown hit. The dose decreases to about one r at a distance of six microns from the center of the particle's path. These calculations indicate that beyond one cell diameter (10 microns) the radiation drops to what should be biologically insignificant levels unless toxic chemical products are diffused to surrounding tissue or some unidentified mechanism extends the radiation effects radially.

In summary, the low-energy heavy primaries are of greatest interest since they frequently terminate as thindowns, whereas high-energy particles usually terminate as stars. The positively charged nuclei are deflected when crossing the lines of the earth's magnetic field in equatorial regions. The low-energy particles (less than approximately 6 Bev per nucleon) can enter the atmosphere only at high latitudes (polar regions) where they come in parallel to the magnetic lines of force. Exposure to the full spectrum of cosmic ray primaries is obtainable along the northern border of the central United States. Animals flown from Holloman Air Force Base, New Mexico, have served as controls, since they are subjected to identical flight conditions, including cosmic ray secondaries, but are exposed to essentially no heavy primary prethindown hits.

This geomagnetic protection effect is especially significant in terms of satellite flight, since equatorial orbits of less than approximately 45° geomagnetic latitude remain within the "zone of protection" produced by the magnetic shielding effect of the earth's magnetic field. Cosmic ray primary exposure in such orbits at less than 1000 miles apogee will be comparable to the control balloon flights from New Mexico. To obtain exposure to the low-energy heavy cosmic ray primaries of specific interest to radiobiologists, either polar orbits or much more distant orbits will be required. Not until flights are made to distances of many earth's radii, such as flights to the moon, will full continuous exposure to cosmic radiation be experienced, since even polar orbits spend part of their time passing through the equatorial zone of protection and receive shielding from the earth's shadow.

Capsule and Flight Technique

During 1954 and 1955 nineteen balloon flights carrying biological specimens were launched from northern latitudes. These flights ranged up to thirty-six hours in duration and attained altitudes as high as 126,000 feet.[11] The animal cabin environment developed for these flights employed a spherical sealed capsule 24 inches in diameter. It was constructed of spun aluminum in two hemispheres.[12] Tracking techniques for maintaining contact with balloon flights for a twenty-four-hour period were refined on these two series of flights.

The composition and pressure of the capsule's atmosphere were maintained at constant values. The animals metabolized the oxygen to carbon dioxide, which was then absorbed in soda lime. The resulting pressure deficit was then replaced on a demand basis with pure oxygen from the oxygen tanks. The 15 pounds-per-square-inch (psi) capsule atmosphere was maintained at 80-100% oxygen to extend the flight time in the event that the oxygen source leaked. On the 1954 flights some evidence of oxygen toxicity was observed among the mice because oxygen partial pressures of the order of one atmosphere had been selected. On the 1955 flights this difficulty was recognized, and oxygen partial pressures of less than 60% of an atmosphere were maintained. No oxygen toxicity symptoms were noted in this series.

The capsules were maintained at nearly room temperature by providing sufficient insulation to retain the animal heat within the capsule at night. The excess heat acquired from solar radiation during the daytime was eliminated by a water-boiler-cooling system.[12] This system was found very satisfactory for this flight duration and capsule loading.

During this period several flights were conducted from Holloman Air Force Base that measured the surface temperature of the capsule through a day and night at altitudes above 90,000 feet.[13] A typical temperature curve obtained on one of these flights shows that during the daytime the maximum temperature on the upper aluminum reflecting surface of the gondola reached over 180° F. At night, temperatures on all surfaces of the capsule plunged below −60° F. The manned flights to date have utilized a similar highly reflective, aluminized surface which produced comparable temperatures.

The temperature of a surface in space is dependent largely on its ratio of short-wave absorptivity (heat gain) to long-wave emissivity (heat loss). By selecting a surface with reflectivity between that of shiny metal and flat white and having the desired heat transfer ratio, it is a simple matter to establish an average capsule temperature within the biologically tolerable range. The wide range from daytime to nighttime conditions can be bridged by adding heat at night and cooling during the day, or by providing a heat sink for the short day-night cycle of a satellite.

Biological Experiments

These flights carried experiments of two different types: one to assess the biological effects of cosmic ray primaries, which would reflect indirectly the damage caused by one or more prethindown hits; the second to examine the specific damage done by individually identified primary particles.

Studies of the indirect effects of cosmic radiation were designed to demonstrate any unsuspected biological effects or extreme tissue sensitivity. Experiments representing this approach include studies of the longevity of exposed mice, cancer incidence of exposed mice, and animal performance study. Only the latter has been completed to date.

Two animals were flown on each of two successive flights from Sault Sainte Marie, Michigan, and carefully examined for changes in weight and general behavior, ability to perform tasks learned before exposure, ability to learn new tasks, and gross neurological changes.

The two animals exposed to heavy cosmic ray primaries showed no loss of weight or alteration of general behavior that could be considered significant as compared to the control. They were able to perform previously learned tasks and to learn new tasks equally as well as the controls. No gross neurological changes were observed in the exposed animals. The details of this experiment have been reported by Harlow et al.[7]

An experiment is being conducted to gain further insight into irreversible changes, such as carcinogenesis produced by heavy cosmic ray primaries, by conducting a longevity study on a group of fifty mice exposed above 90,000 feet for twenty-four hours. This experiment is approximately 90% complete, and preliminary returns suggest that a larger number of animals must be exposed or a longer exposure period provided in order to produce statistically meaningful positive results. This study has been conducted by Lt.

Irwin Lebish under the direction of Dr. Webb Haymaker at the Armed Forces Institute of Pathology, Washington, D. C. The results to date strongly indicate the desirability of continuing this type of study.

In considering experiments of the specific type, the biological significance of primary cosmic particles to a particular body structure depends upon the tissue's radiosensitivity, replaceability, redundancy, and genetic fate. A structure could tolerate indefinite exposure if the unique microbeam pattern of cosmic primaries causes no worse than reversible damage. Indefinite exposure should be tolerable for highly regenerated tissue such as dermis in spite of fatal damage to cells along the path of a heavy primary track. Even nonregenerative tissue such as the neurons of the central nervous system can tolerate loss equivalent to subtle acceleration of the aging process if it has sufficient redundancy, i.e., if adequate alternate pathways are available.

The triggering of irreversible processes such as carcinogenesis presents a foreboding possibility.

Yagoda[18] measured the relative number of medium (M) and heavy (H) nuclear thindown terminations in tissue on a companion flight to the 1955 animal flights and found a decrease in the M/H ratio with increasing altitude. This indicates that the relative proportion of heavy nuclei increases for low-energy primaries as compared to high-energy primaries. Also Yagoda has compared the low-energy heavy-primary mass spectrum in nuclear emulsions exposed on two successive days and has reported that the number of these low-energy heavy primaries varies considerably within a 24-hour period. This places a premium on high-altitude cosmic ray studies of this portion of the spectrum, including monitoring at the time of flight. At present, track plate technique requires tedious scanning and evaluation but is the only method available for determining low-energy heavy-primary flux. Data in the region of greatest interest biologically are distressingly sketchy.

Specific tissues on which meaningful studies have been conducted to date include the central nervous system, crystalline lens, integument, reproductive tissue, and developmental effects.

Evaluation of susceptibility to primary cosmic radiation of the central nervous tissue and the crystalline lens in terms of cataract formation is of acute space-medical interest. Marked sensitivity in either case would influence pilot effectiveness and set limits to tolerable exposure. The integument and development studies and, to a lesser extent, the genetic studies, are not expected to reveal health hazards directly but should provide valuable insight into the radiobiological mechanisms and tissue sensitivity to the unique microbeam pattern of radiation. Assessment of the genetic effects caused by cosmic ray primaries will be of intense interest to individual pilots, although there is no immediate prospect that a sufficiently large segment of the population will be exposed to cosmic ray primaries above 75,000 feet to represent a genetic threat to the species.

Chase[3] observed that four to six melanophores supply all the pigment for the hair growing from one follicle in a black mouse. He also has noted that these cells are relatively radiosensitive, nonregenerative, and nonredundant (have no alternates). Evidence of the death of these pigment cells is multiplied a thousandfold in the growth of a readily detected gray (nonpigmented) hair. Chase has demonstrated that these cells indicate radiation exposures in the range of 100 roentgens (no graying) to 1000 roentgens (total graying). For these reasons the graying effect in black mice is especially suitable for detecting the effects of primary cosmic particles.

On the 1954 and 1955 balloon flights, mice were exposed at northern latitudes in the altitude region of 90,000 feet. This presented an operational ceiling for the 85- to 95-foot-diameter balloons then available. According to the calculations of Schaefer[10] it is also the altitude for maximum exposure to prethindown hits by medium-weight primary cosmic particles of atomic number $6 \geqslant Z \geqslant 10$ (carbon, nitrogen, and oxygen). The same calculations indicated that the relative proportion of prethindown hits by heavy ($H = Z > 10$) primary particles increases to a maximum exposure for graying effect at the 120,000-foot region.

Three International Falls flights in 1955 exposed animals for study of integument. One flight each of mice and guinea pigs was exposed for 24 hours at the 100,000- to 117,000-foot region with the expectation that effects caused by the heaviest primary nuclei would predominate. This flight pattern and results should be directly comparable to the 1954 flights except for the difference in oxygen partial pressure in the capsules.

Chase[2] reported that mice exposed on the 1954 and 1955 flights showed the following changes not observed in control animals:

1. The mean number of white spots per animal exposed on flights 50, 51, and 52 was 13.8 among forty exposed mice compared to the value of 3.2 among Holloman Air Force Base control animals and 1.8 among ground control animals.

2. Numerous clusters of three and four follicles producing white hairs were observed.

3. Follicles producing white hairs presumably due to exposure to cosmic primaries pulled out with the hairs when these hairs were later plucked.

4. One streak of twelve white hairs extended 4 mm and was approximately 200 microns wide.

Animals exposed on the 1955 flights[4] showed the following changes not observed in control animals:

1. Clumps of white hair among exposed mice as observed above.

2. Clumps of white hair among exposed guinea pigs comparable to those observed on mice.

3. Three streaks, one consisting of thirteen follicles producing white hairs among seventeen follicles producing black hairs, were 2.9 mm long and about 200 microns wide.

4. Among fifty-two mice exposed on flight 63 and sixty-nine mice exposed on flight 66, the average number of white spots per animal was 4.4 and 2.7 respectively, compared to 3.3 among ground control animals.

5. No difference was noted between the effects of the 1955 high- and low-altitude flights, although the total incidence of graying was much less on the 1955 low-altitude flight compared to the 1954 flights conducted at the same altitude.

Eugster[6] reported four experiments in which skin grafts were removed, preserved, and flown at altitude, then reimplanted and the implants observed over a period of time for changes. All experiments were monitored either with nuclear track plates or TTC (triphenyl tetrazolium chloride) as indicators of heavy primary hits. In one of the four experiments only six of ten pieces of mouse skin were successfully reimplanted. The nuclear emulsion monitor recorded two traversals by heavy primaries. Eugster reported a granuloma corresponding to the location of one traversal, but no ffect was observed on the other. In another series of experiments ae reported that "at two points marked out by the TTC (i.e., hits) small granuloma developed after two months." In a third series f experiments, four small red points were found, presumably representing reduction of the TTC by heavy primary hits. Within three veeks after reimplantation the TTC colors disappeared, leaving o trace of the event. Five weeks after reimplantation "the beginning formation of a small granuloma with a diameter of 2 mm can e observed at the loci of the hits." A year later two small tumors re described as having a light-brown pigmentation at the same ocation. A fourth series of specimens reconstituted in normal aline and observed histologically were pronounced viable. One arge track was recorded in monitoring track plates. The locus in uestion is reported still under observation with negative results as f May 1956.

The brains of one cat and several dozen mice exposed above 0,000 feet at northern latitudes have been serially sectioned and ystematically scanned for tracks, the former by Campbell[1] and ae latter under the direction of Dr. Webb Haymaker of the Armed 'orces Institute of Pathology. In addition, nearly a dozen mouse rains have been examined by Drs. Schummelfeder and Krogh sing fluorescent microscopy technique. In no case has a pathoogical lesion of the presumed configuration, several cells in diamter and dozens of cells long, been identified.

Two guinea pig brains on a Manhigh test flight received exposure heavy cosmic ray primaries above 100,000 feet for twelve hours. hese brains were monitored and the location of heavy primary aversal to the brain was extrapolated from the location of heavy indown tracks in the monitoring track plates fixed firmly to the ull of each animal. Along the extrapolated path within the brain, lesion in each case was observed, which may represent the result f heavy primary cosmic radiation. Additional examination must e done to resolve this question, since the lesions showed marked ellular changes in a spherical volume approximately 100 microns diameter.

The Aero Medical Field Laboratory conducted a study[11] of dry dish seeds exposed for 250 hours above 82,000 feet on northern ghts conducted in 1954. Calculations indicated approximately 0% of the seeds in the maximum exposure group should have experienced a prethindown hit as defined by Schaefer.[9] No differ-ence was detected between germination of the exposed and control dry radish seeds.

Walton initiated an investigation of developmental aberrations among onion seeds, snapdragon seeds, and grasshopper eggs which were exposed on flights 63, 64, 65, 67, and 68 of the 1955 International Falls series. Examination of the onion seeds included comparison of the sensitivity of "wet" and dry seeds in terms of per cent germination, length of hypocotyl- and epicotyl-unit time, and aceto-carmine smears to check for chromosomal aberrations. Examination of the snapdragon seeds included comparison of the sensitivity of "wet" and dry seeds in terms of per cent germination. Exposed grasshopper eggs were compared with controls for rate of hatching, delayed hatching, and aberrant offspring.

Although the studies by Walton were interrupted by his untimely death, preliminary data indicated that developmental aberration attributable to cosmic ray primaries would have been observable among the grasshoppers. The preliminary results indicated that both types of seeds showed a higher sensitivity to cosmic radiation when exposed "wet."

Numerous northern and Holloman Air Force Base control flights during 1954 carried preliminary genetic experiments for Stone[1] to explore the possibility of developing an experimental system using bacteria and Neurospora to show positive genetic effects. A series of preliminary experiments included on the 1955 series of flights used the adenineless colonial strain of Neurospora crassa which had been evaluated for back mutations. For each flight the material was divided into three lots: (1) a control retained at the Austin, Texas, laboratory; (2) a ground control sent to the launch site and returned with the exposed specimens; (3) an experimental lot exposed above 90,000 feet. Spores from all cultures were plated to test their ability to grow on minimal media in the absence of an adenine supplement. Materials were exposed in test tubes on flights 61, 63, 64, and 67. Since the controls of only one flight showed two positive tubes out of five, it would appear in these preliminary studies that a significant portion of the positive results observed among exposed specimens is due to cosmic ray primaries. Additional studies can now be and are being conducted to clarify these preliminary results.

Summary

Experiments to investigate the biological effects of the unique microbeam produced by heavy cosmic ray primaries indicate positive results in the graying effect on black mice and on the genetic effects on *Neurospora*. The higher total incidence of graying among the mice exposed in 1954 may be due to the higher oxygen partial pressure to which they were subjected during exposure at altitude. The streaks measuring 200 microns in width present an enigma, since the effective path width of the streak is much greater than expected from calculations.

Chase[5] prepared a model of mouse integument to study how wide the effective path would need to be to produce streaks such as those observed. An absolute minimum of thirty microns would be required. This is considerably in excess of the four micron radial spread predicted by Schaefer.

The skin of the mice observed by Chase failed to develop papillomas in areas where clusters and streaks of gray hair indicated penetrations by heavy cosmic ray primaries. Apparently the effects observed in transplanted tissues by Eugster were significantly influenced by the procedures involved. Likewise no papillomas or pigmented areas were observed to develop in the pilot following the Manhigh II flight.

The preliminary genetic experiments by Stone indicate this method can be developed to obtain quantitative data which can then be correlated with control X-ray studies. In this way the mutagenic effectiveness of cosmic radiation can be compared to that of radiation for which acceptable tolerance limits exist.

Indications from a number of sources suggest that "wet" seed material shows a much greater response to heavy cosmic ray primaries than "dry" seeds. This correlates with corresponding experiments using lower energy forms of radiation and is pertinent since human tissue is in the "wet" condition.

Balloon flights of many days at high altitudes and eventually satellite flights with recovery of the exposed animals will greatly increase our knowledge in this area. The problem of physically monitoring the exposure to low-energy heavy primaries is a difficult and serious one. The track-plate techniques used today require recovery, and the plates can be exposed at altitude for only a few days before they become saturated with tracks. New monitoring techniques must be developed for satellite flights of more than several days.

MANNED FLIGHTS

On 2 June 1957, Mr. O. C. Winzen of Winzen Research Inc. launched Captain Kittinger, test pilot, on the first Manhigh flight. The flight, totaling six and one half hours, remained at the ceiling altitude of 96,000 feet for nearly two hours. Mr. Winzen launched the second Manhigh flight, carrying the author as pilot, on 19 August 1957 from the Hanna Iron Mine at Crosby, Minnesota. This flight remained at an altitude of 101,000 feet for five hours and totalled thirty-two hours and ten minutes. Balloon flights to the 100,000-foot region experience space-equivalent conditions in many respects. Biologically the one per cent of the atmosphere remaining is fully space-equivalent, requiring a sealed cabin for life sustention. The temperature-control problem is one of radiation equilibrium—typical of conditions in space—not heat conductivity which is the major consideration at ground level. At this altitude there is significant exposure to heavy primary radiation typical of that experienced in space beyond the atmosphere. Psychologically the environment is as hostile and very nearly as different in appearance as one would expect to observe from a satellite. Physiologically the sustained responsibility for long duration of being completely dependent upon one's own resources presents a comparable challenge. The nutritional problem is identical. The opportunity to make observations of phenomena not previously available for study places a heavy load of responsibility on the crew member.

The Manhigh Capsule System

The Manhigh balloon-capsule system used on both flights consists of a capsule suspended from a large polyethylene balloon by a parachute flown unpacked. A release system which can be actuated electrically by the pilot or by radio control from the ground connects the balloon and parachute. The balloon is normally returned to the ground by releasing helium through a valve at the top of the balloon. The pilot then separates the balloon from the parachute and capsule at the moment of ground contact. It is also possible for him to release several parachute lines from the capsule to prevent dragging in high wind. The balloon is expendable because of its fragile nature and relatively low cost. Both Manhigh flights were completed using this normal landing procedure.

The weight breakdown on the Manhigh II flight included 960 pounds for the balloon and a total of 1700 pounds for the capsule (of which 650 pounds was battery ballast), giving a launch weight of the entire system of 2660 pounds.

Balloon

The Manhigh II flight utilized a 3,000,000-cubic-foot, 1½-mil-thick polyethylene balloon. It had a diameter of 200.2 feet fully inflated and weighed 960 pounds, stretching 280 feet long at the time of launch. Three appendices permitted excess helium to spill on reaching altitude. The seventy load bands, each capable of carrying 500 pounds, were heat-sealed integrally into the meridional seams of the balloon. The total strength of the bands was therefore 35,000 pounds, which provided a theoretical breaking strength of 12,000 pounds, a safety factor of four. A cross-laced suspension between balloon and parachute continued as a six-point suspension system to the capsule and was designed to minimize differential rotation between balloon and capsule.

Capsule

The capsule used for the two Manhigh flights to date (see photo section) would operate equally well, and in a few respects better, at orbital altitudes of 100 to 500 miles than it did at the space-equivalent balloon-flight altitude of 19 miles. It consists of a three-piece hollow aluminum capsule, 36 inches in diameter and 89 inches high. It has the appearance of an upright cylinder with hemispherical ends, with 71 inches of clearance from the floor to the center of the dome. A cast heat-treated aluminum turret provides the attachment member, where all stresses are concentrated. Externally the turret has six parachute attachment brackets, includes six equally spaced six-inch-diameter portholes, and serves as the central suspension for all internal structure. The top and bottom shells can therefore be made of light, thin metal. They are clamped to the turret with Marmon clamps and sealed by silicon-rubber O-rings. The clamps can be released electrically or mechanically either from the outside or by the pilot. The capsule is supported on the ground by a tubular aluminum framework designed and tested to absorb landing shock by crumpling. This framework carries batteries on jettisonable racks for use as ballast. The frame also carries outboard cameras, sensors, and air-conditioning equipment.

The instrument panel displays the dials and controls of the climate system as well as those required for pilotage during the flight. A camera photographs the panel every minute during ascent and every five minutes during the remainder of the flight, recording internal and external temperature, battery voltage, altitude on both the high- and low-altitude altimeters, time, rate of climb, and internal capsule temperature.

The seat used on this flight was specially designed by Lt. John Duddy of the Aero Medical Laboratory, Wright Air Development Center. It consisted of nylon netting stretched over a light, aluminum-tubing framework shaped to conform to body contours. It provided a remarkably comfortable, well-ventilated, adjustable, resilient, and shock-absorbing structure at a marked economy in weight compared to previous structures. A lever released a portion of the seat so the pilot could stand up to stretch and even turn around if he desired. A footrest provided three positions to relieve the somewhat cramped position.

On the first Manhigh flight the inside of the dome was painted a light blue. During the flight the pilot reported difficulty seeing instruments and dials at waist level within the capsule because of the relative darkness inside compared to the intense glare outside. For the second flight the dome was painted flat white. No such difficulty occurred at ceiling altitude on this flight. Unlike the ground situation where very nearly as much light, if not more, comes from the sky as compared to the ground, at 100,000 feet very nearly all the light comes from below, so that the color of the dome is critical for diffusing and reflecting light throughout the interior of the capsule.

Communications throughout the flight were considered critically important both to the pilot and to the ground team-members who were responsible for the flight. A VHF transceiver provided the primary voice communication channel throughout the flight. An

HF transmitter and receiver provided an automatic telemetering beacon and served as the emergency communications channel, using code. The beacon was designed to telemeter respiratory rate and heart rate for the benefit of those manning the ground tracking command post. This transmitter operated during the first half of the flight.

The capsule temperature represents a balance of heat conducted through the capsule insulation and then radiated from the capsule surface, heat absorbed from solar radiation and long-wave earth radiation, plus the internal heat produced by the human subject (equivalent to 125 watts) and the electronic instrumentation (75 watts). The capsule carried sufficient insulation to remain above the freezing temperature by means of nothing more than the internal heat sources. During the daytime it was necessary to remove the additional heat absorbed from solar radiation. The capsule insulation consisted of four layers of aluminum-coated mylar film separated by honeycomb paper. During the daytime excess heat was removed by the water-boiler-cooling system based on the principle previously developed for the animal capsules.[12]

The cabin pressure was controlled by a regulator which maintained the pressure at any selected value equivalent to altitudes between 12,000 and 40,000 feet. This manual control was adjustable in flight, but set at 25,000 feet throughout the Manhigh II flight. This was a demand system which drew oxygen from the converter whenever the capsule pressure dropped below the control value. Since only metabolic requirements are replaced, there is no change in the content of inert gas in such a system so long as the capsule remains hermetically sealed.

A closed, sealed system as described here is essential for oxygen conservation. With a standard oxygen mask, less than 5% of the gas respired is utilized for metabolism. To discard the 95% of the respired gas otherwise wasted would create prohibitive oxygen requirements.

Selection of Atmosphere

The minimum alveolar oxygen pressure ($P\ O_2$) that precludes any symptoms of hypoxia, although highly variable, is generally considered to be 61 mm of mercury. This is equivalent to an atmosphere of 100% oxygen at a total pressure of 144 mm of mercury or a pressure altitude of 39,500 feet and is equivalent to the alveolar $P\,O_2$ when breathing natural air at 10,000 feet altitude.

The occurrence of bends, or dysbarism, constitutes another limiting factor in selection of the capsule atmosphere. This painful condition may occur without extensive oxygen prebreathing between 20,000 and 25,000 feet altitude, depending on the amount of physical exertion performed by the subject. On the other hand, cabin pressure corresponding to an altitude below 18,000 feet presents a hazard in the event of rapid decompression at ceiling altitude. An emergency partial-pressure suit will provide approximately 140 mm mercury pressure (equivalent to 40,000 feet altitude). Navy submarine practice has established a maximum pressure change ratio of 2:1 without danger of bends. The same criterion permits capsule pressurization to a maximum of 280 mm of mercury (25,000 feet), since the 280- to 140-mm pressure change does not exceed the 2:1 ratio.

In addition to the question of gas dysbarism caused by evolved gas, a low-pressure atmosphere must be enriched with oxygen if the pilot is to breathe without a mask or closed helmet. The question arises as to how much increase in fire hazard (or flammability of materials) is associated with decreasing total atmospheric pressure and increasing percentage of oxygen when the partial pressure of oxygen remains constant. Experiments[14] showed that from a normal atmosphere to a 100%-oxygen atmosphere at a pressure equivalent to 39,000 feet, the burning time of paper strips and cloth strips was reduced to one half, while the flame was nearly twice as large. This result warned that there is an increased fire hazard; but with scrupulous care fire should be preventable.

The previous considerations dealt with selection of an atmosphere only in terms of the problems at ceiling altitude. When one considers the necessity of denitrogenating subjects before flight and the implications of using the same atmospheric composition on the ground at 15 psi plus 5 psi for pressure check as well, the problem becomes more complex. As a compromise among all factors concerned, an atmosphere of 60% oxygen, 20% helium, and 20% nitrogen was selected. The Manhigh II flight began with 68% oxygen and the remaining 32% equally divided between nitrogen and helium. By 0935 hours of the second morning the oxygen had increased to 77.8% and by 1519, shortly before landing, it was

83%. This amount of increase was caused by gas lost from the capsule through flushing procedures and pressure adjustments made during the flight.

Air Regeneration

Both carbon dioxide and water were removed from the capsule atmosphere by a chemical air regeneration unit inclosed in an insulated capsule mounted on the landing gear. Moisture was removed by anhydrous lithium chloride backed up by anhydrous magnesium perchlorate to maintain a minimum humidity. Carbon dioxide was removed by anhydrous lithium hydroxide. Air was circulated through this unit by a 25-cubic-foot-per-minute centrifugal blower. Ground tests showed that, if this blower failed, the pilot had approximately one hour before the accumulation of carbon dioxide would become serious.

Pilot Selection and Training

The pilots for both flights met five criteria for qualification for flight: vigorous physical exam, high-altitude pressure suit indoctrination, practice parachute jump, 24-hour claustrophobia test, and qualification as a Civil Aeronautics Administration licensed balloon pilot. The desirability and necessity of being completely familiar with operation of the pressure suit at high altitude were obvious in the event the capsule should unexpectedly depressurize during flight. The parachute jump was required to familiarize the pilot with parachute jump procedures in the event the newly developed system malfunctioned in some unexpected way. The personal chute was to be used from altitudes below 15,000 feet only. The claustrophobia ground tests ensured selection of personnel who tolerated prolonged enclosure well. It secondarily helped to familiarize and condition the pilots to enclosure in the capsule for long periods of time. A chamber test of the capsule before the second flight permitted review and improvement of operating procedures and the resolution of minor but annoying mechanical problems such as the position of lights for night flight. Skill in maneuvering the aerostat and a basis for judgment in valving and ballasting were obtained by making low-altitude flights in the simple, open-gondola Skycar system. This provided invaluable confidence and experience toward successfully conducting the high-altitude flights.

Preflight Preparation

For the pilot the preflight schedule on Manhigh II began with a low-residue diet three days before launch. After that, the schedules were comparable for both flights.

Donning of personal equipment for Manhigh II began at 2100 hours the evening before launch. By 2243 the capsule was sealed and atmosphere-flush and pressure-check procedures instituted. At times during this procedure the helium concentration approached 50%, causing a marked elevation of voice pitch and some change of timbre. At this point excessive internal capsule temperature was prevented by placing a dry-ice cap on the upper hemisphere of the capsule. Half an hour after midnight, the pressure tests were completed and the capsule loaded on the truck to go to the launch site at Crosby, Minnesota. After several complications causing minor delays, the flight was launched at 0922, ten and one half hours after the cabin had been sealed. The flight was launched from a 450-foot-deep open-pit iron mine to protect the huge, delicate balloon from stresses caused by sudden gusts of wind. The first Manhigh flight, using a smaller, stronger balloon, was launched from Fleming Field, South Saint Paul, Minnesota.

The Flight

After reaching altitude a few minutes before noon, the capsule floated quietly in a very stable manner for five hours. As the sun dipped toward the horizon, the gas in the balloon cooled, reducing the balloon volume and allowing it to descend. Despite repeated jettisoning of battery-ballast, the flight did not level off until it had descended to 68,000 feet, where it remained until sunrise the following morning. Partly because of ballasting and partly because of the heating of the helium by the sun, the flight returned to an altitude of approximately 90,000 feet the following day. Shortly before noon, release of helium initiated descent, which was completed at 1732 hours. At lower altitudes the winds carried the balloon toward the east. Near ceiling altitude the trajectory was consistently westward except for northerly and southerly deviations when the flight descended at night.

To maintain VHF contact with the balloon, a communication van which served as command post followed the balloon throughout the flight. The van and much of the launch equipment were made available through the courtesy of the U.S. Navy. Three helicopters and two tracking C-47's operated under the direction of this command post.

A maximum of one half hour was allowed between reports from the capsule, so that Mr. Winzen, who was in charge of the command post with Colonel Stapp, flight surgeon, and Captain Archibald, project physiologist, would be aware of conditions in the capsule. Major decisions during the flight, such as when and how much to ballast, when to terminate the flight, and variations in capsule atmosphere procedure, were made jointly between the pilot and the command post. During the second morning aircraft were unable to fly in the vicinity of the capsule to get DF bearings because of a thunderstorm. Consequently the capsule could be positioned only by omnibearings reported from the capsule. These procedures have been described in detail.[17]

At 1100 hours of the second morning of the flight, it became apparent to Captain Archibald that the pilot's performance in reporting omnipositions was seriously impaired. When he requested a reading on the carbon dioxide level, the pilot reported 4%, an excessive value. This problem was resolved by alternately using the pressure-suit helmet as an oxygen mask for breathing 100% oxygen and then returning to the capsule atmosphere. The trouble arose partly because of the gradual exhaustion of the carbon dioxide absorbents, since thunderstorms had forced extension of the flight beyond the 24 hours for which it was designed. Also the chemicals had become unexpectedly cold during the night. It is interesting to note that submarine practice permits 3% carbon dioxide over long periods of time, but not at reduced total pressures.

Flight Results

The oxygen-nitrogen-helium atmosphere proved satisfactory. It was interesting, however, to notice during helium-flush stages that the pitch of the pilot's voice would go up nearly half an octave. This made communications slightly more difficult. The pilot corrected the voice pitch that was caused by only 20% of helium, so that during the flight there was no noticeable difference in communication efficiency. Throughout the flight the oxygen percentage gradually increased.

A total of 15 hours was spent above 90,000 feet in the region where thindowns of heavy cosmic ray primaries occur. None of the time spent above 90,000 feet was at night when the pilot would have been fully dark-adapted. This precluded the possibility of seeing flashes of light caused by direct stimulation of retinal receptors by heavy cosmic primaries. On subsequent flights which maintain altitudes above 90,000 feet through the night, this experiment can be performed.

The monitoring nuclear track plate on the subject's left arm (which was similar to the plates monitoring the right arm and chest) bore marks indicating traversals of heavy-primary thindowns of sufficient density to be considered "hits" according to Schaefer's criteria. Some of these marks on the plate indicated traversals of medium-weight elements in the region between oxygen and silicon, and some traversals of heavy elements on the order of calcium and iron. These data are provided through the courtesy of Dr. Herman Yagoda, National Institutes of Health, Bethesda, Maryland.

Five months after the flight the skin under the monitored areas has shown no new growths or granulomas corresponding to those described by Professor Eugster. On both arms only two gray hairs have been noticed, and they occurred beyond the monitored area, so it cannot be conclusively proved that they were the result of cosmic radiation. In some respects heavy primary cosmic ray exposure can be considered a form of low-dose radiation and therefore might produce latent effects after some period of time. The fact that no adverse changes were observable after this relatively short exposure is encouraging.

Not only does the environment at 100,000 feet require the protection of a "terrella" (a term applied by Dr. Strughold to describe the life compartment required for man to exist in space) but the appearance of the earth and the sky is completely strange. Instead of the gentle color gradation from horizon to zenith as seen from the ground, the sky appears very dark with bands of color close to the horizon. The first band above the horizon is white, measuring approximately $1\frac{1}{2}°$ in width. Above this lies a narrow band of blue. Compressing the full range of blues seen from the ground, it shades gradually through an angle of about 5° from the white zone beneath through increasingly deep shades of blue to the dark blue-purple of the overhead sky. This sky color when examined closely gives the impression of a spectral violet, except that the color seems at the very limit of vision, like a sound almost too high to hear.

Manhigh Nuclear Track Plate (On Left Arm)

Diagram of the heavy primary tracks observed in the track plate monitoring the left arm of the subject on the Manhigh II balloon flight. The uncircled tracks represent traversals of medium-weight primaries. Each circled track represents a traversal of a heavy primary of approximately the weight of iron. The tails indicate the direction of the relative obliqueness of the primary particle throughout its track. Data by courtesy of Dr. Herman Yagoda.

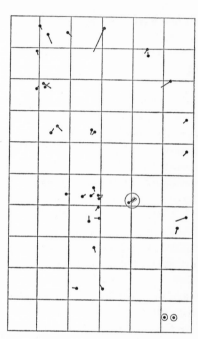

base

When looking toward the horizon, one sees both the brilliant white clouds below and the dark sky above in one view. The sharp contrast makes the sky above appear black, or, more accurately, absent. This gives the impression of being suspended above a large soup bowl without a top and with low, distant, upturned edges. Thus one feels more in space than on earth. Looking out on the faintly curved horizon and narrow banded sky, one needs very little imagination to realize that he is on the very fringes of space.

Throughout the 24-hour period the pilot's attitude toward the flight changed with the time of day and kind of activity. The first afternoon was saturated with observations of many kinds, some of which are listed below. The challenge of taking full advantage of the unique opportunity was uppermost throughout this period. Consequently attention was concentrated outside the gondola in terms of what was there to be observed. The regular reports to the command post tracking van every half hour constituted an annoying interruption. The capsule seemed like a welcome window permitting a fabulous view and precious opportunities, not a prison or an enclosure.

During the night, as fatigue took its toll and external observations became prohibitively difficult because of frosting on the windows, problems and conditions within the capsule assumed increasing importance. The subject matter that was tape-recorded clearly reflects this change in point of view. During this period the capsule seemed cramped and restrictive. It was also interesting to note that rather than being a source of annoyance, the half-hour reports were a welcome contact with friends on earth below.

After a very active period of observation during sunrise, a relaxed and leisurely breakfast seemed in order. It was during this period that the darkening of the sky and narrowing of the blue band above the horizon heralded a welcome return to the high altitude of the day before. While reflecting on his situation during breakfast, the pilot felt an identification with space above rather than with the earth below. It is also interesting to note that the bank of storm clouds below tended to establish a feeling of contact with earth rather than separation from it. From this it appears that the tendency for "breakaway" is reduced by a high degree of activity-saturation and enhanced by contemplative introspection.

In addition to the regular half-hour reports which generally took between ten and fifteen minutes from each hour, special reports were frequently requested on items such as capsule temperature, carbon dioxide percentage, omnirange station readings, etc. One of the major observational objectives was to obtain a photographic record of the appearance of the earth and sky from 100,000 feet. This in itself accounted for a considerable portion of the time.

The performance of the balloon and the stability of the balloon-capsule system were of special interest. The undulating waves observed in the folds of polyethylene shortly after launch were virtually absent throughout the last 30,000 feet of ascent, apparently because of the greatly reduced air density at the higher altitudes.

The reaction of the balloon system to ballasting was also of particular interest, especially in terms of future flights.

The appearance of the earth and the sky from 100,000 feet was carefully noted. During ascent, at approximately 70,000 feet, colors on the ground began to fade so that beyond 45° there was only a gray haze. More directly beneath the capsule, greens and reds were still distinguishable but presented a faded, pastel appearance with a somewhat bluish cast that increased with altitude as if seen through a blue-tinted filter. This latter effect was quite variable with time of day and direction of vision.

At ceiling altitude about 1500 hours, the color of the sky approximately 30° above the horizon was compared to a Munsell color chart, kindly provided by Dr. Stakutis of the Air Force Cambridge Research Center. On this chart a hue of 5.OB (blue) was too green, and a hue of 5.OP (purple) was too red. Apparently a purple-blue hue would have been much closer. The value/chroma readings of 3/6 matched the closest. On this basis the closest approximation that could be made is an interpolation of a dark purple-blue described by Munsell as 5.OPB 3/6. In addition to this observation of color, the actual sky-brightness values were measured with a spectrabrightness meter provided by Mr. Karl Freund of the Photo Research Corporation, Los Angeles, California. The data obtained have been reduced by Dr. S. Q. Duntley of Scripps Oceanographic Institution for presentation before the Optical Society of America.

Numerous original meteorological observations were made during the flight. Throughout the day the pilot observed that there were three different horizons. First the true horizon, representing the intersection of the sky and the limb of the earth itself at a point approximately 400 miles distant. This could be seen only rarely, when there were no clouds throughout the 400-mile range. The second type of horizon frequently formed at the junction of the tops of the clouds and the sky above. This was highly variable in elevation angle and configuration. Thirdly, there was occasionally within the white zone above the horizon a layer of dusty-appearing haziness just above the clouds which formed the only distinguishable line of demarcation.

At approximately 1700 of the first afternoon the smooth line of clouds forming the horizon toward the west-southwest was interrupted by the form of a distant buildup clearly outlined against the horizon. This structure appeared so distant and stood out so distinctly from the other clouds that a special note was made of it. A later check revealed that there had been an unusually violent thunderstorm in the vicinity of Denver, Colorado, at the time of this observation. Denver, was south-southwest of the capsule at that time and some 500 miles away.

Both during the first afternoon and the next morning three distinct yellowish-white lines were observed in the band of blue sky above the horizon. Since these distinct lines were apparently dust layers between 50,000 and 80,000 feet in altitude and were seen only in the direction of the sun, they presumably were composed of particles so small that they were better seen by back lighting than by front lighting.

At approximately 0200 while floating at 70,000 feet, the pilot made the following comment to the tape recorder: "Looking out toward the horizon, toward the moon, there is a layer just on my level that gives a very gauzy, filmy white effect that obscures the stars. It looks like a very, very thin, foggy cloud that is clearly above the top of the thunderstorm activity, that is, like a ground fog that doesn't quite extend to the ground but stays above the ground." This was a source of concern, since there was no way of being certain of its relation to the storm below. Clouds of this type had not been previously reported at this altitude.

During descent at approximately 1430 hours of the second day, and particularly when looking toward the north or west, the pilot noticed a very sharp line of demarcation that had a very hazy, dark-brown appearance below but which appeared perfectly clear above. This layer was located at exactly 70,000 feet, according to the altimeter. At first the pilot thought it must be the tropopause, but after checking the altimeter he realized it was too high for that. Apparently it was a very strong inversion with a great deal of haze and particulate matter below. The pilot had never seen a sharper or more highly contrasting haze layer in over 1200 hours of flying in aircraft at conventional altitudes.

Astronomical Observations

As might be expected, the darkened sky made the sun appear as a white disc sharply defined in a black sky, with no perceptible sky brightness or luminescence surrounding it. This should permit, with proper instrumentation, improved coronagraphic measurements because of the greatly reduced sky brightness close to the sun.

The auroras seen shortly after sunset were clearly visible to their termination just above the horizon, whereas ordinarily the lower portions would have been obscured by atmospheric haze and lights on the earth. From this altitude auroras are observable beyond the normal range of light because of the increased transmission both at the ultraviolet and infrared ends of the visible spectrum.

After sunset the stars shone with an unblinking brilliance never seen from the earth. The complete absence of twinkling brought out the color of each of the stars in strong contrast, so that the blue stars were vividly blue and the red stars brilliantly red as compared to the relatively smeared appearance caused by scintillation. This provides a promising opportunity for astronomical observations not possible from ground level.

At sunrise the unusual green flash was seen just before the sun broke across the horizon. This is rarely seen at such northern latitudes.

Performance

During the ground tests before the flight and again during the flight, subjects consistently found that the upper temperature limit for comfort with the partial-pressure suit and helmet on was approximately 78° F. As the temperature rose slowly or dropped slowly, this was found to be a clearly defined region of demarcation. At lower temperatures the subjects retained initiative, spontaneous interest in external activities, and inquisitiveness. Above this temperature they became human automatons, responding only to external stimulation or threatening situations.

The factors of becoming accustomed to the strange situation at altitude and of fatigue reduced the number of spontaneous observations made on the tape recorder. The first peak in recording observations occurred during the period at launch, the second upon reaching ceiling. The third and fourth peaks of activity occurred at sunset and sunrise. The number of spontaneous observations tapered off through the first afternoon before sunset.

The diet during the flight consisted of sandwiches, candy bars, and IF-8 ration. Since no refrigeration was available in the capsule, it was necessary to eat the lettuce-bacon-tomato sandwich and cheeseburgers during the first eight hours of flight. These were finished before launch of the first day. During the first 24 hours at altitude the observations to be made were of such intense interest that there was no desire to eat. In fact, throughout the first day the flight surgeon, Colonel Stapp, had to suggest it was time to eat again. During this time the six candy bars consumed were tasty, convenient, and required a minimum of time to eat. Knowing that it is a time-consuming process to eat an in-flight ration, the pilot saved this for a special treat.

Liquid waste was collected for later examination of steroid content as a measurement of stress. The problem of solid wastes was circumvented by eating a low-residue diet for three days before the flight and by taking aluminum hydroxide gel tablets throughout the flight to discourage peristalsis. On the flight this was effective.

Future Prospects

This flight demonstrated that manned balloon capsules flown in the altitude range of 100,000 feet provide a remarkably stable platform suitable for making scientific observations of many kinds. Most instrumentation designed for manned balloon observations is directly applicable to satellite observations. Even more important, balloon flights provide a powerful tool for investigating the human-factor problems of space flight at first hand under space-equivalent conditions. For this reason they will provide a crucially important selection and training technique for future satellite crew members. The type of psychological and physiological instrumentation being developed for these tests is identical in its requirements and its objectives to that required under satellite conditions. In the balloon experiments we can learn not only what to study but how best to study it.

Obvious extensions of this work include longer flights of single individuals and flights including many persons for extended periods of time. The latter can best be approached by intensively studying and analyzing the details of the interaction of two individuals under stressful isolation. Crews numbering more than two can be considered special cases of interaction among multiple groups of two.

In preparing the way for man to step into space, a major source of human-factor information will be the data obtained from very-high-altitude manned balloon flights.

Air Force Missile Development Center

CHAPTER 10

Human Requirements for Space Flight

Dr. S. B. Sells and Major Charles A. Berry

The successful transportation of man in space will demand scientific and engineering accomplishments for human requirements as well as for construction, propulsion, and control of the vehicle. Human requirements include two related but quite different phases of research and development. The first phase involves environmental protection and crew compartment features, for which critical information must be furnished to engineers as requirements in vehicle design. Its purpose is to enable survival and to maximize effective performance by the human operators or occupants. The development of personal and protective equipment is an aspect of this phase. The second phase is concerned with the men who will venture into space in the vehicle. It must specify the necessary and desirable characteristics of space vehicle operators and develop selection, indoctrination, and training procedures. This phase is the principal concern of this discussion.

At present space travel is in the larval, undifferentiated stage of its evolution. The scientists and technicians who work on a development project usually follow it through most stages of progress. They participate in the maintenance, countdown, launch, and flight monitoring. Such informal arrangements are at best temporary and must ultimately give way to organization and management as the field advances and expands. These changes will first be seen among civilian manufacturers and the using military organizations and will eventually follow in a civilian space transport industry.

Although these problems are beyond the scope of this discussion, they are mentioned to emphasize the importance of selective staffing of the entire supporting organization in addition to the spacecrews. Every aspect of space travel depends on the complex, coordinated team effort of many specialists. For example, should the need arise during launch to abandon the spacecraft and escape, it is possible that only the range-control officer of the ground crew might be able to actuate the escape mechanism. His actions in turn would be coordinated with the other members of the team. The various occupational specialties that will comprise the teams and the mission, form, and structure of the new teams that will be required are problems that should begin to receive careful attention. The success of the program and the safety of personnel will depend to a significant degree on these factors.

ENGINEERING DESIGN

Adaptation of engineering design to human-factors requirements has received most attention in research and development thus far. Since man could survive neither the strenuous flight through the atmosphere nor the unfriendly environment of space without protection, the development of a feasible spacecraft has had the first priority.

Most of the requirements for environmental protection have been identified. Engineering solutions either have been developed or are considered feasible by responsible workers in the field at the time of this writing.[4] These requirements can be summarized briefly:

• Simulation of a life-sustaining environment by control of oxygen, pressure, temperature, humidity, and gases and of gravitational force if necessary; and provision for food, water, removal of waste, and sanitation. The duration of missions may be limited, first, by the capacity of the system used to provide necessary materials and controls, and, second, by its efficiency. As efficiency progresses—from pressure suits to sealed cabin, from containers of supplies to reconversion and recycling systems for gases, food, and water—the life-sustaining capacity of the cabin environment will be extended. As such improvements remove the need for fatiguing harnesses and restraints on the body of the operator and increase his comfort, his endurance and stamina will also be prolonged.

• Protection against leakage and loss of pressure in the crew compartment. This involves both the structure of the cabin shell and the supplementary equipment such as pressure suits.

• Protection against meteor particles.

• Protection against radiation, both cosmic and solar. A. M. Mayo[5] has reported that no practical solution has yet been found to provide adequate shielding against the very-high-energy cosmic particles, which can penetrate a foot of solid lead.

• Provision of reliable means of emergency escape, particularly during the boost and re-entry phases of the mission. Escape in orbital or space travel has generally been regarded as really no problem since the escape capsule would be no safer than the primary vehicle under those conditions.

• Protection against high g-forces during take-off acceleration.

• Protection against psychologic or physiologic problems attributable to weightlessness. At this time the available knowledge concerning effects of weightlessness is based on exposures in experimental situations of very brief duration. The effects of longer or prolonged exposure must be extrapolated speculatively. From such information as is available this problem is regarded by the present writers as probably minor and one involving the development of new habits and procedures comparable to the adjustments involved in pressure breathing. It is likely that indoctrination may be feasible through a graduated schedule of training missions. These would provide progressively longer exposure to weightlessness during which personnel would practice prescribed maneuvers and the use of special equipment and procedures. If difficulties not now expected should be encountered, aeronautical engineers[5] have expressed confidence that artificial weight can be produced by rotating the craft around its own center of gravity.

The conclusion that space travel is already a practical reality must be regarded with restraint and with insight into the present limitations and remaining problems. It will be many years before operations in space will be as reliable and free of hazard as even high-performance jet flying of today.

The ultimate goal of human-factors contributions to the engineering design of spacecraft is to adapt the equipment optimally to human requirements for environmental protection, comfort, and functioning efficiency. To the extent that this goal is fully realized, demands on the individual as to task performance and adaptability will be reduced. Nevertheless there will remain requirements for crew performance in application of highly complex and technical knowledge and skills under extremely hazardous and stressful circumstances. These additional human requirements for optimal staffing of space operations are at least of equal importance to those of engineering of the spacecraft.

The analysis of staffing requirements presented here assumes that the spacecrewman will be an operator of the spacecraft and will be linked with its control system as a crucial part of a man-machine complex. If he were only a passive occupant of an automatically guided ballistic missile, perhaps as a collector of scientific data, the problem would be somewhat different. However, the difference would be primarily one of emphasis, within the same general frame of reference. In either case it must be assumed that the occupant has been placed on board to perform necessary and useful functions. It seems unlikely that men will be sent aloft in ballistic missiles merely as subjects for physiologic and psychologic experiments in which animals might be used just as well.

The requirements for selection, indoctrination, and training of crew personnel must be initially inferred from the task requirements and environmental conditions under which missions are expected to be performed. Establishment of standards and procedures to implement these requirements will first depend on the judgment of experienced commanders, supported by the advice of experienced flight surgeons and aviation psychologists. Of necessity these standards must be used prior to their validation against actual performance criteria. They will undoubtedly be modified as experience accumulates.

Required Operator Characteristics

In 1957 Beyer and Sells[1] published a detailed set of proposals for the selection and training of space pilots. These covered (a) aptitude and skill requirements, (b) biologic, medical, and physical requirements, and (c) required tolerances of anticipated psycho-logic stresses. These have been reviewed carefully by the present writers, more than a year later and in the light of new information developed in the interim. With minor amendments, the proposals are fully supported by this review. The principal additions are two. The first is the concept of "making up the difference" in estimating human physiologic requirements. This concept applies in cases where equipment available represents a compromise with total protection needed and additional demands must be levied on the man. The second is the estimation of priorities among problems to be faced in relation to the previously discussed rough timetable of successive stages of development.

The personal requirements outlined in the following paragraphs are stated in terms of the trained and qualified space pilot. Practical and economical procurement of required numbers of such per-sonnel must be accomplished through effective selection and train-ing. Selection of candidates with appropriate background and experience may substantially reduce the training and indoctrination necessary. At the same time the initial selection must be regarded as a general screening measure, and the subsequent training pro-cedures as a continuing program of supplementary selection. Attri-tion may be high for inability to qualify on any of the psychologic or physiologic indoctrination phases, on flight checks, and for voluntary withdrawal during training. This combination of initial screening and selection in depth is the most rigorous approach that can presently be visualized. It reflects a policy of attempting to achieve as nearly errorless selection as possible, even at the cost of a high false-positive rate. The responsibility for ensuring success is so great that no precaution can be considered too expensive. It is expected that less drastic procedures may be tolerated as equip-ment is improved and operations later become more routine.

Aptitude and Skill Requirements

The space pilot must be able to perform the following functions with alertness, speed, and accuracy: (a) pilot a high-performance, ultrasonic aircraft through the atmosphere during boost, control it in orbit and re-entry glide, and guide it to a landing; (b) obtain and interpret information concerning vehicle operation, cabin-environ-ment conditioning, personnel functioning, and external conditions and make rapid and accurate computations and decisions, anticipating difficulties by advance planning and action; (c) check, test, observe, and report data as directed for scientific study concerning the spacecraft, its personnel, and the environment.

These functions require personnel with special skills, knowledges, and understandings: (a) proficiency and experience as pilot of high-speed, high-performance jet and rocket aircraft; (b) detailed engineering understanding of the operation and maintenance of the power plant, controls, and environment-conditioning equipment of the spacecraft; (c) medical and psychologic training in human performance and functioning, with particular emphasis on survival and efficiency in the spacecraft; (d) detailed understanding of the operation and maintenance of all communications and scientific observational equipment; and (e) detailed understanding of mission plan in relation to navigational and astronomic frames of reference.

It would be uneconomical to consider any personnel for this program who are not already highly experienced in high-performance jet or rocket aircraft. Test pilots frequently have in addition engineering and scientific training and interest. A requirement for proficiency in high-performance flight and in the engineering, physiologic, communications, scientific, and navigational skills needed would narrow the selection problem greatly.

Even among such highly trained and experienced applicants there are individual differences in aptitude for the additional training and skills required in mathematics, physics, astronomy, and engineering. To maximize the likelihood of success of the applicants that are accepted, aptitude assessment of factors related to success in such technical areas is indicated.

Assessment of flying proficiency and previous flying careers can be done with confidence. Present flight-check techniques are adequate for this purpose, and new methods have recently been devised for quantitative appraisal of career experience and performance. These methods are based on information in personnel and flying records and effectiveness reports.[10] [11] Adequate assessment techniques and aptitude tests are presently available for this portion of the selection of volunteer candidates, but they must be validated and cutting scores established empirically as soon as performance criteria can be obtained.

The need for thorough medical indoctrination and for continuous close monitoring of environment-conditioning equipment was implied but not explicitly stated in the paper by Beyer and Sells. Progress in the evaluation of such equipment during the past year and the recently reported experience of Lt. Col. David G. Simons[8] in his Manhigh II balloon flight have emphasized the importance of the monitoring functions as a realistic requirement—at least until effective automatic control systems are produced.

Biologic, Medical, and Physical Requirements

If and when a sealed cabin equipped with a reliable recycling, closed ecologic system to provide a complete ground environment is available on spacecraft, there should be little reason to prescribe physical standards more stringent than those presently required of rated personnel. The only exceptions might be for body dimensions, which would have to conform to cabin size, for strenuous operations involving unusual strain or fatigue of long duration, or for missions requiring personnel to leave the spacecraft in protective garments for exploratory or other purposes. Otherwise "shirt-sleeve missions" would be possible, since such ideal cabin conditions would require no adjustments to unusual environmental stresses.

Should the system be considered unreliable or require compromises with full cabin protection—as to temperature or cabin gas and pressure levels, for example—then such differences between needed and available protection must be made up. Even if control could be increased by pilot monitoring and adjustment of the system, safety would require supplementary measures. These include protective garments and pressure suits, selection of personnel with superior adaptive capacities, and conditioning of personnel to the expected stresses.

At present neither selection nor physical conditioning per se offers promise of solving these problems. It must be remembered that Mother Nature has been slow to change the structure of man. The 1958 model is very much the same as the 1558 model. Variations in physical characteristics are slight, and evolutionary adaptive change is slow. If man were exposed to a new planetary environment, eons might pass before any physiologically adaptive change appeared.

Protective garments are more realistic but require both supplementary selection criteria and conditioning training for practical use. For example, partial- or full-pressure suits impose a requirement for a more thorough evaluation of cardiovascular status to ensure successful endurance of the physiologic stresses occasioned by their use. Since some failures in the use of such equipment have been caused by decompression sickness, additional criteria would favor youth and reject obesity. The effects of such suits on comfort, mobility, and feelings of confinement must be evaluated in relation to time before their use for periods in excess of 12 to 14 hours is considered.

Personnel must be adapted to any special conditions they will experience on the spacecraft and be given time and guidance in training sessions to adapt their behavior to them. This applies not only to pressure suits and their component anti-g, thermal protective, and helmet sections, but also to warning-signal devices and any special devices for use in weightlessness. Motivation and prior experience in the use of such devices are significant additional determiners of successful adjustment and offer powerful protection against psychologic stresses.

Since early space missions will undoubtedly require "making up the difference" for environmental protection, protective garments will be used. Under these conditions physiologic selection for tolerance of transverse acceleration up to 9 g for 30 seconds to a minute, for cardiovascular efficiency, for resistance to dysbarism, and for tolerance of uncomfortable variations of temperature, humidity, gas partial pressure, and cabin pressure must be considered. Such selection must be supplemented by a well-planned conditioning program for optimal adaptation to these conditions while performing vital tasks.

There are several important psychophysiologic factors for which conditioning is critical even for short missions. Notable among these are diet, that is, adaptation to the in-cabin rations and conditions of eating and drinking, including weightlessness; withdrawal of smoking, cokes, coffee, and snacks; and disruption of normal sleep-waking cycle when a different schedule is required in flight. Additional problems of a related nature may be expected later when mission duration is extended beyond two days and crews of two or more members are used. These may include deprivation of other needs, such as alcohol, sex, recreation, and rest and reactions to sustained isolation, confinement, group coordination, and accumulated strain.

Psychologic Adaptability Requirements

By the time a pilot has logged over 1000 hours in high-performance jet aircraft, most of which are flown at altitudes requiring physiologic training and cabin protection, he may be assumed to have passed a severe stress test of adaptability to the rigors of military flying. Such individuals have already been cited as the most appropriate source of professional airmen of the jet age from among whom the pioneers of the space age must be recruited. As a group they may be considered to have proved not only aptitude and physiologic fitness for high-speed, high-altitude flying but also psychologic fitness as to stability, judgment under pressure, and competency to deal effectively with hazardous emergencies. From the standpoint of motivation, as well, they have the most appropriate experience and background to appraise the challenge of space realistically. Volunteers from their ranks are most likely to have an enduring interest and likelihood of satisfaction in this job. Since tolerance of stress is a direct function of strength of motivation, the requirement that qualified candidates be volunteers is obviously basic.

The assessment of stress tolerance and motivation for space operation is much simplified but not obviated by the proposed preselection. There remains the weeding out of marginal and questionable members of the jet-qualified volunteer group by careful examination of individuals and their life and work histories. This must be followed by further evaluation of the surviving candidates in relation to their expected ability to cope with additional stresses of spacecraft operation that are over and above those of present high-altitude jet flying.

Reliability of equipment. In the early stage of space operation by far the greatest stress problems are expected to be those associated with the reliability of equipment. When Beyer and Sells examined this problem, they assumed that it would be minimized over a longer period of engineering development than has actually been the case. Hence they did not even mention the probability of disaster due to equipment failure as a major stress factor. However the race to space has waxed hot as the realization of the goal has rapidly approached, and space missions are now being discussed that have greater risk factors than previous thinking accepted.

Fortunately this problem may be considered temporary and of relatively minor concern in the broad perspective of staffing a developing space program, once the first major flight-test hurdles are past. During this period stress associated with the reliability of the craft will probably be at its most acute. At the same time the flight-test personnel employed are likely to be the most able. The men who have been selected for the X-15 space trials, for example, are extremely capable and dedicated engineering test pilots. Their intimate knowledge of the craft and its idiosyncrasies, their ego involvement in the project, and their extensive training and preparatory experience ensure the ultimate of human effort and performance in carrying out the tests. Since the most effective counter to fear of unreliability of equipment is successful operation, this source of stress will abate as successful progress is made in engineering development and flight testing. After acceptable reliability of space vehicles has been demonstrated, from launch through flight to safe return, the attractiveness of the challenge of space may be predicted to increase.

The hazard of cosmic radiation has been previously mentioned. Not much can be said about it until further research is completed on absorption in relation to exposure. This is as yet one of the major stress problems that test pilots will investigate, although valuable data have been obtained from the Explorer satellite and other experimental sources. Should radiation exposure be found to be dangerous, it is unlikely that personnel will be further exposed until the efforts to conquer the protection problem have produced a tolerable solution.

Weightlessness. Until more is learned about weightlessness from actual experience under sustained exposure, one can only make educated guesses about this problem. It is not presently expected to be a serious selection problem. Personnel will undergo a program of indoctrination and training in the use of special devices—such as squeeze bottles for drinking, belts, harnesses, and techniques of controlled movement—under a routine of progressively increased exposure. If this program is either inadequate or infeasible, an engineering solution will have to be provided.

Sleep deprivation. Sleep deprivation will probably not be a serious problem for trained personnel on missions of less than two days. Although research has shown that a man in reasonable physical and mental condition may be able to miss sleep for five days without damage, the important issue is maintenance of efficiency. This requires training and conditioning to take maximum advantage of opportunities for rest and relaxation. An important aspect of conditioning is habituation to a day-night cycle of waking-work and sleep-rest consistent with the demands of the mission. Since the restorative effects of sleep can be felt even after cat naps of brief duration, learning to catch up on sleep whenever possible is important. Even more important is the ability to stay awake and react with alertness and vigilance when one is sleepy. Activity, movement, conversation, eating and drinking, and other techniques of self-stimulation including the controlled use of analeptic drugs may be indicated.

Boredom and fatigue. The subjective aspects of boredom and fatigue are similar and frequently confused. Boredom results from repetitive, monotonous activity. It can be relieved by a change, whereas fatigue involves a desire and need for rest. Since the effects of boredom are carelessness and inefficiency, planning is necessary on all missions of more than a few hours to provide a schedule of continuous, diverse activity. This would also have the advantage of helping the individual resist the deleterious effects of fear and anxiety. These tend to arise most insidiously during idleness and can often be suppressed by purposeful activity. In considering extended flights, such as a round trip to Mars, the need for variety of food, reading material, recreation, and other living arrangements will require careful study.

Isolation. Isolation is psychologically complex, since it involves a number of quite different conditions that have a common denominator of separating the individual from significant parts of his environment. One of these is confinement, which means restraint or restriction of freedom of movement or action. Such restraint could occur by command, by threat, by physical enclosure, or by encapsulation. Confinement produced by the dimensions of the cabin, harnesses, garments, and personal equipment, as well as by the possible sharing of space with other crew members, may have harmful effects on individual and group efficiency. Reactions of discomfort, fatigue, annoyance, fear, and even acute claustrophobia must be anticipated and prevented. Anthropometric limitations in selection standards may therefore be important when cabin space is tight. For the same reason engineering for comfort and work efficiency may have additional advantages. Although experienced jet pilots are generally habituated to cabin confinement as extreme as that expected in early spacecraft, their exposure has not yet been for long periods. Before exposure time is substantially extended, research is needed on the effects of prolonged exposure on the thresholds both of emotional reactions and of impairment of efficiency. Habituation tests under simulated conditions must also be considered part of the selection program as well as of necessary pilot conditioning.

Another dimension of isolation of probable concern in space flight is that of aloneness and separation from familiar supports. This has been recognized even on extremely short jet flights as the "breakoff phenomenon." [12] It occurs when pilots become painfully aware of leaving and being separated from the earth's friendly environment and being alone in the hostile and limitless beyond. Some pilots have reacted to this detachment with exhilaration and feelings of omnipotence. Others have felt lonely, afraid, and depressed. This experience has yet to be studied over greater distances and longer times. Much research is needed here to understand the effect of personality type, previous experience, and various component factors on individual and group reactions at different levels of exposure and in association with other stresses. Preselection should screen out the most predisposed, highly dependent individuals who are characteristically unable to adjust to new locales, routines, and associates. Conditioning by prior experience at increasing levels of exposure, effective use of supportive communication, discriminate matching of personalities in the composition of crews, and effective application of group dynamics in crew coordination may prove to be important means of ensuring effective adaptation and performance. Until these ideas are investigated, they can only be regarded as speculative.

A third dimension of isolation that merits consideration in this discussion concerns sensory deprivation or narrowing of the variability of the individual's sensory stimulation. This might occur should the monotony of the space environment and of the cabin interior become a repetitive, undifferentiated, unchanging expanse of sameness. Recent research[7] has provided evidence that mental alertness depends on having a variety of sensory stimulation, e.g., of sight, sound, smell, movement, and so forth. When that variation is drastically reduced, there are measurable effects in loss of efficiency in mental performance. Such effects are seen at a moderate level in monotonous tasks, such as repetitive simple work, monitoring a radarscope in a quiet, dark, confined work space, and studying uninteresting material. It is believed that they can be overcome in a variety of ways, particularly by care in engineering the cabin interior and by appropriate arrangement of work schedules. Avoidance of monotony should adequately prevent the occurrence of the more serious effects discussed here. This problem deserves intensive further study toward the goal not merely of preventing onset of loss of efficiency but of understanding the means of maximizing efficiency.

Cumulative effects. Finally the problems of adaptability and stress tolerance must be viewed in terms of the cumulative effects of all the stresses of the situation on the individual. It is known that the accumulation of a number of minor annoyances, strains, and fears—none of an intensity to evoke a maladaptive reaction by itself—may result after some time in a combined stress of significant proportions. Separate consideration of these problem areas is important both for planning an optimal living and work environment inside spacecraft and for diagnosing and reducing individual susceptibilities. But the final test of both internal environment and individual response for a spaceworthy man-machine complex demands suitability tests in adequate simulators. It will be necessary to test both trained personnel and machine systems at ground-level and space-equivalent flight conditions. The next step will be to conduct actual flight tests.

Personnel Selection

The analysis of human requirements in the preceding sections must be the basis for personnel selection. It is apparent that the operator of a space vehicle must be a motivated, controlled, professional pilot. His interests are directed, as Crossfield has emphasized, toward his primary task of controlling the vehicle. The physiologic and psychologic stresses which concern the aeromedical doctors who advise design engineers and who select personnel do not enter into the pilot's concept of his total job, except in relation to the understanding and operation of various equipment systems and procedures. It is the doctors' job to screen the applicants and to identify the men most likely to measure up to all the demands of this most exacting assignment.

The pioneer space pilots will be men like Crossfield and his colleagues who have excelled as engineering test pilots. They will be identified with the project virtually from blueprint stage. They will be recognized for their proven accomplishments in the most advanced projects yet undertaken. A handful of such men will probably carry the project past its most hazardous stage of reliability testing on relatively short but highly important missions.

After their basic work is accomplished, requirements should increase as more spacecraft are built and further developmental and exploratory missions are scheduled. Volunteer applicants will be required to have experience as pilots of high-performance jet and rocket aircraft, preferably in engineering flight testing. Volunteers who meet experience requirements, which must be defined, will be screened initially by standards based on procedures such as the following:

a. Weight-size restrictions, based on payload and cabin requirements.

b. Review of career experience, based on evaluation of personnel and flying records, effectiveness reports, letters of recommendation, and ratings by fellow pilots and superior officers.

c. Physical examination, including review of medical records, detailed medical history, comprehensive flight physical examination, and a number of special procedures related to tolerance of acceleration and heat stress and the use of pressure suits. According to present thinking, visual standards may be relaxed somewhat, but weight standards in relation to height should be more stringent to eliminate obese persons, who are unduly susceptible to decompression difficulties such as dysbarism. In this connection maximum age standards may also be prescribed. Examination for inguinal hernias, chest X ray to eliminate pleural blebs, and an electrocardiogram at rest and during and after a two-step Masters test will be included. The latter procedure was recommended after it was found that most of the men who failed partial-pressure-suit indocrination had some acute cardiac problem. The cold-pressor test, tilt table, and the Harvard-type test may be included for a further check on cardiovascular reactivity.

d. Psychiatric examination, supplemented by neurologic examination and routine clinical psychologic examination. These examinations assess general personality resources, areas of conflict, dependency needs, reality orientation, and motivation toward the project. Electro-encephalographic examination would be included for clinical neurology, baseline studies, and follow-up research.

e. Psychologic examination for general intelligence, mathematical ability, mechanical principles, dial and table reading, and technical reading and vocabulary, supplemented by a comprehensive experimental selection battery of personality questionnaires and psychophysiologic and performance tests. These would be included for research purposes, to be validated later against operational criteria.

Preliminary standards for screening candidates will of necessity be based largely on "clinical judgment," supported by available scientific research. Standards will probably be too high at first but may be relaxed as experience in the indoctrination and training program proceeds, since substantial attrition is expected as the candidates go through the schooling and conditioning experiences necessary to prepare for actual space work. The initial screening will thus accept for the second stage, selection-in-training, an elite group of professional airmen. Each one will be qualified as an experienced jet (and probably rocket) pilot, highly and realistically motivated for the program. He will also be physically and mentally superior, emotionally calm and controlled, and possessed of certain technical aptitudes necessary for performance of the task ahead.

Indoctrination and Training

The principal areas of training may be divided into (a) survival indoctrination and habituation, (b) operation and maintenance of all equipment systems and subsystems, and (c) navigation and communication. Each of these areas comprises didactic classroom training or ground school and practical application in ground simulators, balloon trainers, rocket vehicles, and spacecraft.

Survival indoctrination is basically an extension of the physio
logic training presently given for high-altitude flight. For the space
man the curriculum must be extended to cover all the components
of the synthetic cabin environment essential to life, including the
physiologic processes, possible dysfunctions, and corrective action
In addition he must be taught practical survival principles and the
facts concerning physiologic and psychologic aspects of nutrition
fluid balance and dehydration, temperature regulation, fatigue
sleep, boredom, isolation, anxiety, fear, and loneliness. To use thi
knowledge most effectively, each man should be trained in such a
way that he can apply it meaningfully to himself and, when ap
plicable, to his comrades, with insightful knowledge of his and
their physical and mental characteristics.

To complete the survival training, indoctrination must be fol
lowed up by realistic individual (and later group) habituation to
the actual conditions of work room and living room, tasks, and
equipment to be encountered on space missions. This phase will
consist of a progressive series of practice sessions: first in the
laboratory, later in ground simulator mockups and balloon gondola
simulators at altitude, and finally in rockets and spacecraft. These
sessions will provide exposure to the various stresses during per
formance of simulated required tasks. Pilots must learn to function
effectively while using flight rations, drinking from squeeze bottles
recognizing signs and signals indicative of their functioning, rec
ognizing and coping with emergencies, and tolerating fatigue, dis
comfort, and deprivation of smoking and other habits of long
standing. In short they must be adapted to living comfortably and
efficiently in the spacecraft.

Flight training and training in navigation and communication
must be laid out on the basis of the functioning abilities and back
ground of the personnel selected and of the particular equipmen
and operations involved. The traditional training sequence o
ground school, simulator trainer, and transition to operational craf
must be adapted to this situation.

Every aspect of the training program will also provide for furthe
selection and attrition. The graduate will actually have passed a
comprehensive series of stress and performance test hurdles whil
going through his preparation. It is not too much to expect that h

will measure up to the standard set forth by Major General Dan C. Ogle,[6] Surgeon General of the United States Air Force:

Such a person must be all that the best aviator is today as well as being constitutionally and emotionally suited for the physical and emotional traumatic influences of sealed cabins speeding, heaven knows where, through the awful silence of a timeless and a darkened sky.

School of Aviation Medicine, USAF

CHAPTER 11

Experimental Studies on the Conditioning of Man for Space Crews

Dr. Bruno Balke

As we progress in the many areas of research that must fit man into his spacecraft and enable him to do a useful job of work while he is there, one of the problems that we must examine very carefully is the choice and conditioning of the first space flyers. In this radically new venture little can be left to chance in their selection and training. The first space flyer must be capable of the most exacting human performance, must have the highest degree of tolerance to stress, and must have a demonstrated endurance to prolonged marginal conditions. Our research must identify the kinds and degrees of stress that he will undergo, must determine the human capabilities that will best withstand such stresses, and must discover means of conditioning and strengthening the necessary human defenses against the anticipated rigors of space flight.

Man's capacity for stress varies not only among individuals but also within the same individual, fluctuating with differences or changes in the proper adaptive responses. Generally, low or high tolerance for a given stress situation correlates with poor or good levels of "fitness."

The human organism, if properly conditioned, responds readily to acute and chronic changes of demands. A strictly sedentary life or forced inactivity can reduce functional reserves to a point at which metabolic requirements that exceed the basal metabolic rate by five to six times are well beyond adaptive capacities. On the other hand, properly conditioned and regularly active men might be safely stressed to 15 to 18 times the resting level of their energy metabolism. A cardiovascular and respiratory system which, through extensive physical training, has become adapted to such extraordinary requirements will stand up under almost any other stress situation. At the least such cardiorespiratory reserves will serve as a good background for further attempts to increase the tolerance for other stresses by additional special training.

It is all too true that human life exists in a very narrow zone compared to the diameter of our own planet earth and to the vastness of the space beyond the earth's atmosphere. From this point of view the 100 to 200 feet of water depths reached by divers and the 28,000 to 29,000 feet of altitude conquered by mountaineers delimit a ridiculously narrow belt of life. And even in this narrow zone what physiological adaptations are necessary! Of all the more highly organized living organisms, only man so far has demonstrated the ability to adapt to its extremes.

Our search is therefore for the qualities of the superman, and the subject of the following discussion will be the experimental work on man's tolerance limits to some of the anticipated singular stresses, with some emphasis upon cross-adaptability for complex stress situations.

General Physical Conditioning

Any normal healthy individual who fulfills the present standard requirements for Air Force pilot selection has the physical potentialities to become eligible for eventual space operations. Spacemen should be required to have a maximum of body reserves. The key to high body reserves is regular physical activity of a kind making high metabolic demands. This has been shown by experimental research in which running was employed as conditioning exercise. Aside from walking, running is the simplest and most natural form of physical activity. It is also one of the most disliked of exercises. Considering the great metabolic requirements involved, that dislike is easily understood.

In work-capacity studies at the School of Aviation Medicine, USAF, it was found that 40 per cent of more than 500 Air Force personnel were in "poor" physical condition. Their functional capacities were adequate for a maximal oxygen intake of only 35 milliliters (ml) per minute per kilogram (kg) of body weight. The physical condition of an additional 40 per cent of test subjects was classified as "fair." Their maximal oxygen intake was 38 ml/min/kg. In the accompanying table the maximal oxygen intake, the classification of performance capacity, and the maximal performance in walking upgrade are correlated with running speeds. It can be seen that slow running, or "trotting," calls for maximal functional adaptations in the average man. No wonder that in even brief periods of running exercises he experiences pains, severely labored breathing (dyspnea), and general discomfort.

Maximal oxygen intake (ml/min/kg)	Status of physical condition	Grade walking at 3.4 mph. Maximal grade in per cent	Running speeds Maximum in meters/min.	1 mile in mins
35	poor	14%	140 m.	11'30"
38	fair	16%	160 m.	10'00"
43	good	19%	190 m.	8'30"
48	very good	22%	215 m.	7'30"
53	excellent	25%	245 m.	6'30"

The table illustrates sufficiently the great functional demands involved in running and the great value of this type of exercise for a physical-conditioning program. In such a program the emphasis has to be put on the so-called "interval training," a carefully balanced interchange of speedy running and recovery-walking periods.

Experimentally, such daily training of 30 to 45 minutes duration for a period of 10 to 12 weeks had these physiological effects:

1. It reduced the pulse frequency at any given work intensity. This means, since the oxygen intake for the same work intensity remained unaltered, that (a) the stroke volume of the heart, or (b) the oxygen utilization by the tissue, or (c) both of these factors had been altered in the direction of a more economical circulatory function.

2. The maximal oxygen intake increased by about 25 per cent, a reflection of a substantial increase of the maximal cardiac output.

3. The maximal breathing capacity during work increased about 40 per cent. However, for comparable work intensities the effort of breathing was slightly reduced so that for equal oxygen intakes, or for equal work loads, less ventilation was required.

These three findings meant that the functional reserves were considerably increased.

The training period also had a valuable effect on the metabolic reserves. Pretraining tests on the control group revealed that an average amount of 220 grams of carbohydrates was utilized before the subjects became extremely exhausted by a steady-state type of heavy work. Posttraining exhaustion occurred much later, after an average amount of 315 gm of carbohydrates had been mobilized. The extent to which carbohydrates from the glycogen stores in muscles and liver become available and the extent to which stored body fat is readily converted to fuel for muscular activity can be of great importance for the pilot of present-day aircraft and more so for the space pilot.

The increase of functional and metabolic reserves accompanying regular physical activity has more implications than those of work capacity alone. With more functional reserves physical fatigue is delayed or even prevented, or is such as not to be of too much concern from a performance standpoint. Regular physical exercise can help control body weight and prevent the functional disorders generally accepted as the natural deterioration of aging. Finally, the high body reserves achieved and maintained by regular activity can assist one's adaptation to other stresses, as, for instance, hypoxia or temperature extremes.

Experiments to Build Up Physical Reserves

In an effort to build up functional and metabolic reserves still further and to improve the tolerance for various physiologically adverse conditions, the experiments were transferred from near sea level at Randolph Air Force Base, Texas, to the higher altitudes of the Peruvian Andes and the Rocky Mountains in Colorado. In Morococha, Peru (14,800 feet), as well as on Mt. Evans, Colorado (14,160 feet), various phases of acclimatization to high altitude were studied for their effects on

1. Performance capacity
2. Altitude tolerance
3. Adaptability to hyperventilation
4. Tolerance for pressure breathing without protective counter-pressure
5. Susceptibility to dysbarism at various stages of natural partial denitrogenation at low barometric pressure
6. Tolerance for increased carbon dioxide levels in the inhaled air,

Since all these experimental studies are pertinent to the physiological problems of space flight, the results will be briefly reported.

Performance capacity. At high altitude the work capacity is reduced. Even the native Indians who live at altitudes between 13,000 and 16,000 feet, and who work and play harder at those altitudes than most people in lower countrysides, do not attain the same maximal performance as do well-conditioned subjects at sea level. Their circulatory and respiratory adaptive response to work does show, however, signs of greater efficiency and economy than do the responses of individuals temporarily acclimatized to these high altitudes. There is some indication from experimental studies (Pugh) at altitudes up to 21,000 feet in the Himalayan Mountains that man, when temporarily acclimatized to more extreme altitudes, behaves more like a native Peruvian Indian after he returns to altitudes of 14,000 to 15,000 feet.

During the experimental period on Mt. Evans in 1958 physical training was regularly continued at altitude. The improvements in body reserves, although not determined experimentally, can be appreciated from the work performed in mountain climbing. In the initial phase of the 6-week period, climbs of 2-hour duration were very fatiguing. Toward the end of the mountain episode remarkable work in climbing steep slopes was accomplished for periods of 5 to 8 hours without the usually essential rest intervals or intake of food and liquids. The caloric requirements for such work amounted to approximately 3500 to 5000 calories and were furnished from the body stores without undue fatigue symptoms.

Altitude tolerance. In control tests of altitude tolerance in the low-pressure chamber which employed a gradual ascent to simulated altitude, the subjects reached on the average a critical level of 24,000 feet. After physical conditioning the subjects became unconscious at 27,000 feet. After five weeks at altitudes above 10,000 feet but only 10 days at 14,000 feet, the average critical altitude was 30,000 feet. At a level of 21,000 feet the average performance scores on a neuromuscular coordination test were higher than under all previous more normal conditions.

Utilizing a low-pressure chamber in Morococha, Peru (14,800 feet), and exactly the same procedure of gradual ascent as in the Mt. Evans experiments, a group of native residents reached an average critical altitude of 31,000 feet. The author, after living five weeks at Morococha and spending a few hours almost every day on hikes up to altitudes of 17,000 feet, was still conscious at 33,000 feet, at which time he took the precaution of turning on his oxygen supply.

The time of useful consciousness (TUC) at 30,000 feet, after discontinuing oxygen breathing, exceeded one hour in the permanently acclimatized natives as well as in the temporarily acclimatized subject. Velasquez has recently reported a TUC of one and one half minutes for natives exposed to a simulated altitude of 40,000 feet.

The TUC attained at simulated altitudes of 25,000 and 30,000 feet was also tested during the Mt. Evans experiments in 1958. All subjects stayed conscious far in excess of 30 minutes at a level of 25,000 feet where normally TUC lasts only four to five minutes. At 30,000 feet the TUC exceeded the normal one- to two-minute period and went beyond the 30-minute mark in one experiment.

Adaptability to hyperventilation. Noticing the increasing tolerance for severe deficiency of carbon dioxide in the blood (hypocapnia) during frequently repeated hyperventilation experiments, a group of subjects volunteered to hyperventilate for 30- to 60-

minute periods daily during three weeks. The hyperventilation was assisted by a respirator delivering alternately a positive and a very slight negative pressure at any rate desired.

The test results before and after the hyperventilation training confirmed the hypothesis that there is an adaptive response to chronic hyperventilation in healthy individuals. At high altitudes where hyperventilation becomes a necessity for proper oxygenation of the blood, the tolerance for hypocapnia reaches a maximum. There an excessive hyperventilation is limited by eventual breathing fatigue rather than by the deleterious effects of hypocapnia.

Tolerance for pressure breathing. Breathing against positive pressure is considered to interfere seriously with adequate blood circulation (hemodynamics). Experiments in our laboratory have shown that good physical condition, special training in pressure breathing, and proper breathing mechanics enable an individual to tolerate continuous mask or helmet pressures of 20 to 40 mm of mercury (Hg) for a considerable length of time without circulatory complications.

Breathing oxygen under pressure is the means utilized to increase man's altitude ceiling, at least for emergency situations. Pressure breathing without protective counterpressure is limited by fatigue of the hard-working respiratory muscles and by hypoxia. With increasing altitude both factors become greater handicaps. At an altitude of 50,000 feet the oxygen pressure delivered from the oxygen regulators presently in use is approximately 30 mm Hg. This is the equivalent of 18,000 feet altitude in ambient air. At 60,000 feet with a positive mask or helmet pressure of 40 mm Hg, which trained men can tolerate from several minutes up to one half hour, the equivalent altitude in ambient air is 26,000 feet.

So far seven subjects have been exposed to ceiling altitudes of 54,000 to 58,000 feet in pressure breathing without counterpressure after they had become partially acclimatized to an altitude of 14,000 feet. Neuromuscular coordination at these ceiling altitudes was only slightly impaired. The subjects did not represent a selected "tiger type" but rather a cross section of normal airmen. The average age was 33 years in a 20- to 52-year range. These experimental results reaffirm the usefulness of conditioning and special training as a keystone for greater reserves.

Susceptibility to dysbarism. Besides hypoxia the most urgent problem during acute exposure to altitudes above 35,000 feet is the development of severe pains—the so-called bends or chokes. The symptoms are caused by formation and growth of air bubbles in tissues of inadequate capillarization. The gas bubbles originate whenever there is a great difference between the partial pressures of the gaseous nitrogen dissolved in the body and of the nitrogen in the surrounding atmosphere.

Breathing of 100-per-cent oxygen for several hours before leaving for a high-altitude flight lowers the partial pressure of nitrogen in the lungs, blood, and body tissue in that sequence. In the subsequent ascent to high altitude the amount of nitrogen remaining in the tissue is minute, bubbles do not form, or at least do not grow to any considerable size, and decompression sickness is prevented.

For experimental research on the prevention of dysbarism the following assumption was made: since partial denitrogenation by breathing oxygen for a few hours results in bends protection, then living at higher altitudes with naturally diminished partial pressures of nitrogen should also provide sufficient protection after adequate time has been allowed for a complete equilibrium between the partial pressures of nitrogen in the body and in the atmosphere. The experimental work was done at Randolph AFB, Texas, in the Peruvian Andes, and in the Rocky Mountains in Colorado. A standard exercise test was employed in the low-pressure chamber at a simulated altitude of 38,000 feet. At Randolph AFB all subjects experienced third-degree pains after an average time of about 20 minutes. After living three to four days at an altitude of 10,000 feet, third-degree bends did not occur and second-degree pains occurred only after an average time of 50 minutes. After staying 48 hours at an altitude of 14,000 feet there were only two incidences of slight pains among seven subjects tested, and at Morococha (14,800 feet) all ten individuals tested remained symptom-free.

These findings, although mainly of basic research interest, may have some application in determining the desirable cabin environment in a space vehicle.

Tolerance for increased levels of carbon dioxide. Just as frequently repeated hyperventilation increases the tolerance for hypocapnia, so a more chronic subnormal decrease of air in the lungs (hypoventilation) favors adaptations to higher levels of carbon dioxide. Divers who can hold their breath for two to three minutes, or top athletes trained for long-distance running who still breathe smoothly at a murderous pace, or patients who are inadvertently underventilated during treatment in an iron lung—all these conditioned people develop a lower sensitivity to the ventilatory driving force of carbon dioxide.

The two main causes of environmental emergency situations in the sealed crew compartment of vehicles flying at altitudes above 80,000 feet are likely to be the loss of oxygen pressure or an accumulation of carbon dioxide (CO_2). While altitude acclimatization provides considerable protection against severe hypoxia, it might not be compatible with sufficient tolerance for higher levels of CO_2 in the inhaled air.

To investigate this latter problem two types of experiments were carried out: (1) Rebreathing tests were performed, starting with a volume of 100 liters of a 30:70 per cent $O_2:N_2$ gas mixture, and employing light work on the bicycle ergometer to raise the inhaled CO_2 concentration approximately 1 per cent each minute. The control tests at sea level were compared with the tests made at an altitude of 14,160 feet on subjects having a few weeks' acclimatization. (2) During extended periods of confinement in a sealed chamber simulating effective altitudes between 12,000 and 20,000 feet, two groups of two subjects each were exposed to an accumulation of CO_2 at the beginning and again at the end of 8-day and 10-day experiments.

In both types of experiments the limiting CO_2 concentrations in the inhaled air were practically identical for the normal and the acclimatized man, although at comparable carbon dioxide concentrations the pulmonary ventilation of the acclimatized man was increased by 25 to 33 per cent. Compared on the basis of inhaled or alveolar CO_2 tensions, however, the respiratory response to comparable tensions was almost three times and five times, respectively, that of the normal response. These findings indicate a great increase in the sensitivity of the respiratory center to carbon dioxide during the process of acclimatization to altitude. For all practical purposes, however, this increase in sensitivity to CO_2 did not lessen the CO_2 tolerance of the acclimatized man.

The reason for this apparently contradictory situation may be that during progressing acclimatization to altitude, assisted by regular physical activity, the maximal breathing capacity increases with the higher demands on the respiratory muscles. Maximal values of 180 to 200 liters of pulmonary ventilation per minute have been observed during work capacity tests in the mountains, compared to maximal values of 120 li/min at sea level. At any altitude the metabolic requirements for any given work are the same and the same volume of carbon dioxide is exhaled during a given time by the acclimatized or the unacclimatized subjects. Thus in a closed system without provision for the absorption of carbon dioxide the accumulation of CO_2 can be assumed to be of equal magnitude. Although the acclimatized man responds with greater ventilatory volumes, he does not become dyspneic sooner than the normal man because of the considerable increase of his maximal breathing capacity.

The measurements of pulse frequency and blood pressure during these experiments—averaging 130 pulse beats per minute and 200/110 mm Hg systolic/diastolic pressure—indicated a considerable cardiovascular stress when carbon dioxide concentrations exceeded eight to ten per cent.

Cross adaptability for complex stress situations. The conditioning training of the experimental subjects at Randolph AFB before leaving on the mountain expedition in Colorado affected not only their work capacity but also their heat tolerance. The workouts were usually held during the noon hours when the temperatures were between 32° and 36° C. On some training days the relative humidity reached 80 to 90 per cent. The subjects ran distances varying from three to five miles. When each subject's work capacity was tested on the treadmill, once at room temperatures of 22° to 24° C and again at temperatures of 33° to 34° C, no essential difference was found. Under the additional heat load the critical pulse rate of 180 beats per minute occurred, on the average, one minute earlier during the gradual increase of work intensity.

In the mountains the experimental group adapted not only to altitude but also to a rather cool environment with temperatures around the freezing point. Immediately after the return to Texas in mid-August the daily workouts were continued. The subjects ran four to six miles in temperatures ranging from 34° to 38° C.

Subjectively and objectively there was no deterioration in performance.

Ten-day sealed chamber experiment. A crucial experiment was carried out by two individuals four weeks after they had returned from Mt. Evans, Colorado. They spent 10 days in the mobile low-pressure chamber that had been used during the experiments in the mountains. The purpose of this experiment was to study various physiological, mental, and possibly psychological reactions of thoroughly conditioned and cross-trained men to an excess of combined stress situations.

The chamber environment was kept at barometric pressures equivalent to 14,000 or 18,000 feet, and the oxygen content was regulated so that the effective simulated altitude was controlled at levels between 14,000 and 20,000 feet. The chamber temperature varied from 26° to 36° C with average temperatures of about 29° C at night and about 31° C during the day. Carbon dioxide and water vapor were absorbed by lithium hydroxide. The capacity of lithium hydroxide for water vapor absorption is far less than that for carbon dioxide. Thus the relative humidity varied between 70 and 92 per cent, while the level of carbon dioxide was kept below 1 per cent most of the time.

The most severe environmental conditions were encountered when at an effective altitude of 16,000 feet the levels of carbon dioxide, humidity, and temperature were allowed to build up. When the chamber temperature reached 36° C, the humidity 92 per cent, and the inhaled CO_2 concentration 4.5 per cent, the enormous sweating rate was most uncomfortable but the circulatory and respiratory reserves were only slightly affected. A cold spell, unusual for that time of the year in Texas, terminated the heating part of the experiment. Attempts to counteract the effect of the drop in outside temperature by more rigorous exercise on the bicycle ergometer failed. Despite a high energy expenditure for a period of 30 minutes the inside temperature dropped to 34° C. The relative humidity, on the other hand, rose to almost 100 per cent and the carbon dioxide content to 5.5 per cent. Five hours later when the carbon dioxide level reached 8 per cent the temperature had fallen to 31° C, and the subjects were in good physical and mental condition. When at this point the subjects attempted to clean up the chamber, the increase in physical activity caused an unexpected respiratory and cardiovascular response. Within 30 minutes the pulmonary ventilation increased to maximum, and the rise in pulse rate and blood pressure also indicated impending limitations in the CO_2 tolerance. Intense efforts were required to make the last physiological and environmental measurements before putting on the oxygen mask.

Immediately after this experiment was terminated, the chamber pressure was lowered to a simulated altitude of 40,000 feet for a bends test. During a period of two hours at that altitude the subjects experienced no symptoms of dysbarism, confirming the earlier findings that natural denitrogenation at altitude levels of 14,000 feet and above provides satisfactory protection from decompression sickness.

Under the severe environmental conditions of the experiment the energy, fluid, and electrolyte balance was disturbed. Meals and beverages were not cooked but consumed lukewarm at the prevailing chamber temperature. The highly chlorinated water was very distasteful and the canned baby food—as canned food in general—was unappetizing. Occasionally one or the other subject became slightly nauseated, probably as a result of hypoxia or of heat and dehydration. The daily energy intake did not exceed 1600 calories on the average, while the expenditure was estimated as approximately 2600 calories. The total loss of body weight during the 10-day experiment averaged 10 pounds per person. Undoubtedly the great metabolic reserves achieved during the period of extensive physical work high in the mountains had been adequate to cope with any of the acute or temporary energy requirements of the experimental situation.

Both subjects demonstrated satisfactory mental alertness at all times and never failed under any of the severest experimental conditions. Although the hourly checks of all the environmental factors became routine, the instrument manipulations and the necessary calculations required accuracy, good coordination, and a clear mind. A simple adding test of one-hour duration and a neuromuscular coordination test were performed daily. Sufficient physical activity was provided by changing the CO_2 absorber, cleaning the chamber, riding the bicycle ergometer, and practicing putting on the pressure suit as fast as possible. Under the prevailing environmental conditions all that work caused a great degree of physical fatigue, which was not relieved by compensating rest and sleep. Restlessness, headaches, nausea, the narrow bunk bed, odors, and the feeling of air stagnation, high temperatures, etc., cut the time of sleep to three to four hours in each 24-hour period.

No definite psychological observations were made. Both subjects expressed the subjective opinion that confinement to the very primitive and odd chamber interior had no effect on their spirit. Boredom was unknown. Any free minute was used either for relaxation or for technical or entertaining reading, especially during the night shifts. The matter of how two people would get along together for 10 days in such a tiny compartment proved to be no problem at all: the mutual respect and regard and the readiness to serve and help each other at any moment were accentuated under the more severe stress situations. Anxiety and fear, of course, did not enter into this type of earth-bound experiment. It is felt, however, that most specific situations in space causing anxiety and fear can be anticipated and can be obviated by training. Any experienced pilot or deep-sea diver or mountaineer might agree with this hypothesis.

Experimental evidence exists that the human organism has a great capacity to adapt to superhuman requirements of a biological nature. With proper conditioning and training each man can achieve his own physical, mental, and psychological maximum of adaptive capacity. Since the limitations of these capacities are not known before considerable efforts have been made to increase the psychosomatic reserves, the selection of an eventual spacecrew becomes possible only after such special efforts have been made. Certainly there are numerous ways open for proper conditioning and training. In the experimental research described simple methods were successfully used. These methods might also be effective to increase g tolerance. For a preadaptation to the state of weightlessness, exercises requiring highly developed neuromuscular coordination might be helpful.

School of Aviation Medicine, USAF

CHAPTER 12

Escape and Survival During Space Operations

Colonel Paul A. Campbell

Manned space operations, especially in the pioneering stages, will be fraught with many problems. Among the most serious and complex will be that of escape and survival from a damaged or malfunctioning vehicle. The multiplicity of distinct and widely different environmental and operational conditions—beginning at the launch pad, extending through the atmosphere into space, and continuing during the return through the atmosphere and the landing on the earth's surface—adds immeasurably to the problems that the engineers and human-factors groups are called upon to solve. The communications problem, the location problem, the survival problem—all represent segments within themselves. In this stage of the development of space operations any article on escape and survival must be largely speculative and must raise more issues than it solves.

Protection of the individual, like many other aspects of space flight, depends to a large degree on energies available at the time when and the place where they are needed. Available controllable energy in most of the space situations is a critical item costing additional weight and volume for which there will be many competing needs.

The philosophy of protection has never as yet been completely resolved in conventional military aviation. A few basic principles are applied, however, and some of these can be extrapolated into space operations. First of all, weight and volume of protective gear must never prevent or even seriously interfere with the successful accomplishment of a mission. In other words, the occupant or occupants should never be protected to the point of uselessness. Second, protective equipment should never be used as a substitute for the reliability of a primary vehicle. Third, insofar as practicable protection should be multipurpose and designed to meet as many hazardous situations as possible. Fourth, 100-per-cent protection is unrealistic, just as almost all situations in ordinary life present a certain degree of hazard. And fifth, where weight costs are critical as in space flight, protection should be planned and designed only after very careful analysis of the hazards and their possible incidence. The weight-cost ratio must always be borne in mind.

Except in instances where the fate of our nation is at stake, it is unrealistic to consider that a man or a group of men will be sent or allowed to go into space until there is a *reasonable* chance of safe return or of safe recovery in case of an accident or mishap.[1] The term "reasonable chance" is a debatable one and requires at least that an attempt be made to equate possible costs and dangers with possible rewards. "Safe return" implies reliability of the primary system. "Safe recovery" implies effective protective gear and adequate means of return, location, and retrieve.

Space Flight—Types and Situations

When considering any aspect of space operations one must distinguish between various types of space flight, as each type will require somewhat different equipment design and recovery systems. This chapter is concerned with three: first, a simple penetration of the earth's atmosphere along a ballistic trajectory and return through the atmosphere to a designated area; second, an orbital flight around the earth one or more times; and third, a penetration into outer space along an ellipse. These three types of space flight become more complex in ascending order as do the protective gear and recovery systems required. Duration of flight and distance of flight from the earth also are very important factors, and as their magnitude increases they will require certain alterations of the systems.

Similarly there are also at least five basic situations in space flight, some of which require special provisions of escape and recovery systems. These are the situations which occur on the launch pad; during the period of rapid acceleration through the atmosphere; while in ballistic trajectory, in orbit, or in ellipse; during re-entry into the earth's atmosphere; and after landing on the earth's surface. They will be considered in order.

The launch pad situation. On the launch pad the occupant or crew will be in the immediate vicinity of a very large quantity of highly explosive, highly corrosive material. Consequently provision must be made for safe, almost instantaneous escape from the standing vehicle to a protected area. The ejection should be capable of initiation by the crew, by the blockhouse control group, or by some automatic sensing device activated by excessive heat or other critical malfunction. According to R. M. Stanley[2] there are ejection systems presently in existence by which a crew could escape, and there is probably sufficient knowledge to employ such an arrangement for the purpose. He states that the existing Stencel ultra-fast-opening parachute could bring the occupant down safely from low trajectory. Stanley suggests that if the vehicle is of the orbital type the final stage of the vehicle itself might form an escape system, using the same energies which will probably be present in that stage for separation and for control during re-entry and landing. In his opinion the entire operation would have to be programed for automatic action. The only human action would be initiating the escape maneuver.

Accelerative stages. Stanley also believes that the same system could be utilized for escape during the second situation—the accelerative stages within the earth's atmosphere. In a nonorbiting vehicle of ballistic trajectory a properly encapsulated seat or compartment would probably suffice. The same systems, he suggests, can be employed during re-entry. He places a velocity limitation of mach 2 on all the systems and points out that slowing is required if speeds in excess of this limitation have been reached before the emergency.

In ballistic trajectory, orbit, or ellipse. In the upper reaches of the atmosphere or above the atmosphere in space, the escape situation becomes much more complex. The complexity increases proportionately with distance from the earth and with the velocity of the vehicle. The type of emergency is also of importance, as ability to remain in the primary vehicle and attempt repairs simplifies the problem considerably. Analysis of possible causes of emergencies during this stage of operation indicates that cabin leaks through malfunction or meteoric penetration will be the most likely. Most writers on the subject agree that, barring disintegration of the craft, the best protection for the occupant would be an automatically inflated pressure suit activated by a pressure-drop sensing device. Such a suit would preserve useful consciousness while repairs were attempted.[3][4]

It should be pointed out here that the time of useful consciousness[5] during complete exposure to the ambient atmosphere or ambient space above the 50,000- to 55,000-foot-altitude range is limited to approximately 15 seconds. Thus automatic inflation is a requirement. In a one-man operation a pressure suit seems imperative. In multiplace vehicles one of the crew members should always be in his pressure suit on alert, with self-contained oxygen, pressure, and communications systems ready for instantaneous operation. Remaining with the primary vehicle has many advantages, most of which can never be duplicated by a secondary or lifeboat type of substitute vehicle. As has been pointed out many times, an effective secondary vehicle would require practically all the structural integrity, controllability, and basic equipment of the primary vehicle; thus it would seem impractical. Furthermore the location problem would appear to be simplified by remaining with the primary vehicle, as presumably the general position of that craft would be known to ground monitoring stations.

If in orbit at the time of an emergency, the situation becomes further complicated from many points of view. First the damaged vehicle must be got out of orbit by some method of slow, controlled orbital decay, followed by controlled re-entry. These maneuvers require a high degree of programed automaticity. Thus the integrity of the control system must have been preserved. The energies inherent in the final-stage re-entry vehicle would appear ideal for this purpose.[2][6] If the damaged vehicle is incapable of controlled orbital decay and controlled re-entry, new complications are compounded upon the old ones.

Norman Petersen[7] and Krafft Ehricke[8] analyzed this situation in their presentations at the Second International Symposium on Physics and Medicine of the Upper Atmosphere and Space, in San Antonio, Texas, on 10-12 November 1958. Petersen presented a detailed analysis of rescue through retrieve, and Ehricke presented the considerations required if the lifeboat or secondary-vehicle type of approach were necessary. The retrieve operation would require a vehicle to be sent into orbit from earth, from a satellite station, or from a companion vehicle which by its own energies would match a segment of its orbit with that of the derelict vehicle. The retrieving vehicle, after contact and coupling, could assist in repairs, transfer energy if required, or take the occupants on board. This would be an extremely difficult operation but it is probably not outside the realm of future possibility. From the standpoint of the secondary-vehicle approach, a possible solution might lie in the utilization of more than one vehicle in the same space operation. Both might take off together or possibly one might separate from the mother vehicle while in orbit and both continue thereafter in the same orbit in close proximity with each other. This could make mutual aid possible in event of emergency. Many readers undoubtedly will consider these approaches so complex as to be unreal. However, our achievements during the past half-century have demonstrated the feasibility of many operations formerly considered fictional.

The re-entry and pickup situations. Re-entry into the earth's atmospheric mass will for some time be the most dangerous portion of a space flight, with the possible exception of that on the launching pad. The magnitude of deceleration, the heating effects, and the dissipation of tremendous amounts of kinetic energy within a relatively short distance in a short period of time account for the difficulty. This situation has been analyzed by many. It does lend itself to emergency solutions. These solutions eventually will weld the final link of the achievements that will put man into outer space and return him safely. Protective gear for this segment of his flight will not be too unlike that for his flight up through the atmosphere after launching, with the exception of the equipment needed to prepare for final contact with the earth and for return to zero velocity. His safety during this period will depend upon the effectiveness of ground-monitored re-entry control and the means of rapid pickup.

Some means of flotation would have to be provided for water landings. Markers, radio beacons, etc., would be used by the monitoring and the pickup groups to spot the drifting craft or its occupants. Provision would be made for survival if pickup were delayed.

We would be remiss to conclude this simplified sketch of escape and recovery from space without pointing out that man in many ways is the weakest link in the man-machine complex of a space system that may be built around him. His tolerances to almost all the situations of space flight fall short of those provided by other materials and components. Yet the entire system must be built up in a manner to protect him from exceeding his limits of tolerance. Tolerances to acceleration have been established by Stapp,[9] Preston-Thomas,[10] Ballinger,[11] and others; temperature tolerances by Taylor,[12] Blockly, J. Lyman, McConnell; time of useful consciousness by Luft[5] and others. Tolerance to weightlessness or zero-gravity requires a question mark.

One situation has received too little attention. That is tolerance to tumbling and spinning, singly or together, or in combination with other forms of acceleration, either positive or negative. Man simply does not tolerate tumbling or spinning of appreciable magnitude. The exact tolerances have not been worked out, but it can be stated that spacecraft crews must be given a relatively stable platform if they are to remain effective.

This has been a brief attempt to analyze the problems of rescue and recovery from space operations. One cannot escape the conclusion that the maximum chance for safe return depends upon the reliability of the primary vehicle and of the ground-support system. If these have sufficient reliability, then many protective measures, much equipment, and therefore much weight can be eliminated from the operation. Weight reduction itself in certain instances increases reliability.

School of Aviation Medicine, USAF

CHAPTER 13

Time Dilation
and the Astronaut

Major Evan R. Goltra

Engineers and biologists interested in satellite and space vehicles need to examine the theory of relativity to determine if it predicts any physical effects that can be of use. The portion of the theory that has received most publicity in connection with the prospect of space flight is the prediction of time dilation at great velocities.

The phenomenon of time dilation has been verified by experiment and has been demonstrated repeatedly and conclusively in scientific literature. An example of it may be found in the existence of the pi and the mu mesons. These subatomic particles would not even endure to reach the earth from their source without operation of the time dilation. At the velocity they attain in their paths, they remain in existence one hundred to one thousand times as long as if they were at rest.

Before the possible applications of the time-dilation phenomenon to moving biologic systems such as the astronaut are explored, it may be helpful to consider a few rather simple mathematical principles without which the theory of relativity is quite obscure.

The Lorentz Transformation

It is highly desirable that the formulations which constitute the body of a physical theory be the same for all observers under all conditions of motion, i.e., that they be invariant upon transformation of the coordinates of reference. In the three-dimensional world of human experience we refer events to a three-dimensional reference system. This reference system is called a Cartesian reference system in deference to the mathematician Descartes who developed it. Several hundred years ago Galileo demonstrated that the laws of motion, when expressed by observers in two different reference systems, were related by the following relationships:

$$x' = x - vt$$
$$y' = y$$
$$z' = z$$
$$t' = t$$

where v is the velocity of the moving system and t is the time variable. In formal mathematical language, the laws of classical me-

Systems of relative translatory motion. Two different reference systems, the two Cartesian systems C and C', are in uniform relative motion at a velocity small compared to that of light. Assume that there are observers, Q and Q', in each of these systems and that each observer is at rest in his own system. Both Q and Q' perform an experiment involving the motion of a body. Each tosses a rubber ball upward along the Y axis and catches his ball when it falls. Each measures, in terms of his own coordinate system, what happens to the ball in the other coordinate system. Q sees his own ball rise vertically and fall straight down. Q' sees Q's ball describe a curved path because of the relative motion of the two systems. The comparable phenomenon is apparent to Q

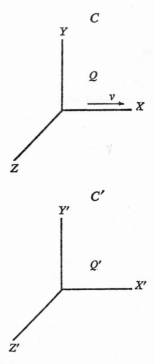

concerning the ball tossed by Q'. The two observers can reconcile their observations only by application of a suitable "transformation." Galileo demonstrated that the motion of the body, as governed by the laws of classical mechanics and expressed by one of the observers in terms of his own frame of reference, can be expressed in terms of other reference systems, or "transformed" to it, by means of certain relationships formulated as a set of transformation equations.

chanics can be said to be invariant with respect to the above transformation, which is known as the Galilean transformation.

In the late nineteenth century the new science of atomic physics began to develop at a rather rapid pace. The physicists of that time assumed that the Galilean transformation would apply to the submicroscopic world of the atom and the electrical field. Experiment revealed that this assumption was incorrect because unexplainable inconsistencies developed when attempts were made to treat this new world by means of the Galilean transformation. A Dutch physicist of the time, H. A. Lorentz, solved the problem of what transformation equations would be satisfactory under these new conditions for observers in two Cartesian systems, one of which is moving at a uniform velocity with respect to the other. That is, Lorentz demonstrated that if the equations of this new world were not invariant for the Galilean transformation they were invariant for another linear transformation of the coordinates only a little more complicated than that of Galileo. The Lorentz transformation is:

$$x' = (x - vt)(1 - v^2/c^2)^{-\frac{1}{2}}$$
$$y' = y$$
$$z' = z$$
$$t' = (t - vx/c^2)(1 - v^2/c^2)^{-\frac{1}{2}}$$

where v is the velocity of the system under consideration and c is the velocity of light in *vacuo* (300,000 km/sec).

The Lorentz formulations indicate that time and space are not independent variables but that time and space are covariant, i.e., that they vary with each other and that time measured by an observer in one coordinate system is different from the time measured by an observer in another coordinate system and that it depends upon the velocity with which one system moves with respect to another as well as upon the space coordinate x. In other words, in naming what we choose to call simultaneous events we cannot be certain about the accuracy of our statement unless we know the relative distance of the two events. For example, we cannot say that lightning struck simultaneously at two locations unless we take into account the passage of the light signal, the flashes, by which we observe and measure the strokes. Inspection of the Lorentz transformation reveals, however, that the formulation reduces to the well-known Galilean relationship when the velocity of the moving system is small compared to the velocity of light.

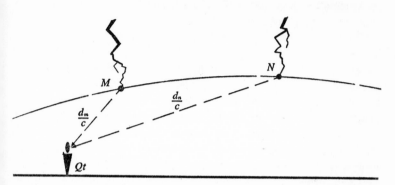

The relativity of the simultaneous. To say that two lightning bolts struck at the same time, the observer must take into account their distance from him and the consequent time required for the light signal originated by the flashes to reach him. Observer Q sees lightning flash simultaneously at locations M and N according to his own time t. But if the distance of stroke M from observer is less than that of stroke N, then the strokes were not simultaneous, as observed. This fact Q may discern by comparison of $t - d_m/c$ and $t - d_n/c$, where c is the speed of light and d_m and d_n are the distances of the origins of the flashes M and N from Q.

Relativity Theory

In 1905 Albert Einstein proposed his monumental Special Theory of Relativity and eleven years later his General Theory of Relativity. The Special Theory treats of objects or systems that are moving with respect to each other at a constant velocity or not moving at all (unaccelerated), while the General Theory treats of systems which are accelerated with respect to each other. The word "special" is used to imply that the principle is restricted to the case where one coordinate system has a motion of uniform translation relative to another but that the equivalence of these two systems does not extend to the case of nonuniform translation. In 1904 Poincaré had proposed the need for a principle of relativity in which the laws of physics would be the same for any two observers, one of whom has motion of uniform translation relative to the other. Examining the known data of the day in the light of this principle of relativity, Poincaré declared that an entirely new type of kinematics was required, characterized by the law that no velocity could exceed that of light.

The program indicated by Poincaré was carried out by Einstein in the following year. The Special Theory of Relativity is based upon two physical hypotheses: the principle of constancy and the principle of relativity. The principle of constancy states that light is propagated in empty space with a finite velocity which is independent of the state of motion of the emitting source. The principle of relativity states that a reference system may move along a straight line with respect to another system and if the initial conditions relative to the first system are given, then the further motion and light propagation of the second system are determined. In different language, the laws of physical phenomena are equivalent when stated in the terms of two reference systems moving at a constant velocity relative to each other.

It is evident that Einstein's two principles are true physical hypotheses and not mere definitions of terms. It should be pointed out that the Lorentz transform arose naturally in mathematical development of the Special Theory of Relativity and that the previous work of Lorentz was completely unknown to Einstein. The transform arose as the appropriate description and formulation of the relationship which exists between the spatial and temporal coordinates of two observers one of whom has uniform motion relative to the other.

The theory of relativity has been criticized for giving a central theoretical role to the propagation of light in that the theory constructs the concepts of time upon the law of propagation of light. It is immaterial what processes are used for the definition of time; but in order to give physical significance to the concept of time, a process which allows one to establish time relationships between different places is necessary. The velocity of light serves this purpose particularly well because of the certainty of our knowledge concerning the laws of the propagation of light.

In classical mechanics, points of space as points or instants of time were spoken of as if they were absolute realities. It was not observed that the true element of this space-time specification, or "event," was the event itself specified by the terms of its Cartesian coordinates and its time coordinate. Einstein states in *The Meaning of Relativity:* "It is neither the point in space nor the instant in time at which something happens that has physical reality but only the event itself." In summary then, Einstein's principles are equivalent to a restatement of the relation between observed motion and the velocity of light.

Inspection of the Lorentz transformation reveals that at great velocity, with respect to the velocity of light, time in the moving system will be longer or in terms of the reference system it will in a sense be dilated. Because of the nature of the terms in the denominator of the transform, a squared fraction, the dilation proceeds very slowly and becomes appreciable only at large fractions of the velocity of light. At 60 per cent of the velocity of light, for example, the time dilation is approximately 20 per cent; and 60 per cent of the velocity of light is 180,000 km/sec!

It is of course possible to measure time dilation in a suitable orbital vehicle at a suitable altitude and velocity if it is appropriately instrumented with atomic clocks. But it must be pointed out that these experiments would do nothing but confirm an already fully established scientific fact. In performing such experiments it is necessary to pay attention to the slowing of clocks in gravitational fields (the red shift). The Special Theory time effects in orbit are of the order of 3.5×10^{-10}, while General Theory time effects are of the order of 7×10^{-10}. Current cesium atomic clocks are capable of an accuracy of 10^{-10}, and plans are under way to construct cesium clocks of 10^{-13} accuracy. Accuracies of this magnitude are necessary because of the small differences that would be measured.

Time and the Space Traveler

For the sake of fiction let us assume that we could construct and launch a vehicle and accelerate it at a constant 1 g toward some distant fixed star, say a thousand light years from the earth. The course of this flight would be as follows: After 1.4 years in the reality terms of the crew a velocity of 90 per cent of the speed of light would have been attained. After a total of 5.5 years, again in the reality terms of the crew, a velocity of 99.9999 per cent of the speed of light would have been attained. Let us assume further that the flight continues at this velocity until the destination star is reached. This would occur in another 5.5 years, so that after a total of 11 years in flight the crew would reach their destination. This measurement of 11 years' time passage would be made by means of the very accurate chronometer in the space vehicle. This chronometer had originally been synchronized with equally accurate chronometers on the earth. In terms of the chronometers on earth, one thousand years would have passed. The return trip is made under the same circumstances, and a total time of 22 years in terms of the crew would have passed while two thousand years would have passed on the earth.

Now we may speculate about the observations of the crew during this flight and about some of the biological consequences of the flight. Midway through the flight the crew would measure their distance from the earth as 5.5 light years, instead of the approximately 994 light years that one might expect from simple subtraction. The approximately 200-fold discrepancy is the result of a relativistic change in length in the distance between the earth and the destination star taking place during the flight. The problem is analogous to the experiment of the tossing of the balls such as Galileo saw in his transformation, but here the observer's perception of distance is modified by the velocity with which he is moving. What would the crew visualize as they approach their destination star? As the vehicle accelerates, there would be a motion-picture-like unfolding of events on the destination planet. The events of the past one thousand years on the destination star would unfold like a progressively speeded-up motion picture film during the 11 years of the space flight, and the crew would arrive in their own "present time."

Other events that can be predicted from this journey are those related to the variation in the wave length of the spectrum emitted by the destination star. For example, the light emission from the destination star of approximately six thousand angstrom units would be apparently changed to approximately 12 angstrom units. Radiation of this latter wave length is in the X-ray portion of the spectrum. All other radiations emitted by the destination star would suffer a contraction in wave length in a similar manner and magnitude. In other words, all radiation would undergo a shift to the violet. The energy levels of these radiations can be computed but are not a pertinent part of the problem. Suffice it to say that the energy levels computed would be of the same order of magni tude of the X rays known and described on earth today. Therefore, the question is raised about the hazard of radiation to which the crew might be exposed. The same phenomenon would operate in reverse on the return trip.

It must be stressed that this entire description of time differential between the age of the crew members and the observers on earth is an observational phenomenon associated with the terrestrial observer, and in the reality terms of the crew the rate at which they age and the measurement of the passage of time by their chronometers does not change in the slightest. It can also be pointed out that this observational phenomenon of the earth inhabitant would be quite different for an observer in another frame of reference moving at a different velocity relative to the spacecraft.

What other biological consequences might be considered? The following statements seem to follow from relativity theory, with the admission that many of these statements or assumptions are totally unverified by experimental procedures. Life in a system of uniform, unaccelerated motion would be unaltered. The thermodynamic process that we call life can be called constant for the frame of reference in which we operate—or is this statement true? The living system, as we describe it, is essentially an open thermodynamic system capable of accepting energy from an external source and of giving up energy. In other words, it is a system which is continuously exchanging energy with an outside source.

A question that might be posed is, what would transpire in such a system in which the energy level of an outside source is significantly altered as it would be in the fictional situation described in the preceding paragraphs? Does the process of life, as we describe it, depend upon unalterable constants which must be maintained for optimum performance or even survival, or do these so-called constants alter in a changed metrical field? The reason for these questions lies in the conception that we live in and depend upon a flux of photons emitted by the sun. Is this true, or will other necessary dependencies as yet unconceived be discovered? What influence does this flux of photon energy have upon the fields surrounding the earth, and what might happen to an earth-evolved man forced to operate and survive when these fields are altered in a new environment?

The objection is raised that the theory of relativity is concerned only with physical systems and not with living organisms. This objection seems untenable in the light of one of the basic assumptions of biology that no biological system may violate any law of physics. The ultimate constituents of all living things or systems are atoms and subatomic particles. And if every atomic period, that is, the period of the electron within the atom, is retarded to the same degree under the influence of motion or of a metrical field, it follows that physiological phenomena would necessarily reveal the same retardation, since these phenomena can be considered as the integration of many atomic periods.

The author submits that the implications of the relativistic time dilation for the astronaut are of academic interest only. We are several fundamental steps away from a propulsion system which might allow us to reach velocities of sufficient magnitude that the effects of time dilation would be important or even measurable. The greatest velocity so far attained by a man-constructed vehicle is approximately 10 kilometers per second. The velocity of light in *vacuo* is 300,000 kilometers per second. The ratio of these two velocities is 1:30,000. Perhaps this ratio emphasizes the magnitude of the velocity of light.

School of Aviation Medicine, USAF

CHAPTER 14

The Spiral Toward Space

By the Editors of *Air University Quarterly Review* *

The dawn of the space age—at least for the general public—came on 4 October 1957 with the launching of the first earth satel-

* With the assistance of Major Arthur Murray and Mr. Chester McCollough of the X-15 Weapon System Project Office of Headquarters, Air Research and Development Command.

lite. Here was proof that man could put a vehicle outside the earth's atmosphere and use the laws of nature to keep it there.

To the airman the promise of the space age had perhaps been apparent some years earlier. But even he, caught up in the events of the present, is apt to lose sight of the broader patterns that mark more clearly the means by which man will expand his activities into interplanetary and eventually interstellar space. Even he, caught up in the almost concurrent development of the big missile and the application of this missile's power plant to the purposes of the earth satellite program, is apt to lose sight of the two parallel strands of vehicle development—the missiles and the aerodynamic systems. At their present stage both are married to the rocket engine for propulsion. As long as man must depend on the rocket's brief, violent surge of power to spring free of the earth's atmosphere or its field of gravity, probably both the missile and the aerodynamic vehicle will have useful roles.

But as the next major cycle of propulsion comes into being, perhaps in the form of packageable atomic power, and as a true space combat capability comes within reach—in terms of being able to operate in space against other craft in space as well as against ground targets—then it would seem that the aerodynamic vehicle would soon crowd the missile to the wall. For then the requirements that molded the airplane will be superimposed on those dictated for space flight by the laws of nature. The vehicle will have to be able not only to re-enter the atmosphere but to land at any of a number of points on the earth's surface. The vehicle will have not only to fly a trajectory in space but to maneuver with intelligence and versatility, to make judgments and choices of a kind that come better from a human pilot than from the memory bank of a computer.

The first flight of the X-15, now scheduled for early 1959, serves as a reminder that the aerodynamic vehicle is moving apace the ballistic missile in controlled space flight. This is by no means an accident of technological timing, for the X-15 is the culmination of a distinguished family of rocket-powered research aircraft. Designed to fly at hypersonic speed and at altitudes up to 100 miles, the X-15 is a test not only of a machine but of man in a machine in space. The major objectives of the X-15 flights will be to study the effects of frictional heat during re-entry into the earth's atmosphere, the problems of stability and control at high speeds and altitudes, and the psychological and physiological effects on the pilot of weightlessness and of rapidly accelerated and decelerated flight processes. The X-15 may well be an historic landmark in the development of the aerodynamic space vehicle.

Research Concepts

In considering the point now reached in the state of the art of research aircraft, we might well think first of the role of research aircraft in relation to such ground test facilities as wind tunnels, high-speed sleds, and free-flight models. Although these ground facilities provide much valuable information, they have definite limitations in simulating the conditions of actual flight. For example, wind tunnels, now capable of surpassing for a fraction of a second the minimum speed necessary to propel a vehicle beyond the earth's gravity into space, provide important data on the heat problem of atmospheric re-entry; but it is impossible to duplicate the size of the vehicle in wind-tunnel tests. Also, high-performance data are obtained only for short durations. Sled tests are useful in investigating such problems as escape at high speeds, but here limitations are imposed by the length of the track, which requires high starting and stopping accelerations in order to achieve the necessary speeds. Free-flight models provide helpful aerodynamic and thermodynamic information, but operations are on a small scale and yield only limited data.

Larger unmanned test vehicles, which are extremely expensive, may be used for essentially one data point in each experiment, and recovery of the vehicle for re-use is sometimes impossible. With the possible exception of sophisticated, remote-controlled vehicles, which would have the disadvantage of great expense and unwieldy complication, none of these tools is capable of investigating the flying qualities of an aircraft with a human input in actual environmental conditions.

Manned research aircraft obviously are not limited in full-scale simulation of flight conditions, since the craft actually enter the environment of flight. They do, however, have certain limitations. To design and build a research aircraft and to maintain the organization necessary for research testing are expensive operations. The amount of data recorded is somewhat restricted by the space and weight that may be devoted to instrumentation. Since research aircraft are to probe certain unknown areas of flight, there is some risk involved for the pilot. Electronic devices cannot be substituted for a human being because there are no practical means of adapting the equipment to the flight situation until the environmental conditions and the characteristics of the vehicle in flight have been explored.

In the evaluation of the advantages and disadvantages of the various methods of obtaining data discussed thus far, the need for the manned research aircraft is clear. The main attraction of such an aircraft is that by no other means can the effects of the actual operating environment on piloted vehicles be accurately determined. This is considered justification for the expense and risk to human life involved. Manned research vehicles have been accurately described by E. Kotcher of Wright Air Development Center as "necessary full-scale flight laboratory facilities to confirm, supplement and consolidate the model data obtained from ground test facilities before undertaking prototype development of manned operational vehicles."

In the design and construction of research aircraft, many of the requirements of operational aircraft are subordinated to obtaining research information. The payload is the instrumentation required to bring back the information. Range is of no importance and flight duration is important only at the points of flight being investigated. The brute force of rocket propulsion necessary to get the craft to desired speeds can be built into the vehicle at the expense of ordinarily important features. The research aircraft is designed to operate in one vicinity only (Edwards Air Force Base, California, in the case of the X-15). Consequently there is no need for the aircraft to be able to withstand certain conditions such as high humidity and salt spray. The pilot obviously does not need equipment for arctic, tropic, or other unusual conditions. Lengthy flight preparation is acceptable in a research aircraft. It may be air-launched at high speeds and altitudes, thus offsetting the high propellant consumption of rocket vehicles. The flight plan may be selected so that dry lakes are available for landings. This feature, together with the fact that once landed the craft may be picked up by auxiliary equipment, permits the use of skid-type landing gear.

Background of the X-15 Project

Toward the end of World War II the United States embarked upon a series of projects for the development of manned aircraft designed to probe the unknown areas of aeronautical technology. This program led to the historic breaking of the sound barrier in 1947 by the Bell X-1. The German V-2 guided missile had exceeded the speed of sound, but the Bell X-1 was the first inhabited aircraft to accomplish the feat. Like the others of the series, this airplane was designed for the purpose of pure research. It was a rather conventional aircraft except for the liquid-rocket engine which developed a thrust of some 6000 pounds. An alcohol-water mixture was the fuel and liquid oxygen the oxidizer. Major problems in development were making the plane strong enough to withstand the rigors of supersonic flight and crowding the necessary equipment, especially instruments, into the limited space available. It is interesting to note that the Bell X-1 was the first of the research aircraft projects in which the National Advisory Committee for Aeronautics (NACA), the military services, and the aircraft industry participated.

The Bell X-1A attained a speed of two and one half times the speed of sound in 1953 and the following year exceeded an altitude of 90,000 feet. This plane had a skin of duralumin and the general contour of a .50-caliber bullet. It was approximately 35 feet long with a wing span of some 28 feet. The craft was powered by the same type engine used in the Bell X-1 except for the use of a pump feeding device instead of high-pressure propellant tanks. A big problem with this plane was aerodynamic control in the rarefied atmosphere of high altitudes. Aerodynamic heating was no special problem because flights were made at altitudes where aerodynamic heating is not acute in speed runs of short duration. The altitude and speeds of the Bell X-1A necessitated the wearing of a partial pressure suit.

New records in both speed and altitude were set by the Bell X-2 in two flights in September 1956. The aircraft reached more than three times the speed of sound and an altitude of almost 25 miles. Pencil shaped with swept-back wings, the Bell X-2 was powered by a 15,000-pound-thrust, double-barreled Curtiss-Wright rocket engine. With this aircraft, altitudes and speeds were such that the effects of aerodynamic heating presented a considerable problem to the design engineers. So the aircraft was constructed primarily of K-monel, a new metal at that time which possessed good qualities of heat resistance.

The latest research aircraft to be developed is the X-15. The origin of this program may be traced to a resolution passed in the spring of 1952 by the Committee on Aerodynamics of the NACA directing the laboratories of NACA to initiate studies of the problems likely to be encountered in space flight and of the methods of exploring them. Ground facilities, missiles, and manned airplanes were considered. By the spring of 1954 the NACA had a team at work to determine the characteristics of an airplane suitable for exploratory flight studies. This work led to an NACA proposal for the construction of an airplane capable of investigating aerodynamic heating, stability, control, and physiological problems of hypersonic and space flight.

When on 9 July 1954 NACA representatives met with members of the Air Force and Navy research and development groups to present the proposal as an extension of the cooperative research airplane program, it was discovered that both the Air Force and the Navy were already actively interested in similar types of research. This fact made for early acceptance of the NACA proposal for a joint effort and eventually led to the X-15 project.

Areas of responsibility were designated by a memorandum of understanding signed in December 1954 by the Special Assistant, Research and Development, of the Air Force, the Assistant Secretary of the Navy for Air, and the Director of the NACA. Technical direction of the project was assigned to the Director of the NACA acting with the advice and assistance of a Research Airplane Committee composed of one representative each from the Air Force, the Navy, and NACA. The Air Force was charged with the responsibility of developing the X-15, which included establishing the contract as well as coordinating the various development phases of the program. The responsibility of conducting flight research after acceptance of the airplane as an airworthy article was assigned to NACA. The Director of the NACA and the Research Airplane Committee were to inform the military services and the aircraft industry of the progress and results of the program. The memorandum concluded with the statement that this project was a matter of national urgency.

After Department of Defense approval was obtained, the Air Force was authorized in December 1954 to issue invitations to prospective contractors to participate in the design competition for the X-15 airplane. Approximately one year later North American Aviation, Inc., was awarded the contract.

Development and Flight of the X-15

By October 1955 it was fairly certain that the development contract would be awarded to North American. In that month a meeting of representatives of this company, NACA, and USAF was held to establish the requirements and features of the aircraft and to coordinate generally the X-15 program. A list of customer comments and requests concerning the configuration submitted by North American was presented and discussed. Most of the items were quickly settled when contractor representatives agreed to the proposed changes. In those cases not settled, it was agreed that the contractor would provide studies to enable more accurate evaluation of the questions. At this point in the program, one of the more difficult problems was the type of escape to be used. A second meeting was held in November 1955 to discuss the results of the contractor studies. Important among the results of this meeting were evaluations of possible engine and propellant variations.

In February 1956 a letter contract was executed with Reaction Motors, Inc., for development of the XLR-99 throttleable liquid-rocket engine. Anhydrous ammonia was chosen as the fuel, with liquid oxygen as the oxidizer. The propellants account for well over half of the launch gross weight and are contained in tanks which form an integral part of the fuselage. Separator baffles counteract the surge of the liquid propellant in flight. Sustained firing time of the engine, at varying thrust, is up to six minutes.

By July 1956 the cockpit arrangement had been established and the decision had been made to use a full-pressure suit for altitude and acceleration protection. This lightweight, flexible suit is considered one of the significant accomplishments of the program thus far and will doubtless be of value to pilots of our present high-speed and high-altitude aircraft. The instrumentation bay and pilot's compartment will be pressurized to 35,000 feet and cooled by expansion of liquid nitrogen. A stabilized ejection seat will be used for emergency escape.

Of the human problems, the physiological and psychological effects of weightlessness and of acceleration and deceleration forces are the areas where new information is most needed. A condition of weightlessness, in which the gravitational pull of the earth is nullified, will be experienced by the pilot of the X-15 for several minutes as the plane coasts over the peak of the flight path. Recently pilots of other high-performance aircraft have been subjected briefly to this condition without serious impairment of their ability to function properly. Though the effects of weightlessness seem to vary considerably with individual pilots, some becoming nauseated and others experiencing a feeling of exhilaration, the duration of this condition in the X-15 flight trajectory is thought to be insufficient for it to be one of the severe human problems of the program.

It is felt that the pilot of the X-15 will have good control over the forces of rapidly accelerated and decelerated flight processes. He will be subjected to about 2 g as the engine is ignited and the plane begins to climb. This force, roughly comparable to that experienced in a catapult launching of an aircraft, will tend to immobilize the pilot but not to the extent of preventing him from performing the tasks necessary to control the aircraft. As the fuel load is rapidly consumed, the speed is increased and the g-forces become stronger. Maximum g-force is reached as the engine burns out prior to the peak of the flight path. It is in the latter stages of the flight, however, that deceleration and pullout forces can combine with atmospheric disturbances to give the pilot most trouble in controlling the X-15. An entirely new control design has been created to avoid involuntary pilot inputs. To study this problem area a series of simulation tests have been conducted in the Navy centrifuge at Johnsville, Pennsylvania.

An inertial flight-data system is being built into the X-15. The equipment includes a lightweight computer and a three-axis gyro-stabilized platform on which accelerometers are mounted. The output of the accelerometers is fed to the computer, which derives speed, altitude, rate of climb, and other data. This information is supplied to the pilot through conventional instrument presentation. Built to withstand accelerations more than ten times the force of gravity, the system has the advantage of being adaptable to other space experiments.

Aerodynamic control will be accomplished by movable outboard portions of the upper and lower vertical stabilizers and by differentially operated, all-movable horizontal tail surfaces. The movable portion of the lower vertical stabilizer will be jettisoned before landing. One of the surprising features of the X-15 is the wedge-shaped vertical tail, which measures no less than 12 inches thick at the trailing edge. These surfaces are moved through an irreversible hydraulic control system, with the pilot using a control handle on his right console along with conventional rudder pedals.

Small peroxide rocket motors will provide control at altitudes where aerodynamic controls become ineffective. Two motors controlling movement about the pitch axis and two motors controlling movement about the yaw axis are mounted in the nose of the aircraft in the form of a cross. Movement about the roll axis is controlled by a motor mounted in the tip of each wing. The pilot will operate these motors by means of a single control on the left console.

A difficult problem in development has been the effects of high temperatures on the aircraft. Air friction will heat the skin of the X-15 to approximately 1000° F, the heat being greatest on re-entry into the atmosphere. At the other extreme, temperatures will be as low as −300° F in sections of the plane containing liquid oxygen. To withstand skin temperatures up to 1200° F the aircraft will be constructed for the most part of Inconel-X, a new metal consisting primarily of nickel. About 70 per cent of the structure will be welded, with only about 30 per cent bolted. Passage through the highest temperature is expected to be accomplished so quickly that the metal will not be heated beyond the design point.

Although the X-15 was originally conceived as a "state-of-the-art aircraft" (i.e., built with the materials, techniques, and knowledge available at the time of requirements), there have been many difficult technical problems in the development phase of the program that required new techniques and new knowledge. One such problem was in the area of structure. Like K-monel, of which the Bell X-2 was constructed, Inconel-X had never before been used in building an airplane. A pioneering effort was necessary, a type of activity which in itself is of value to the aircraft industry.

Other landmarks in the development phase of the program that should be mentioned include the two industry conferences, one in October 1956 and the other in July 1958, to review progress on the program; and a development engineering inspection of a mockup of the vehicle in December 1956 at which comments and suggested changes were presented. Also there was the decision in the summer of 1957 to use a B-52 as the carrier instead of a B-36. By the end of that year the basic design configuration had been established and manufacturing had begun.

The first powered flight of the X-15 is expected to take place on schedule in early 1959. The B-52 carrier will take off from Edwards Air Force Base and fly northeast toward Wendover Air Force Base, Utah, some 500 miles distant. Just before drop, the pilot will carry out final preparations such as checking electrical circuits. In the vicinity of Wendover the X-15 will be air-launched at approximately 40,000 feet from beneath the right wing of the carrier. After launch the engine will be started and the aircraft will then fly a semiballistic path, during which research data will be recorded both internally and by telemeter at the three stations of a special radar range. Early in the flight the X-15 will be trailed by a jet "chase plane" from a nearby base. Re-entering the earth's atmosphere at the correct angle will be one of the critical tasks of the pilot. Two aft skids and a nose wheel will permit landing the X-15 on the dry lakes around Edwards Air Force Base. Because of delays in development of the XLR-99 rocket engine, an interim engine package of two XLR-11's from the Bell X-1 program will be used for initial flights. The program of demonstration flights by North American will continue until the fall of 1959, when the aircraft is expected to be accepted by the Government and turned over to the NACA-Air Force Flight Test Center Joint Operating Committee for initiation of the flight research program.

Research flights of the X-15 will be flown by pilots from the NACA, the Navy, and the Air Force. These pilots will take the airplane through the full exploration of its performance capabilities.

The Future

Just as the accomplishments of earlier research aircraft paved the way for the design of aircraft now operating in our first line of defense, so it is expected that the information obtained from the

X-15 flights will be useful, mainly to the aircraft industry, in the design and development of more advanced vehicles for atmospheric and space flight. Data pertaining to all the major areas of interest in the program—the aerodynamic, thermodynamic, and human problems of space flight—will be of value in conjunction with information obtained from ground test facilities. This phase of development must precede the prototype development of manned operational aircraft. Technical reports regarding the results of the project will be disseminated to interested concerns in accordance with the memorandum of understanding mentioned above. North American Aviation, Inc., will retain no proprietary rights concerning the techniques and devices developed and the information gained through the program.

The project which is perhaps closest to a continuation of the X-15 program is the development of a boost-glide aircraft called Dyna-Soar, a name derived from "dynamic soaring." The Air Force and the NACA are now engaged in developing this advanced test vehicle, thus continuing the productive partnership that resulted in the earlier research aircraft and the forthcoming X-15.

Preliminary investigations indicate that it will be possible to vary the original thrust and thus the velocity of Dyna-Soar, enabling the pilot to complete one or more orbits around the earth and make a normal landing. The vehicle will operate from space altitudes down to well within the atmosphere where it can maneuver and be recovered undamaged. It will utilize both centrifugal effect and aerodynamic lift.

The Martin Company and the Boeing Airplane Company have been selected as development contractors for the Dyna-Soar. These companies will each head a team composed of five or six of the ablest contractors in the aircraft industry. Martin will draw heavily on the aeronautical pioneering experience of the Bell Aircraft Corporation. The specialized abilities of contractors throughout the country will contribute to development by both teams. Early efforts of the two teams will be competitive to ensure that the Air Force receives the most advanced and complete designs. The Air Force, NACA, and the aircraft industry have been obtaining and assessing data and knowledge on the boost-glide concept since 1951.

Possible operational craft following the test version of Dyna-Soar will be capable of various missions, including bombing and reconnaissance. As a weapon this vehicle promises to have some of the best features of both guided missiles and aircraft. It will have long range and great destructive capability, especially with nuclear pay-loads, and the judgment of the pilot will make for reliability and versatility. Such a weapon would be particularly useful in case of loss of our overseas bases.

It would naturally be almost impossible to predict the exact course that space technology will take. We can say with some assurance, however, that the information gained from flights of the X-15 and similar aircraft will be extremely valuable. In fact, later craft in this same line of development may well play the predominant role in the conquest of space.

Air University Quarterly Review

CHAPTER 15

Human-Factors Support of the X-15 Program

Lieutenant Colonel Burt Rowen

The X-15 research program is being conducted as a national effort by the National Aeronautics and Space Administration (NASA), the United States Air Force, and the United States Navy. It was initiated in the spring of 1952, when the National Advisory Committee for Aeronautics (NACA)—recently absorbed as part of NASA—directed its laboratories to study the problems likely to be encountered in flight beyond the atmosphere. In December 1955 North American Aviation, Inc., was given the go-ahead to con-struct three of these airplanes. Construction was started in Sep-tember 1957, and the roll-out and delivery of the first one came on

15 October 1958. The program through completion of the third vehicle is expected to cost about 120 million dollars in direct contract costs, plus sizable indirect costs consisting primarily of laboratory and wind-tunnel testing by NACA and Air Research and Development Command.

The X-15 will carry over 1300 pounds of instruments involving about 600 temperature pickups, 140 pressure pickups. By way of contrast the X-2 used 15 temperature probes and no pressure recordings and the over-all research instrumentation weighed 550 pounds. Also included in the X-15 is equipment to monitor the pilot's physiological condition. This aspect represents a new concept in research aircraft. Primary research interest is to obtain (1) knowledge of actual flight conditions beyond the earth's atmosphere, (2) determination of aerodynamic heating, heat-transfer rates, and their effects on aircraft structure, (3) quantitative physiological data during actual flight. Additional research objectives include (4) knowledge of missions involving exit from and re-entry into the earth's atmosphere and (5) man's reaction to space flight.

The X-15 will be air-launched from a B-52 mother plane. As the altitude and speed envelope is expanded, the launchings will be accomplished farther from Edwards Air Force Base and nearer Wendover Air Force Base, the farthest point along the 400 nautical miles of specially designed and instrumented range. Intermediate radar sites have been established at Ely and Beatty, Nevada. These are coupled to the master site at Edwards AFB.

Physiological Telemetry

An interesting aeromedical support mission presents itself in the field of such research aircraft. For approximately ten years aeronautical engineers have been recording in-flight data from instrumented aircraft sending back telemetry signals to ground read-out indicators. The pilot's physiological status was never recorded. This was the situation during the X-2 program. During the flight phases of the X-15 program, physiological data will be telemetered so that a flight surgeon observing ground read-out indicators can tell when the pilot is approaching the limit of his physiological tolerance. This will quantitatively identify the most stressful portion of a particular mission profile. Then in future flight programs the aeronautical engineer will know what portion of the mission profile most critically needs stability augmentation or possibly automatic-control inputs. The full-pressure suits to be worn during the X-15 program have been specially designed with 24 electrical contact points to facilitate the necessary connections between the physiological sensors or transducers and the telemetry transmitters.

Before the first flight of the X-15 takes place in 1959, pilot physiological data will be telemetered to ground recording stations to evaluate and prove this technique. A TF-102A aircraft has been assigned the Air Force Flight Test Center specifically for this project. Items such as helmet-pressure versus suit-pressure differential, cockpit-pressure versus suit-pressure differential, pilot's body-surface temperatures, and electrocardiographic data will be monitored by a flight surgeon. The pilot's body-surface temperature will be correlated with recorded cockpit temperature. A quantitative index of the effectiveness of pressurization and air-conditioning systems can thus be established. For certain missions specific data can be collected by recording galvanometers. The transducers for these measurements are all miniaturized and will not hinder pilot performance in any way. Flat, round electrocardiographic pickups, for example, have been miniaturized and are now approximately the size of a quarter.

Initially only the first two items, the pressure differentials, will be telemetered. These items are most critical in maintaining a livable environment for the pilot. Therefore it is important to monitor them for the pilot's safety. Since the cockpit pressurization of the X-15 is engineered to 3.5 pounds per square inch (psi) of pressure differential between the inside of the cockpit and the outside air, it was not considered feasible to install a breathable atmosphere in this aircraft. At sea level, oxygen comprises about 20% of the normal atmospheric pressure of 14.7 psi. A breathable atmosphere would then require 20% of 14.7 psi, or about 3 psi of oxygen in the 3.5-psi cockpit. To date, the problems of combustion and fire associated with this 86%-oxygen atmosphere have been insurmountable.

To avoid this difficulty, liquid nitrogen, pressurized by helium, will be used for cooling, cockpit pressurization, and MC-2 suit pressurization. Nitrogen is an inert gas and lacks fire and explosive characteristics. The helmet will be pressurized with 100% oxygen.

It is separated from the suit by a rubber seal at the neck, and a two-inch column of water provides the extra pressure needed to keep the nitrogen from seeping into the helmet and contaminating the pilot's oxygen. Future research aircraft and manned orbital systems will be supplied with breathable atmospheres. Increases in available thrust will permit use of a higher cockpit-pressure differential because the added thrust will offset the added structural weight this system entails. The combustion and fire hazard will be proportionately reduced because the artificial environment will approximate sea-level atmospheric conditions.

Body-surface temperatures and electrocardiographic readings will be recorded on oscillographs early in the program. The ultimate objective is to have all physiological data telemetered to the ground master station of the NASA High Speed Flight Station at Edwards Air Force Base, California. It is here that a flight surgeon familiar with the X-15 project will monitor the pilot's physiological status in the same manner that the aeronautical engineer monitors the aircraft's performance. The procedures for accomplishing these goals are in existence today; they need only further refinement in an operational aircraft to make their use a reality when the X-15 begins its flight program. A physiological package is also being developed by North American Aviation for both telemetering and on-board recording of physiological data. This system has a growth potential for additional recording of physiological variables. The School of Aviation Medicine, USAF, is currently developing miniaturized blood-pressure and respiratory-rate sensors that will be used in this telemetry system as soon as they have been satisfactorily demonstrated. Tests to prove their feasibility in flight were begun in December 1958 at the Air Force Flight Test Center in the TF-102A.

Evaluation of the North American Aviation physiological-data package began at the Air Force Flight Test Center in December 1958. The objectives of the Center's TF-102A program are (1) training and familiarization for the X-15 pilots in the MC-2 full-pressure suit assembly; (2) physiological instrumentation research and development and establishment of physiological criteria for future crew selection; (3) development of pilots' base-line physiological data; (4) standardization of MC-2 suits; (5) product improvement of the MC-2 suit assembly for future weapon systems;

and (6) testing operational capability of the MC-2 suit. Approximately 15 hours of actual flight time have been accumulated by pilots wearing the MC-2 suit assembly.

Cosmic Radiation

Another interesting aspect of physiological monitoring of pilots associated with the X-15 program is the technique of determining whole-body radiation. The University of California operates a whole-body radiation counter at the Los Alamos Scientific Laboratory, about 110 miles north of Albuquerque, New Mexico, in the Los Alamos prohibited airspace area. This device, shielded by 20 tons of lead, has been used as an investigative tool in measuring whole-body radiation levels of over 3000 persons. This gamma counter measures radioactive potassium (K^{40}), a constituent of striated muscle tissue, and identifies radioactivity as so many counts per second. Preflight K^{40} activity will be obtained from pilots in this program. This becomes the base line which is later correlated with postflight levels. Any increased activity represents a quantitative increment of cosmic radiation effects.

These measurements will become available for the first time from a human subject flying a research aircraft. Using one of the two known whole-body radiation counters in this country, this program is easy to implement. The only portion that needs to be hurried is the trip back to Los Alamos Scientific Laboratory after landing from a high-altitude flight. Since the induced whole-body radioactivity of K^{40} has a half-life of 12.8 hours, the pilot's postflight radioactivity returns to normal in about three days. The technique of performing the whole-body count is very simple, requiring only three minutes, and does not involve the use of drugs. It is anticipated that the Air Research and Development Command will obtain a whole-body radiation counter in the near future for installation at or near Edwards Air Force Base.

The Air Force Cambridge Research Center has expressed interest and complete cooperation in obtaining quantitative data of cosmic-ray activity on the pilot and on the surface of the X-15. These results, when compared with the pilot's whole-body radiation activity, should be extremely informative concerning the relationship between pilot and aircraft exposure to cosmic-ray activity. The initial proposal includes cosmic radiation detection by emulsion preparations. The means of implementing this program are currently being formulated and refined.

Simulation and Training

The contractor began a static simulation of five degrees of freedom for the X-15 performance in October 1956 and expanded to a simulation of six degrees of freedom in May 1957 (yaw, pitch, roll, and accelerations vertically, longitudinally, and radially). The cockpit instrumentation and analog computer tie-in are installed at the main plant in Inglewood, California. The simulator's cockpit layout is a duplicate of that in the X-15. Since 1956, innumerable static simulated missions have been flown by all pilots participating in the X-15 program. In June and July 1958 the third series of dynamic closed-loop simulation runs was completed at the Naval Air Development Center, Johnsville, Pennsylvania. The Johnsville facility is the only known centrifuge with a manned, gimbaled gondola and an analog computer tie-in capable of simulating six degrees of freedom, with the centrifuge accomplishing the three linear accelerations.

The dynamic loads on the pilot experienced in the centrifuge program established a confidence in continuing the simulator program. The data derived in this manner will allow the flight tests to proceed at a more rapid pace. Experience gained at Johnsville indicated that all trained pilots associated with the program can successfully control the X-15 aircraft throughout its designed speed and altitude envelope. Additional and more realistic training is currently being obtained with F-100 series aircraft equipped with eight-foot drag chutes to simulate rates of descent anticipated during the unpowered glide approaches to lake-bed landings. The F-104A can be made to approximate the X-15 rates of descent and is a very useful approach trainer for the X-15 pilots.

Protective Equipment

The MC-2 full-pressure suit assembly represents the efforts of three separate subcontractors. The suit, helmet, and controller units were made to specifications drawn up by ARDC's Aero Medical Laboratory, following meetings with the National Aeronautics and Space Administration, North American Aviation, and Air Force Flight Test Center representatives. The suit is built by the David

Clark Company, Worcester, Massachusetts, the back-mounted controller unit is manufactured by the Firewel Company, Buffalo, New York, and the helmet is a product of the Bill Jack Company, Solana Beach, California. The suit has been extensively tested in the low-pressure chamber and is in the process of actual flight evaluation at the Air Force Flight Test Center. The outer silver garment has demonstrated high resistance to dynamic pressure and to heat. It incorporates an integrated parachute-restraint harness. Also provided are g protection and variable suit ventilation. Design refinements resulting from experience with the MC-2 suit assembly in the X-15 program will be incorporated in future protective equipment for higher and faster manned flight programs.

Escape System

After a lengthy appraisal of escape systems North American Aviation concluded that the pressure suit combined with the open ejection seat would provide a minimum emergency escape system for the X-15. This combination, while less than desirable from the standpoint of escape, was accepted in the interest of reducing development time. The contractor-designed seat incorporates fins and twin booms for roll and yaw stability. A 24-foot back-type parachute is mounted in a special container on the ejection seat. Upon actuation of the ejection handles, the canopy deploys ballistically, initiating the proper sequence of events. This rocket-actuated catapult seat is in a continuing stage of design refinement and is being tested in dynamic runs on the high-speed track at Edwards AFB. Man-seat separation and parachute deployment are dependent upon preset altitude and dynamic pressure sensors. From all available test data, it appears that the escape system will operate safely in the region of 600 knots indicated airspeed or a dynamic pressure of 1500 pounds per square foot.

This briefly is the human-factors support program for the X-15. Those engaged in this effort feel that they are contributing to the safety, comfort, and efficiency of the X-15 and of future manned research aircraft operations.

Air Force Flight Test Center

CHAPTER 16

The U.S. Air Force Human-Factors Program

Brigadier General Don Flickinger

The dramatic announcement of the first artificial earth-orbiting satellite by the Russians on 7 October 1957 presaged a new era of science and technology which contains challenges and promises of an unprecedented scope and magnitude to all of mankind. Significant though this achievement was, it has long since been completely overshadowed by the tremendous strides which have been made in space science and technology during the extremely short intervening period of but 15 months. One can no longer deride or minimize the Russian accomplishments as being merely propaganda "stunts," but instead must accept the undeniable and compelling fact that our nation faces the most serious trial in its history and must respond, not solely as scientists and engineers, but as a highly-motivated, commonly dedicated total body of people if we are to survive as a free nation.

In this short space of time the art of missilry has matured with amazing rapidity. An increasing number of progressively heavier and better instrumented vehicles have been placed at ever greater distances from the earth's gravitational field with a predictability and reliability unprecedented in past technological progress. The Russians have continued to lead the way, so to speak, by placing the first animal, the dog Laika, into orbit and maintaining its viability for a significant period (6-7 days). They further placed a large instrumented satellite weighing 3000 pounds into an elliptical terrestrial orbit from which considerable data are now being reported on the physical characteristics of space. Their most recent reported achievement is that of adding the first artificial man-made planet to our solar system with the successful launching of a 3200-pound lunar probe which missed the moon by some 4300 miles but continued into interplanetary space to become another solar-orbiting body in our firmament.

Progress on the American front has been equally rapid and significant—if not in comparable terms of payload, certainly as regards the amount of scientific information obtained per pound of payload and dollar cost of the various efforts. Both the lunar probes (Pioneers II and III), though technical failures in the sense that their mission objective was not realized, nevertheless were scientific successes of considerable magnitude. By their means the depth and intensity of the Van Allen layer of ionizing radiations were accurately plotted for the first time. Initially the discovery of this unpredicted and unexpected band of radiation comprised, as so aptly put by Dr. Hugh Dryden of the National Aeronautics and Space Administration, one of the many "surprises" which space has in store for us and an unwelcome one it was to those of us interested in developing a manned space vehicle capability. Subsequent findings, however, though not minimizing the impact of the Van Allen finding on manned space travel, provide some hopeful evidence that polar exits, shielding, and some degree of maneuverability of the manned vehicle may permit the traversing of these bands without undue or unacceptable risks to the occupant.

One of the most significant events which has occurred in America during this 15-month post–Sputnik I period has been the establishment of the National Aeronautics and Space Administration, with its charter of prime responsibility for the direction and prosecution of the national program in space science and technology. The stated objectives are those which would be expected of a free country and are directed toward peaceful and constructive purposes for the benefit of all mankind. A portion of this national space program is concerned with developing a competence in manned space flight, and it is in this specific area that the very considerable aerospace medical resources of the Air Force are being brought in direct support. Because of our commendable national tradition and philosophy which place the highest value on the safety and welfare of the individual, all of our Armed Services have developed knowledge and skills in the fields of occupational, environmental, and preventive medicine which have no counterpart in the world today. The monumental task of providing adequate safety and effectiveness for crews operating high-performance aircraft, submarines, and even more-conventional ground weapon systems has been met with commendable skill, ingenuity, and intelligence by the life scientist and engineer. Upon this broad foundation of knowledge and techniques a preeminent national capability can be built to provide for the unprejudiced survival of our future spacecrews.

The Air Force has and will continue to have into the foreseeable future requirements in the field of aerospace research and engineering which closely parallel those contained in the first manned earth-orbiting satellite. The demands for adequate pilot performance and safety in the X-15 research aircraft, the Dynasoar, and even the B-70 supersonic chemical bomber are stringent indeed. In many respects they are directly comparable qualitatively with those of the first generation of space vehicles. Time duration in the vacuum of space and additional requirement for the life-support components to operate in a zerogravity field are the principal differences involved.

Further, in the field of animal experimentation in the exploration of new, incompletely known, and potentially hazardous physical environments, the Air Force has an enviable record of past accomplishments, with the first space mammal being sent 36 miles above the earth and returned safely back in 1951. During this past year all the Armed Service medical-research groups have combined their talents to continue this type of biologic exploration of space, as payload and humane considerations permit. The Air Force mice and the Navy-Army primate have traveled in nose cones over appreciable ballistic flight paths, and the telemetered physiological information indicates that neither the vehicular-induced nor space-intrinsic hazards were found incompatible with uncomplicated survival, although in neither case were the search and recovery techniques capable of retrieving the subjects.

Under supervision of the Advanced Research Projects Agency and with cognizance of the National Aeronautics and Space Administration, the Air Force will carry out several biosatellite experiments as a part of the "Discoverer" series of missile shots during 1959. This work gives every promise of contributing timely and useful biomedical data to the NASA man-in-space program, particularly as regards the re-entry, search, and recovery phases of orbital flight. In passing, it is of interest to note that despite many notable achievements in space exploration reported since Sputnik I, no one yet has reported the successful re-entry and recovery of a satellite vehicle from orbit with its payload reasonably intact.

The Air Force Medical Corps is perhaps justifiably proud of its pioneering work in the new and challenging field of space medicine and eager indeed to contribute in full measure as a competent team member to the national space program.

Objectives of the Program

Many objectives can be offered as reasons for putting man in space, depending upon what particular aspect of national interest and philosophy is being expressed. One may say that man must inevitably invade space personally since it is the last frontier left for him to conquer and explore. In this sense one could simply say that, being constituted as he is, man must inevitably invade space. Next one might wish to put man into space for political reasons, to enhance national prestige. Certainly an excellent case can be made for putting man in space to further scientific knowledge. We know that the more we learn about ourselves and the physical phenomena in our environment, the more benefits accrue to mankind generally.

For the Air Force, however, there can only be one objective. That is one directed toward improving our capability to maintain and safeguard the security and integrity of our nation. Thus our aim is to develop a manned space-vehicle system in which the unique capabilities of the human component can be successfully utilized and exploited toward greater net military effectiveness than could be realized from an unmanned space-traversing system. Man as an item of extra payload alone becomes an expensive passenger; but man integrated into the system and enhancing its military usefulness is quite a different matter. Therefore our primary objective becomes that of developing a manned space system having demonstrable and decisive military advantages over any weapon system in our Air Force armamentarium.

Air Force Space Objectives

The attainment of this primary objective proposes natural and expected extensions of Air Force doctrine and capabilities:

- To establish a technical competence to launch and recover a manned space vehicle.
- To establish the functional usefulness of man in the space weapon system.
- To establish an over-all operational reliability of the manned space system which imposes no greater risks to the crew member than now exist in the operational use of first-line combat aircraft.

Engineering Application

Both the bioscientist and the behavorial scientist produce data regarding man's needs, tolerances, and capabilities which must be transposed into mathematical values that the engineer (and military planner) can use in setting down design specifications for the actual item to be produced, whether it is an oxygen mask or a complete weapon system.

Assignment of R&D Tasks

There is no attempt made to segregate the total Air Force life-science program into separate and distinct packages for prosecution only by School of Aviation Medicine or Air Research and Development Command, nor should this separation be made. In general one might say that SAM pursues the more basic problems in the aeromedical, biomedical, or space-medical field. The assignment is to develop the basic knowledge of the organism man both as an isolated functional biologic unit and as related to the particular environment in which he is placed to perform his job.

ARDC is more on the applied research side, concerned more directly in the specific stress factors involved as related both to the environment and more particularly to the machine or system in which the man is to become a functional component. In the trade, ARDC life scientists are commonly referred to as being "hardware oriented" in their primary efforts. This is mainly correct, but it is also true that the ARDC Office of Scientific Research sponsors and directs a long-range program of exploratory and imaginative research in the biosciences. Though focused generally in areas that are estimated to be of maximum potential benefit to the Air Force, this program is held free of any time-tagged requirements for existing weapon systems or components.

The key to success in any combined research, development, and test organization rests fairly completely upon two essential factors:

1. The imagination and vitality (motivations) of the individual scientists and engineers at laboratory level. Only from these men can come new and potentially useful knowledge.

2. The perception and judgment of the management (command and control) echelon in providing intelligent guidance, stable yet stimulating working environments, and, last but not the least important, timely utilization of the useful end-product.

Original ideas are the province of the individual mind and when they arise should be promptly ascertained and developed. Any rigid organizational structure or policy which blocks or retards the implementation of this basic premise is doomed to scientific oblivion. An equally hazardous situation arises when policy, practice, or "expert" opinion requires that each new idea for investigative scientific work or exploratory development be successively reviewed and coordinated by progressively higher-echelon groups of advisers, councils, coordinating committees, ad infinitum, who have neither the direct responsibility for widening the base of Air Force science and technology nor the means of supporting such efforts. In this post-Sputnik-I era of apprehension and uncertainty as regards our true scientific capability vis-à-vis that of the Russians, it is of far greater importance to react intelligently and constructively for the long pull ahead than to attempt through super committees and crash programs a temporary patching up of our national scientific prestige. Perhaps the saddest commentary that could ever be heard expressed by a highly motivated laboratory chief or project scientist is that his program or project has been "coordinated into mediocrity."

The preceding comments have been both diverse and philosophical and certainly contain a large measure of personal opinion. The writer has found it necessary to burden the reader with such a preamble in order to establish at least in part an understanding and, hopefully, an appreciation for the following generalization of the

USAF human-factors program in support of man in space. The plain truth of the matter is that as of the time of this writing the complete scope and extent of the program in astronautics and bio-astronautics as authorized for Air Force prosecution have yet to be determined. What therefore is presented herewith is the program as presently authorized and funded, along with the planned augmentation of our future efforts in support of an Air Force manned space-vehicle capability. For purposes of both brevity and clarity the program will be presented by problem areas rather than task designations with no attempt being made to specify which laboratory in the SAM or ARDC complex is carrying out the work. Neither will funding information be broken out since this has little meaning unless estimates of dollar value for "in-house" work were given, and this is not susceptible of accurate definition. Suffice to say, the present Fiscal Year 1958 and an estimated Fiscal Year 1959 budget authorization for all life-science research and development work amounts to 1.6 per cent of the total Air Force R&D budget. Of these funds approximately 40 per cent is allocated to biomedical programs which are contributory to the NASA man-in-space objective.

I. Biodynamics of space flight
   A. Launch and recovery g-forces; accelerations and decelerations
      1. Determination of human limits, using centrifuges, spin tables, and rocket sleds.
      2. Development of restraining, positioning, and protective gear against g-forces.
      3. Test of protective equipment, using both animal and human subjects in centrifuges, sleds, and capsules dropped from balloon-hoisted platforms.

   Present status.—Computed time—g-force profiles for launch and re-entry indicate a present capability to position and protect the human against these forces. Peaks of 8 to 9 g during launch and 9 to 10 g during re-entry, while not allowing much purposeful function by the man, can be accepted for the time period required.

   Future work.—Continued study to determine:
      1. Methods of increasing human tolerance to g-forces.
      2. Limits of human performance during simulated launch and re-entry patterns on large centrifuge.

3. Fabrication and test of capsule components; "barber-chair," couch-and-seat, head-and-body restraints.
4. Animal flight in sealed capsule in missile nose cone to define true force profile and to test the efficacy of protective devices.

B. Escape during launch and re-entry phases
1. Study of force and control requirements to provide successful escape during prelaunch, launch, and re-entry phases.
2. Determination of blast effects on animals and equipment during simulated escape at supersonic speeds on rocket sleds.
3. "Boosted" vehicle re-entry and ejection simulation, using balloon-launched platform.

Present status.—It appears feasible to use third-stage vehicle boost to eject manned capsule on launch pad and during certain phases of launch to orbiting velocities. Launch trajectories may be "tailored" to provide escape during entire trajectory with acceleration and heat loads contained within tolerable limits (less than 10 g).

Escape during re-entry phase appears feasible but will require considerable further study, development, and test of both conventional (parachute) and unconventional (flaps, retrorockets) drag devices.

The requirement for continuous data acquisition from ground to vehicle and ejected capsule in order to provide timely rescue will require further improvements in tracking and locating devices.

C. Thermal loads and tolerances during launch and recovery
1. Establishment of criteria for human tolerances and performance capabilities under various conditions of temperature extremes.
2. Basic studies on biologic effects of heat and cold on animals and humans to explore possibilities of "adaptation" and of increase in tolerances.
3. Development and test of ventilating garments and capsule "conditioning" units to maintain temperatures between 55 and 85 degrees F.

Present status.—Computed heat loads during most rigorous type of re-entry place humans at 150 degrees F for less than 5 minutes. This is well within acceptable limits.

Future work

1. Continued basic studies on effects of temperature on humans with special emphasis on the additive effects of temperature extremes in the total environmental stress profile.
2. Engineering studies on ablating materials, insulation, heat suits, protective garments, and temperature control methods for the satellite capsule.
3. Instrumented animal flights in ballistic nose cones to more accurately define temperature flux and methods of controlling it within tolerance limits.

D. Weightlessness (during "coasting" phase in orbit)

1. Basic studies on animals and man to determine the relationships between "muscle-position" senses, visual apparatus, and middle-ear sensors (labyrinths and otoliths) in providing man with true gravity-sensory capability.
2. Instrumented parabolic flights in supersonic aircraft to determine actual effects of subgravity states on physiologic function and on performance capability of the human operator.
3. Study of performance capabilities using synthetic devices, such as a "frictionless" platform which gives rotational component of weightless state.
4. Instrumented animal flights in ballistic nose cone to obtain further data on subgravity effects on body function and performance limits.

Present status.—Weightlessness has been aptly named the "great mystery of space flight," and it is the most difficult factor of all to evaluate, since its full impact on man's function cannot be realized until he is actually faced with it in an orbiting situation. Parabolic flight paths yielding 42 to 85 seconds of near weightlessness have produced or will produce considerable information about its effects on eating, drinking, breathing, blood circulation, and excretion of urine. New techniques have been devised to handle the eating and drinking problem, but further work must be done to estimate the complete effect of weightlessness upon normal physiological functioning of the human body.

Future work

1. Continued basic and applied work to delineate total effects of weightlessness during longer periods. Scheduled X-15 flight paths will give several minutes of weightlessness.

2. Consideration being given to various methods of putting laboratory animals (and later man) into a semiballistic flight path which would provide 6 to 8 minutes of weightlessness.

3. Providing recovery techniques can be resolved, it is planned to place a specially trained small animal into actual orbit, which would enable us to telemeter both physiologic and performance data to ground observer points. It appears that the Russian dog Laika was able to eat, drink, and maintain adequate heart and lung function during a number of days in orbit. This provides us with some restrained optimism regarding this problem. If weightlessness proves to be a limiting factor in space flight, we are faced with an engineering problem of some magnitude to provide a degree of artificial gravity during orbital coast.

II. Biologistics of space flight

A. Provision of habitable environment

1. Studies to delineate man's critical needs for ambient pressure, oxygen, water, food, and waste gas and material disposal per unit of time in space vehicle. Corollary studies to determine possibilities of preconditioning or acclimatizing man's system to function normally under conditions less optimum than at sea level.

2. Studies of biologic regenerative systems using photosynthetic principles (*Chlorella* algae) to provide resynthesis of CO_2 and water into O_2 and carbohydrates.

3. Studies of chemical and electrochemical regenerative systems to resynthesize gases and waste products into metabolically and aesthetically acceptable products.

4. Studies on "closed" respiratory gas systems which, though requiring replenishment of oxygen, nitrogen, and helium, together with nonreclaimable CO_2 absorbers, nevertheless provide 24 to 48 hours of a livable gaseous and pressure environment within estimated weight allowances for the orbiting manned capsule.

5. Study of noxious environments to determine man's tolerance to ozone, carbon monoxide and dioxide effects, and other potentially toxic gases.

6. Development and test of space environment protective assembly (full- and partial-pressure suits) to provide emergency protection in event of failure to maintain a habitable environment either through capsule penetration or failure of gas pressurization.

B. Space cabin design and simulator tests

1. Use of sealed-cabin "space simulators" to study various patterns of ambient pressure and vital and inert gas environments against recorded physiological function to determine optimal internal atmosphere within predicted weight and cubage allowance of the space vehicle.

2. Testing of prototype capsules and components by balloon-lift, as in Manhigh Project, in which the subject remained in a sealed cabin for 32 hours aloft and 6 hours on the ground.

3. Use of large centrifuge plus reduced ambient pressure to determine component reliability under both g and lowered ambient pressure conditions.

C. Development of environmental control and monitoring devices

1. Devise methods of instrumenting the space capsule to give both visual and aural warnings of significant deviation from the desired atmospheric configuration. Provision of simple controls for correction of atmospheric composition defects by the operator.

2. Methods of monitoring and telemetering the physiological functions of the operator to the ground as continuous events with some capability of ground command control of atmospheric constituents are being actively pursued.

Present status

1. Existing techniques and components will provide the necessary habitable atmosphere for one man through a 48-hour period, within structure, weight, and volume restrictions imposed by basic thrust available.

2. Simulated space flights have proved the capability of an operator to function normally from a purely physiological standpoint in an atmospheric pressure equivalent to 18–20,000 feet with partial pressure of oxygen equal to practically sea-level conditions. Reduction of pressurization requirements enables the capsule to be constructed at half the weight it would require to provide sea-level pressure.

3. The Manhigh balloon flights have revealed the inadequacy of our monitoring instruments and control equipment for the internal capsule atmosphere. A significant increase in CO_2 concentration went unobserved and uncorrected by the subject until his attention was called to the situation by the ground safety observer who noted vagrancies in subject's radio reports.

Future plans

1. Augmented efforts will be directed toward the discovery of new techniques and development of prototypes to provide complete regeneration and reclamation systems capable of recycling all gaseous, liquid, and solid materials needed and utilized in normal human metabolism.

2. Improvements in comfort, mobility, and protection in the space-environment clothing assembly. The X-15 full-pressure suit marked a major breakthrough in pressure-suit development, with outlook bright for continued improvement.

3. Environmental control, monitoring, and telemetering equipment will require considerable improvement in both qualitative performance capability and reliability prior to first manned flight.

4. Further Manhigh flights will be made with both two-man and five-man crews to provide a test vehicle capability to

evaluate the entire capsule assembly at space-equivalent altitudes.

5. Prototype development of both man and animal capsules
of a size and weight capable of being integrated into
ballistic missile third-stage and nose cone assembly.
Actual tests of these capsules in a semiballistic flight path
may be achieved in the next 12 to 18 months. Such tests
will provide considerable data on total capsule configuration under energy conditions partially simulating re-entry
from a modest orbit of 150 miles altitude.

III. Protection against occupational health hazards
   A. Noise and vibration
      1. Estimates and measurements of sound intensities in the
         nose cone of a ballistic missile during launch indicate a
         possible requirement for protective devices. The vibra-
         tion spectrum during launch or re-entry, particularly if
         drag augmentation devices are used in the latter, is not
         well defined. Human tolerance studies are being run on
         the vertical accelerator and thus far indicate that no
         critical problem exists within data on hand.
      2. The effects of noise and vibration on human commu-
         nications are being actively studied with new types of
         transducers and circuitry developed toward better com-
         munications in a high-intensity noise field.

   B. Space ambient radiations
      1. Basic cellular and genetic studies are continuing to deter-
         mine the relative biologic effectiveness of the heavy
         cosmic primaries which will be encountered in space.
         It appears likely that improved accelerator techniques
         may enable us to simulate quite closely the high energies
         and ionizing effects of the heavy nuclei. This will con-
         siderably expedite our knowledge of their potential bio-
         logic hazard in space flight.
      2. Solar X rays, neutrons, and other ionizing particles are
         being studied as related to predictable galactic phenom-
         ena and capsule shielding requirements.

3. Collection of data from presently orbiting and instrumented satellites yields preliminary indication that previous estimates of cosmic ray activities are valid.

4. Animal research continues, using artificial ionizing source to define tolerance limits and protective requirements.

5. Animal and human studies are being continued, using long-duration (24- to 48-hour) balloon flights to give exposures above 80,000 feet.

6. Techniques and equipment developed by the Atomic Energy Commission for determination of total body radiation are being investigated for possible use in the spacecrew monitoring and conditioning program.

C. Toxicological health hazards

1. Considerable work is being done to investigate the potential health hazards involved in the ground handling of fuels, lubricants, and gases used in ballistic missile operations. Environmental monitoring devices, protective equipment, safe disposal methods, and clinical screening procedures are being developed to ensure the health and safety of ground crews.

2. Estimates are being made of both long-term and short-term health hazards arising from chemicals and by-products accidentally contaminating the space capsule. A power source in the space vehicle will be required both for stabilization in orbit and for the institution of re-entry proceedings. Hydrogen peroxide and solid-propellant engines are being investigated for any potential health hazards to the space passenger.

Present status

1. For the duration of space flight that our present ability to provide a habitable atmosphere can sustain (24 to 48 hours), it is not felt that space ambient radiations will be a limiting factor at relatively low orbits.

2. Noise and vibration energies during launch and re-entry require further study but evidence indicates no intolerable levels.

3. Potential health hazards within the capsule, arising from accidental or unforeseen contaminants as by-products of intrinsic energy sources, appear to be negligible at present.

Future work.—Exposure of subhuman specimens to simulated cosmic particles will begin as soon as more data on the physical nature of the particle are available and accelerator techniques prove adaptable.

IV. Human performance in space vehicles
   A. Space mission tasks and job engineering analysis
      1. Digital-analogue computers with simulators interposed in the closed loop are being used to determine man's capability to handle and process data and to exercise monitorship and control under various simulated space mission profiles.
      2. Hypothetical mathematical models are being used to determine optimal crew composition and crew–machine relationships as a function of problem sharing and decision making on a real-time basis.
      3. Work-space layout designs are being functionally tested, using known restrictions of position, body movement, and visual scanning ability.

   B. Psychophysiological aspects of crew performance and stress tolerance
      1. Isolation and confinement studies are being continued, using both single and multiple crew simulators. Varying degrees of sensory deprivation are being studied.
      2. Simulated mission activities are fed into a space capsule to determine decrement of performance proficiency under various patterns of a work-rest cycle. Factors such as synthetic atmospheric configurations can be added to provide a fairly close simulation of the actual mission with the exception of weightlessness, actual radiation exposure, and the actual stress of being isolated in orbit.
      3. Manhigh balloon flights provide most of the psychophysiologic factors in an orbiting space flight, with the major exception of weightlessness. Continuation of these flights with one-, two-, and five-man capsules will yield

considerable data on performance decrements and stress tolerances for both the individual and a composite crew.

C. Selection, training, and conditioning of space crews
   1. Biomedical, psychomotor, and sociologic screening tests indicate that a high degree of reliability can be achieved in predicting individual and crew performance under standing operating and emergency conditions.
   2. Conditioning and acclimatizing regimes appear feasible and practical as a means of improving the individual's basic psychophysiologic tolerance to expected stresses of space flight. Material improvements in performance have been validated under simulated conditions in both the physiologic response to stress and proficiency of performance.

Present status
   1. The answer to the question, what will man be required to do on a space mission and what can he add to the effectiveness of the system, is as yet indistinct. On the basis of what we can extrapolate from high-performance aircraft and predictions as to what the task will comprise, it is felt that he will indeed provide a useful and needed function.
   2. The psychophysiologic stresses of space flight have been closely simulated and exhaustively studied. Properly selected, trained, and conditioned individuals are capable of completely reliable and effective performance under all conditions of space with the possible exception of weightlessness, which has not been adequately studied. It does not appear that these stresses imposed under actual conditions will deteriorate performance or increase safety requirements.

Future work
   1. Work at both the basic and applied levels of this problem will be considerably augmented to provide a more complete understanding of bodily mechanisms in response to stress from the cellular level on up through regulatory systems to the complete functioning organism. With more fundamental knowledge of cellular biology

and regulatory systems interrelationships, particularly as concerns brain mechanisms, we stand an excellent chance not only of identifying the premium man for the premium job but also of producing more premium men through natural and artificial adaptation techniques.

2. On the applied end, a crew selection and conditioning unit will be established in an area where there is a high population increment of pilots who are required to perform premium tasks. When the reliability of the space vehicle has reached an acceptable figure, it is confidently expected that an equally reliable crew component will be ready and waiting.

We can say, then, that the present research and development program covering the life-science field will provide for the safety and effectiveness of a human component in a space vehicle for a mission duration of from 24 to 48 hours. The engineering problems involved in final integration of all components of the system to provide the required reliability and margin of safety are formidable and complex. Yet from the existing state of the art of components and of systems engineering technology, their satisfactory resolution appears feasible in the near future.

Headquarters Air Research and Development Command

CHAPTER 17

Blueprints for Space

Brigadier General Homer A. Boushey

"In the country of the blind the one-eyed man is king."

The writer of this oft-quoted adage has expressed, in a poetic and dramatic way, the basic truth of relativity. Some of us see better than others. And as regards "seeing" I refer to the ability to more clearly foretell the future—and specifically, to predict the role which the space age will occupy in our future. I would like to summarize my beliefs. This is not to say that I consider myself a superior prophet. It is only that my work has led me to study and think a great deal about this subject and that the possibilities are so startling and limitless that we need as many views on its potentialities as we can get.

In twenty years, I believe both the moon and Mars will have permanent, manned outposts . . . but perhaps that is getting somewhat ahead of myself. Working up to these achievements, I believe you will agree, we will launch and utilize many, many scientific and military satellites. Even a few commercial satellites may prove economically desirable. Satellites will not only circle our earth but will also orbit the moon. And we will probably give Mars three or four small moons to add to her two natural ones. Even Venus will probably rate a satellite. Each will relay information back to the earth, or perhaps to the moon, since I believe the moon will prove to be a better site for electromagnetic reception. Probes to the near vicinity of the sun will undoubtedly be used. Perhaps there will be a need to explore the outer fringes of our solar system with unmanned space vehicles. And all this effort will surely increase our scientific knowledge.

Uses of Satellites

But what are some of the practical uses of satellites—specifically earth-circling satellites? Perhaps the most obvious is as a global weather detecting and reporting satellite. Even rather crude television will provide enough resolution to determine cloud coverage and accompanying wind patterns. This should permit storm warning and accurate air-mass weather prediction.

Another use will be for communications. Either a simple reflector type of satellite which merely serves to bounce a signal back toward earth can be used, or a relay type might be employed.

The passive, or reflector-type, satellite has one great advantage: all the payload can be devoted to the reflecting surface. There would be no power-supply problems or electronic failures to cope with, and during the very extended period it would remain in orbit —perhaps hundreds of years—*it would function!* Another type, the delayed relay type of communications satellite, would receive messages in electronic "fast time" while, say, over New York and store them on tape. About eighteen minutes later, over Paris, the satellite would spew out, again in electronic "fast time," the messages addressed to that location. At the same time it would receive a batch for delivery to other cities—and so on, as the satellite circled around the world.

Here it is interesting to discuss the possible advantage of a retrosatellite, one fired westward rather than eastward. Since the earth at its equator has a rotational velocity of about 1000 miles per hour toward the east, it is only sensible that rocketmen make use of this "free," initial velocity provided by our earth's eastward spin. In the case of a communications satellite, however, the speed of delivery of the messages might make a retro-orbit desirable even though more chemical energy would be required to place it in orbit. The difference in ground speed between the retrosatellite and the normal, or east-moving, one would be 2000 mph, or twice the earth's rotational velocity. At an orbital altitude of 1000 miles, for example, the time for orbit going eastward would be two hours, but in westward orbit the time for one circuit of the globe would be one hour and forty-six minutes, or an improvement of almost twelve per cent. Such an improvement seems attractive enough for us to consider employing a "wrong-way sputnik."

A navigation satellite is another very practical use. The desirable features for a navigation satellite are: constancy of orbit so that precise forecasts of its future positions can be tabulated, large reflecting surface so that the satellite can be readily seen visually both during daytime and at night when sun-earth positions are right, and a strong radio transmission signal so that the satellite can be identified and tracked accurately through clouds or even in clear weather during sun-earth positions when the satellite could not be seen visually.

Think how navigation could be simplified by a few such satellites. Imagine if you will that they are placed at an orbital height which is best for navigational observations. Each satellite would of course have an identification. For visual use, a pair of binoculars might be all that would be needed to identify the object as, say, "navigational satellite, number three." By use of sextant, a chronometer, and a prepared ephemeris for these "navigational satellites," the precise latitude and longitude could be readily determined. Or if you prefer, a small radio receiver could be used. It would tell by a triple beep or other code that the object viewed was "Navigational Satellite Number 3." If the satellite would frequently broadcast its own latitude and longitude (which it could easily do by playing back a tape recording), even the chronometer and ephemeris could be eliminated. Only angle measurement would be required. This would certainly be a help to small surface craft and airplanes.

Next, I believe satellite vehicles can prove immensely useful to mankind. Appropriately utilized, they could provide a manned space patrol for peaceful purposes. They can provide attack warning and assist in mutual inspection programs. They can be of use in enabling us to improve our geographic knowledge of the world. A similar satellite could, through mapping and charting, provide information leading to far greater accuracy in positioning our continents relative to one another.

Another use would be purely military—bombardment—and accomplished by space vehicles. I use the term vehicles rather than satellites because I believe these weapon systems will be manned. By usage we seem to be adopting the terms *satellite vehicles* and *spacecraft* for man-carrying machines, and *satellites* or *space-probes* for the unmanned. Now, what would be the purpose of manned, bombardment-type space vehicles, and how could they function? Obviously they would serve as a deterrent to armed aggression, just as our Strategic Air Command bombers safeguard the peace of the free world today. But could they bomb, and would such bombardment be accurate enough to be practical? It has been claimed that the idea of bombing from orbit is ridiculous. It is pointed out that "one can't drop anything from a satellite—things *won't drop*—they will remain in orbit and circle along with the satellite vehicle itself."

To cause objects to re-enter the earth's atmosphere and fall, energy must be applied to the bomb to reduce its velocity so that gravity will overbalance centrifugal force. And so it has been stated, that unless quite a lot of energy were applied, the bomb would need to be released halfway around the earth and the accuracy at the target would be off by perhaps hundreds of miles. Why not, say the critics of space bombing, do things the easier way, and fire ICBMs?

Let me give you my reasons. First, our government would surely not launch its intercontinental ballistic missiles on incomplete information. But if it waited for full confirmation, our launching sites themselves might be destroyed. This problem is certainly a serious one. It is eased somewhat by the use of man. A manned vehicle can be launched on only partial, or even garbled information, for without a definite command confirmation some 15 to 20 minutes after launch the man would not press home an attack but would peacefully return to a U.S. base.

Next, I do not share the misgivings about "not being able to drop anything from orbit." Certainly energy would be required to bring an object out of orbit—a considerable amount. But if a sufficient rearward impulse were imparted to a bomb, it would plummet earthward along a vertical trajectory, and the time of fall to the earth's surface from an orbital altitude of, say, 150 miles would be only four or five minutes.

But it would not be necessary or even desirable to program a bomb or warhead to fall vertically. If the warhead were merely slowed down a proper amount, it would fall to earth in a steepening curve, traveling forward under the moving space vehicle. As the warhead entered the atmosphere, it would decelerate more rapidly. But the important fact is that if the amount of rearward impulse were properly selected, the pilot of the space vehicle could guide the warhead during its fall and increase its accuracy considerably. It is true that today we have very little excess payload capacity in a satellite vehicle to allocate to fuel for the deceleration of a warhead. But I think such arguments are much like those faced by Wilbur and Orville Wright.

In 1903 it was difficult for them to lift one man into the air, let alone transport any useful load. Today just one of our operational aircraft can take off with over 300,000 pounds of useful military payload. Likewise, as we improve our capabilities to operate in space, the loads which we can carry into orbit will be sizable, and the operational advantages which I have mentioned will predominate.

I believe space will be used effectively for both military and civilian purposes. The uses which I have briefly discussed—weather reporting, world-wide communications, navigation, surveillance, and bombardment—are all vital military uses, and in my opinion can best be accomplished by space satellites and space vehicles. But one thing is certain: for each new offensive weapon, a military opponent will attempt to provide a defensive or counterweapon. Thus it appears logical to assume we will have antisatellite weapons and even space fighters. These and other counterweapons will become highly specialized and, I imagine, also highly lethal. Each new fantastic space weapon will probably generate a requirement for an equally fantastic defensive weapon. Thus we could go on and on in our imaginations, playing such a checker game of the future—with weapons and counterweapons and even counter-counterweapons.

But I believe it will be sufficient to sum up my impersonal views by the simple statement that space will prove immensely useful from a military viewpoint. Our very security depends upon our military abilities, and while scientific or commercial exploitation of space is certainly desirable, there is not the overwhelming urgency as for a military space capability.

Manned Outposts in Space

Now I would like to discuss manned outposts on both Mars and on our moon.

From one standpoint Mars poses a somewhat easier problem. It has an atmosphere, even if it is roughly equivalent to that at the top of Mt. Everest. Entry through the atmosphere of Mars, because of the lesser gravity and more gradual density changes, is easier than re-entry through the atmosphere of our own earth.

Once on the surface of Mars, temperatures are well within the limits of survivability. A few pieces of protective equipment would provide ample insulation against the extreme cold at night. I imagine an atmospheric compressor will be necessary to maintain a livable pressure. It is hoped that free oxygen in the Martian air will be available, and perhaps the atmosphere will be of such composition that one only needs to compress it for use by man. Water is probably present in sufficient quantity. The biggest single problem appears to be survival during the voyage. Estimates of the duration range from 57 days to as long as 244. Keeping man, or men, alive during such prolonged voyages in sealed, closed-cycle containers is not an easy task. All other aspects of establishing a habitable site on Mars seem to me to be easier of solution. But even this formidable problem I believe will be overcome, and within the next twenty years we shall have a permanent, self-sustaining outpost on Mars!

The moon in many ways poses some even more difficult survival problems than Mars. But since the moon is only perhaps two to five days' travel time from the earth, I believe the establishment of a lunar base will precede a Martian site.

A Trip to the Moon

To better understand the problems involved, let us exercise our creative imaginations in describing a single pioneering venture: the landing of the first human observers on the surface of the moon and their return to earth.

Essentially what we are dealing with here is the reconciliation of two opposite environments. We are sending men on this trip. Therefore with them we must send a capsule of the earth environment to which the human organism has become adapted through the millenniums of its evolution. We are sending these men through a strange—perhaps hostile—environment, so they must be protected completely from all foreseeable hazards. Finally, unless these men can do something useful, there is no reason for landing them on the moon in the first place. So we must give them a goal, a job to do. And it must be a job that will contribute to scientific and military colonization of the moon.

Now since the critical element in this flight is the men themselves, let us think for a moment about them. After more than ten years of ingenious and fruitful research, Dr. Hubertus Strughold and his associates at the Space Medicine Division of the Air Force's School of Aviation Medicine have formed some rather definite ideas about these space-age Marco Polos. Biologically they will have to be exceptionally well adapted to this sort of adventure. They will have to be economical organisms, so to speak. They need not be heavily muscled, for example. Weight is a handicap rather than an advantage in space. The desirable attributes are coordination and physical endurance.

Psychologically they will have to be free of any mental quirk or habit which would detract from their usefulness. Obviously confinement in the limited room of the space vehicle would rule out anyone who might be subject to claustrophobia, and this doubtless means that the first space travelers will never have served a Pentagon tour.

Given this human package of qualifications as raw material, we then process them through a rigid qualification program. You may safely believe me when I say that no training for anything before in history will compare with this program for thoroughness. Every detail of physical conditioning will be covered. Every move these men will make, every action they will be called on to perform, will be rehearsed repeatedly to ensure success of the mission. Perfection! That is what we must expect of the men entrusted with this work.

Concurrently with the selection and training of these men we will be conducting the final testing and assembly of the vehicle itself. A few simple calculations show us that the gross design weight for such a vehicle will be on the order of one million pounds. This gives us an option. Either we can wait until we have developed and accepted a propulsion engine capable of lifting this mass and sustaining it throughout the voyage, or we can adopt a smaller unit and utilize it through a series of space refuelings. This space refueling idea seems to me to be highly practical and to offer an earlier realization of the moon flight project.

All of you are familiar with the history of refueling in the air. You will remember the crude beginnings of the idea, and some of the endurance flights that were made using any old way to get more fuel aboard the airplane. And you know that refueling in flight is now a highly refined technique, one that is practiced successfully in the Air Force about every three minutes around the clock.

There is no reason why space refueling could not be accomplished. We could place a cluster of propulsion units (fuel tanks with a rocket engine) in orbit around the earth a month prior to the actual launch of the space vehicle. The launch trajectory of the vehicle itself could be predetermined so as to intercept the power package in the orbit. Pick-up could be accomplished in any one of several ways and the new units attached to the space vehicle for the voyage out to the moon and back.

This permits us to consider the use of a fairly small space vehicle —something on the order of 15 thousand pounds, or about the weight of an F-86 fighter. This vehicle could be mounted on the present ICBM boosters. And having tracked the orbiting power units and having established a meticulously accurate interception curve, so to speak, we are now at the beginning of the final countdown.

In the last critical minutes, the physically conditioned crew goes aboard, suited up and ready to undertake this challenging voyage into the not unknown but little-known extraterrestrial reaches of space.

When the countdown ends, the surge of the rockets against their supported and protected bodies gives them a nine-g initial thrust upward and outward. After the burnout of stage one, the vehicle coasts upward for about five minutes, and then is kicked along again with the nine-g thrust toward orbital speed.

Here is where our crew members find themselves for the first time in a prolonged period of weightlessness. This is one of the critical problems which must be explored and solved before lunar flight can be considered. Can a man work, can he do the numerous tasks involved in this project, when he seems to have no substance at all? This condition cannot possibly be simulated on the earth. Nothing short of free flight in space itself can tell. And that is why we are involved in other projects to gain priceless experience and knowledge prior to launching the manned lunar flight.

Consider these men. Once an orbit is established, they have work to do. The intercept with the power unit has been practically perfect. Only a few hundred yards—perhaps a few miles—now separates the rocket from the power package it must now pick up. It will have been accomplished in practice many times before. But like parachute jumping, you have to be perfect every time. Otherwise the crew will find that they have picked a very poor place to run out of gas.

The automatic controls will have to be turned off and the manual controls engaged for this refueling maneuver. Vernier rockets can be used to bring the space vehicle up into close contact with the orbiting power package for the final adjustments.

How long will this take? Will it be half an hour? One hour? Or more realistically, will it require several orbital periods around the earth? While this is a vital phase of a lunar voyage, the time required for accomplishing the refueling is not critical. No expenditure of fuel is needed to circle the earth once an orbit has been established. So except for the moderate consumption of air, food, and water there would be no critical penalty involved in orbital refueling.

For the lunar course there is a certain minimum energy curve, so to speak, which must be precisely calculated. But here again we enter a new field. Precisely calculated with reference to what?

At launch, and to this point in the flight, orientation is naturally gravitational; the center of the earth is the point of reference. But now this orientation is losing all usefulness. This flight is projected beyond the predominant influence of the earth, and the only useful reference becomes a mathematical concept—the ecliptic of the orbits of the earth and the moon. Obviously this is no slide-rule exercise. This is the time to yell "Hey, Doc!" and to get an answer. "HaDOC" is the oral shorthand designation of a computer, specifically the Handy Dandy Orbital Computer designed and built by John Miller of the Minneapolis Honeywell Regulator Corporation. First mechanized on an analog machine, this small device seems capable of developing the accuracy of a digital differential analyzer—and it will need this degree of accuracy to be effective on this flight. A pilot can feed into HaDOC the values of thrust, direction, and duration and get back results on a repetitive basis. With it the commander of the space vehicle can always tell what action is called for and when. It will also feed him the cost of the action in terms of energy needs. Naturally such a computer in the cockpit would be invaluable.

After the hook-up of the power plant the commander computes the precise point along the orbit around the earth where he must fire the first unit so as to depart this orbit and set off along course to his destination, which is the surface of the moon. During the maneuvering to pick up his power units, he would probably have cut off the automatic controls and put his craft under manual control. But for earth departure and for the long voyage to the moon he will probably engage the automatic control systems during the entire time, with the crew merely monitoring for override actions if needed. At any rate the commander has determined time and trajectory from his computer by now. At the precise instant indicated, he fires the first of the five rockets in his power package. The actual flight through space is now under way.

Here is where we have to consider the two opposite environments we mentioned in the beginning. Within the spacecraft itself we will have a cabin environment bringing along something of the earth environment, enough of it to keep our crew alive and functioning. Weightlessness? During the flight proper, since there will be no up-and-down-and-sideways orientation with respect to anything but the cabin itself, it may be possible to use a slow rotation of the craft to create at least a fractional g-force. It would not take much. Just enough, in fact, to keep the few movable objects from going adrift and floating aimlessly around the cabin. By movable objects, I mean such items as the highly concentrated foods, packed either in plastic containers as liquids or in collapsible tubes in paste form. After all, nobody wants his steak-paste to float away from his faceplate in the middle of a meal, nor is it easy to round up a weightless blob of milk floating like a monstrous amoeba across the interior of the cabin. Let us at least have a way to make things behave. There are enough new experiences to deal with on this trip without building others into the plan.

Of course the cabin interior will be pressurized, but not like passenger airplanes are. Pressures will be low, approximately that of an altitude of 15,000 feet or lower. And humidity, initially low, will begin to build up, simply as a result of human physiology. The humidity can be controlled to within acceptable limits. I am sure, for instance, that we can keep the humidity within much closer limits than what we find to be normal for a summer in Washington, D. C.

Yes, the internal environment will be sufficiently man-directed, biologically and physically, to enable our crew to function efficiently. But on the outside, just a shell of metal away, things will be very different. And there is a possibility that a chance contact from that tremendous void outside the craft would change the inner environment abruptly.

Consider the meteorite and how it flies, for example. A pinhead-sized meteorite, just a grain of celestial sand, so to speak, moving through space at a speed of 20 to 60 miles per second, could easily puncture the steel hull of our craft. As a matter of fact, it would be less a matter of puncturing it than of blasting its way through the hull. The heat generated by the impact would cause a minor explosion of the site of the hit. Result? Decompression within the craft, with a span of perhaps 15 or 30 seconds for the crew to act before losing consciousness. Even that short time would be enough for the crew to plug the hole and gradually bring the cabin pressure back to the desired level. But all this is a lot of effort to have to expend for a collision with a grain of sand.

What about the larger ones? There is little doubt that a collision with a meteor weighing just one ounce would end this voyage at once. This sobering fact prompts us to ask what the probabilities are of such an encounter. And the information we have now, from instrumented satellites and other sources, leads us to believe that the probability is so small as to be inconsequential. A spacecraft of the size we are talking about could cruise for hundreds of years without meeting such a catastrophe. Meteors of this size are just that rare in space.

Other information relayed to us from our satellites indicates another hazard to space travel. This is the radiation encountered there. You have all read of this layer, so powerful that it overran the radiation counters in the first satellite. It is believed, but not yet proved, that this is a layer which can be traversed at high speed with no danger to the crew members. Proper shielding of the craft coupled with short duration of exposure within the layer would cancel the hazard completely. What we all want to be sure about is that it is, in fact, a layer. Should this zone extend indefinitely into space, we might be confronted with a serious barrier.

Cosmic rays alone are a serious consideration. We have found heavy primary particles in the course of our upper atmosphere studies, particles ranging up to an atomic weight of 40 or more. These rays can be very dangerous. The particles crash into the atmosphere with energies millions or even billions of times greater than can be produced in our laboratories. To keep them out of our spacecraft entirely, the craft would have to be sheathed in steel armor plate at least two inches thick. And such a weight of steel is out of the question for an early spacecraft. So the crew must accept the fact that they will be exposed to a certain amount of cosmic radiation, not only of the heavy primary particles but of powerful secondary particles and gamma rays. Again, and fortunately, these particles of such tremendous energies are rare. Their density in space is extremely low. Cosmic radiation dosage would be safely low for short trips, such as our lunar flight. But in the more distant future, when we are concerned with interplanetary or even interstellar travel, this possible danger must be considered.

Now, having placed these hazards in what we believe to be their proper perspective, let us look for a moment at what our crew is doing while en route. The velocity attained at burnout of the first rocket engine should bring them within the pull of the moon's gravitational field in approximately two days. It is during this free-flight period that the presence of human minds trained for this work takes on added importance. These minds can form judgments from complex data. They can make decisions based upon many and diverse information inputs, some of which may not have been anticipated initially and hence could not be fed into the electro-mechanical programmer. Valuable work can be done in monitoring and analyzing the different sources of navigational data. Radio aids, celestial fixes, and inertial equipment will all be in use. The human intellect alone can evaluate and select the data from each. And if by any chance a change in the original commitment becomes necessary, the human mind can make the change.

All of this will be done, of course, within a schedule of time-allocation for each crew member. Relaxation, sleep, and work, on a schedule unlike the normal earth routine, will be ordered into effect once the craft has left the earth orbit. The commander, of course, must bring his crew to destination in the best possible condition.

At the end of two days of free flight, the ship approaches the moon, fires its second rocket as a lunar retrorocket while entering the gravitational field so as to establish an orbit. The sole purpose of orbiting is to study the surface of the moon and to interpret data previously furnished by unmanned lunar probes. One problem will be the selection of the most advantageous landing place. Several tentative points will have been selected, but the final choice will rest with the commander. Let us assume that he decides upon a polar landing, since it appears that this may permit the best use of the moon's quota of solar radiation. At an altitude of over 1000 feet at a lunar pole the sun would be continuously in view. At this location solar power would not be curtailed by the two weeks of lunar night. But will the crew actually land on a peak? Some of the peaks are thought to rise 30 thousand feet above the lunar plains. Or will they select one of the adjacent plains, or "seas," or perhaps a level crater bed? And what is the nature of the surface selected? Is it rocky, or dusty? And if dusty, how deep is the dust? Inches? Feet? Well, let us go in and see!

But only after we have carefully disconnected one of our refueling packages, leaving it to orbit the moon. This is the round-trip part of the ticket for this trip, and the orbit must be very carefully established. It would not do to lose this fuel package now.

When everything is right, then the craft goes on in with a rocket approach. Because of the lack of atmosphere, no aerodynamic approach is possible. Retrorockets will have to be used to control this landing and prevent a crash—a ticklish maneuver indeed. And always that dust problem is the unknown factor. The blast from the retrorocket could throw that dust about, and an induced electrostatic charge on the ship could attract it in clouds or create a violent discharge spark upon landing. This is one of the unknowns the pioneers will have to contend with.

After touchdown, the crew will go into its well-rehearsed exploratory routine. They will don the suits designed especially for the moon's surface. And, by the way, the design of such a suit is quite a challenge. It must be light, comfortably pressurized, and equipped with its own air-oxygen supply, be nonelectrostatic, have an integral communications system, and still enable the wearer to maneuver and do something useful. Otherwise he might as well be at the club playing snooker.

There is a solar-energy collector and power converter to be set up and put into operation. This system must be so arranged as to take maximum advantage of the sunlight available throughout the day-night cycle. This system will provide the permanent power source for a reporting station, fitted with sensing and reporting instruments, and continuously sending its findings back to earth. There will be gravimetric readings to take. Photographs must be made. And above all, these men will have to knock off a little chunk of the moon to bring back with them. Can you imagine the sensations of a group of chemists and physicists and mineralogists assembled to examine this first piece of man-imported matter from the moon? I am reasonably sure that the Board of Directors of the Smithsonian Institution would be glad to make space for even a small piece of it in the new hall of gems and minerals. Probably, in view of the money and effort expended to get it, it would belong in the gem collection, where it would rank far above the diamonds in value.

There is one thing the crew will welcome on the moon, and that is the return of some sense of gravity. Even though only one sixth of what they experienced on earth, it will be much more than they felt during the trip.

Personally, I want to find out if it is feasible to dig in on the surface of the moon. My interest is sparked by the realization that some way must be found to provide protection from meteorites, all forms of radiation, and the extremes of high and low surface temperatures, if we are to use the moon for scientific and military purposes.

Meanwhile back on earth where the lunar trip started, final orbital verification has been made on the second power-unit package which was placed in orbit perhaps a month prior to the start of the lunar voyage expressly for use by the returning craft. Join-up information is ready to transmit on call from the spacecraft as it approaches the earth.

When the exploratory work is finished—and it will be brief on this first trip—the crew goes aboard, secures the ship, and blasts off to intercept the orbiting rocket above the moon's surface. This refueling technique is getting to be second nature to our crew by this time, and the hook-up goes smoothly. Then the course for earth is set and they are on the return trip.

Maybe a bit more rest is permissible on the return flight. These men have accomplished the most spectacular job of exploration in human history, and yet the most difficult step remains before them. This is the matter of approaching the increasing gravitational field of the earth in an orbit to coincide with that of the circling power package. And once it has been hooked up, to continue in orbit until the conditions below will permit them to land at their selected terminal base.

Pure ballistic re-entry is possible, of course, with a vehicle equipped with a heat sink or ablation material. But our vehicle will most likely incorporate some aerodynamic lift and drag to permit slower re-entry and landing under full control of the crew.

Seven days have elapsed since the launch. Seven earth days—one half a lunar day. Has it been worth the effort and the expense? You know and I know that to make this trip possible, the effort will tax a good segment of American industrial capacity and will cost vast sums of money. It will draw upon the best talent in the nation, and it will demand the utmost of that talent.

But there is one thing that would cost even more. That would be the failure to be first on the moon. We cannot afford to come out second in a territorial race of this magnitude. We must either succeed in this drive or fail utterly because of some as yet unknown factor. If we fail for this latter reason, we shall know that no one else can succeed, and that no other nation will pick up an advantage through our default. This outpost, under our control, would be the best possible guarantee that all of space will indeed be preserved for the peaceful purposes of man.

Headquarters United States Air Force

CHAPTER 18

The Military Impact of Manned Space Operations

Major General Lloyd P. Hopwood

World War II was the adrenalin shot that mobilized American scientific and engineering talent in the field of weapons and weapon systems to a degree beyond anything in our history. Out of this stimulus came fission and ultimately fusion, electronics, jet propulsion, and the beginning of rocket propulsion.

All these were quantum breakthroughs, melodramatic to the point that military concepts, doctrine, and strategy tended to be submerged in a secondary role. The power, speed, range, and flexibility afforded by these breakthroughs were such that the requirements for imaginative strategy were lessened during the decade in which we enjoyed a monopoly in decisive power.

Circumstances have changed significantly. We are entering an era of another quantum breakthrough into the hypersonic speeds of space. We know at the same time that man's judgment and discrimination in realistic military readiness are more important than ever before. Air and space vehicles, however, are delivery systems which offer the highest promise of positioning man's judgment in that part of the complex equation where effectiveness is optimized. Whether the system is to be ground-monitored or is to employ mobile launching pads with command posts represented in manned aircraft must be determined by sober consideration of which system or combination of systems offers the best solution in a period of dynamic evolution and severe threat. We must be wary of the term "ultimate."

Unless we are extraordinarily careful and professionally responsible, the dawning era in which the conquest of space will be achieved may invite a continuing deficit in conceptual evolution. Much has been written on the complexities and characteristics of space hardware. This book has concerned itself primarily with the equally complex factors of making man and "hardware" an effective and compatible system.

Throughout history man with a club, man with a gun, or man with an airplane has been a more or less fallow combination until given the purpose inherent in mission and concepts and the strategy in support of an objective. Since objectives are the product of man's desires and intellect, then the concepts of men that evolve the doctrine on which strategy is built to support those objectives are the fundamental keystone on which the usefulness and reality of space systems must be developed.

It is not always fashionable to look to history for guidance to the future, particularly among airmen. But perhaps tradition and habit tied to the glories of the past or to obsolete weapons are the real culprits rather than history. History suggests that since the beginning of recorded time man has been preoccupied with the conquest of space. Until the time of Kitty Hawk it was necessarily a two-dimensional conquest.

Up through the years national proprietary rights have become formalized for two-dimensional space. Three-mile, ten-mile, and twelve-mile limits have been established and generally accepted as seaward extensions of national sovereignty. Progressive nations have tended to be those with the imagination and initiative to exploit the oceans beyond the recognized territorial waters. It was so during the expansion of the Roman Empire, throughout the Spanish era of greatness, and in the *mare nostrum* time of the British Empire. It was so in the days of the American clipper fleets and whalers.

In a very real sense aviation in its first fifty years has repeated the pattern of history in the conquest of the "territorial" atmosphere. Commercial aviation has achieved something like a six-mile limit, and advanced military aircraft are now approaching the 12-mile limit. At least one venture has been made into the greater space at 25 miles. The X-15 might well be christened the "Santa Maria" when it ventures many miles beyond the shore of three-dimensional space, or perhaps this title should be reserved for the much greater conquests to follow.

One of the lessons history should teach us is the futility of differentiating between "territorial" and "open" space if we are to fulfill our obligation for free-world leadership in the future. This has been a pattern of logic as well as tradition. It was ability to exploit two-dimensional sea space completely that best assured the fulfillment of at least four dominant principles of war:

First, optimum mobility afforded flexibility in establishing the *objective*.

Second, ability to carry the war to the enemy instead of being restricted to defense by range limitations achieved the capacity for the *offensive*.

Third, freedom of action to move anywhere as required by national policy permitted the assumption of *initiative*.

Fourth, *economy of force* and concentration of force derived from naval units which could operate as fleets under single command wherever necessary.

The logic of history distilled by able men over hundreds of years should not be forgotten in the urgency of conquering three-dimensional space in the shortest possible time span. The lessons and logic of centuries are as valid now as they were then.

Armies also have always sought the capability to dominate two-dimensional space. Resort to horses, elephants, and, more recently, mechanized vehicles has improved the capability for faster movement even though the rate of territorial acquisition tends to remain slow. However, ground strategy has always been more circumscribed by man's propensity to put up fences, borders, and various natural or artificial boundaries. This is not surprising. All but a very few of our 49 states have at least one border drawn along some natural geographical feature which has no relationship with functional logic. We see many "twin city" complexes that might have been more productive if they operated as a functional entity.

Because property lines, section lines, county lines are the things we live with, there is the constant temptation to solve every problem with more lines. Perhaps our best hope of keeping three-dimensional space the entity it must be will lie in the considerable difficulty of putting granite monuments and bench marks into precise and stationary orbit.

Out of this preoccupation with lines and limits comes the hazard of point defense. Our best historical precedent to which we should look for guidance is again in naval strategy and tactics. Once the ability to maneuver on the high seas had been achieved, we find no major battles in which naval forces dropped anchor and fought to preserve a position on the ocean's surface. They did, however, seek to deny enemy access to sea space that would constitute a threat to coast lines or harbors.

The history of air defense has been closely tied to points. In our own country, Army concepts emerged along clear traditional lines. The old coast defense artillery was proved obsolete in its point defense of harbors by the advent of amphibious tactics which could circumvent its fixed field of fire. Our first antiaircraft defense units were the insignia of the Coast Artillery Corps and carried that title with the parenthesized qualification "(antiaircraft)." Considerable commotion arose when the Field Artillery Corps entered the arena of air defense. Both antiaircraft forces were confined to point defense by the limitations of their weapons and their concepts. These concepts were from the outset as outmoded as the demonstrably outmoded concept of harbor defense. Yet they persist today to the tune of megamillion-dollar budgets.

It is probably true that many of the airman's initial concepts for air defense came from the only classic example of air defense, afforded in the Battle of Britain. Limitation in bomber and fighter-escort ranges of the Luftwaffe confined the attack on Britain to a relatively small area of a relatively small island. The Royal Air

Force Fighter Command won an air campaign that was essentially one of point defense. But these are not the circumstances on the North American continent. They were not the case in defense against air-breathing bombers, and they are even less the case against ballistic missiles. As long as massive fallout effects can be exploited by an enemy, space denial rather than point defense offers the best ultimate solution, though one which has apparently been rejected or at least deferred. The time lost may be hard to regain.

There is another feature of change which invites consideration. Since time immemorial, military forces have sought to exploit their characteristics of mobility and firepower against the vulnerability of their adversary. In creating our forces we sought the positive factors of mobility and firepower while designing into our materiel and our tactics those elements of security needed to reduce our own vulnerability. The only modern exception was the Maginot Line, in which mobility was rejected in favor of assumed security. By this rejection France became committed to a defensive strategy that automatically ruled out victory and left stalemate or defeat the only alternative.

Today, however, the evolution of nuclear weapons has given us what to all intents and purposes is the ultimate in firepower. We find all forces turning attention to the remaining two characteristics of mobility and vulnerability. And emphasis on missiles, aircraft and aircraft carriers, and submarines evidences a recognition that exploitation of three-dimensional space affords the highest rewards in mobility and invulnerability.

In a period when the availability of nuclear weapons compacts the time of decisive action into a relatively instantaneous exchange, mobility itself is not a meaningful characteristic. Instead we now think in terms of delivery capability. This, in turn, is a two-pronged proposition. In its most obvious sense it involves the capability to place firepower on any target complex the neutralization or destruction of which is essential to the achievement of our objectives. This is, among other factors, a function of penetration survivability and lies at the heart of the urgency to include a greater missile capability in the composite strike force. Such a combined force is as logical and as inevitable as the careful balancing of specialists in a professional football team.

The less obvious aspect, but perhaps the more urgent, is the timeliness of the delivery. This is not by any means a matter of dragging the old skeleton of preventive war out of the closet. At the very least it must be the recognized capability to strike at unacceptable cost to the enemy, regardless of what he does. In this recognition lies a continuing deterrent capability.

The conquest of space has more than an academic bearing on this requirement for timeliness. Today the Kremlin planner enjoys two very significant and potentially decisive advantages: surprise and initiative. In the time period of hypersonic speed when countdown time is longer than flight time to target the advantages of initiative to an aggressor are less than those of surprise. If surprise can be denied, the gamble on an initiative can become unacceptably risky. To the nonaggressor, on the other hand, who by definition does not intend to exploit surprise, a proper positioning with regard to space capabilities offers both intelligence of enemy intentions, thereby denying him the certainty of surprise, and a proximity for counter action that establishes an ever-present initiative potential from which to "wage the peace."

Thus with the conquest of space beyond current territorial limitations, military air power gains opportunities vastly greater than those afforded by air-breathing vehicles limited to the coastal complications of sovereign space. Since these opportunities will require infinitely sound judgment, the capabilities of man must be available in their exploitation.

The consequences of failure to meet the challenge are so catastrophic and the promise of achievement is so great that we must ensure that the functional evolution from concept to doctrine to strategy to achievement of objectives is revitalized and thereafter maintained at the highest order of leadership, dedication, intellectual brilliance, and imaginative courage that the nation can develop. This will be best achieved through fixed and undivided responsibility on those best qualified by experience to meet the challenge. It must be so in peace, as the catastrophe of an H-hour will afford no time for reorganization and reconsideration.

Success lies beyond the scope of the individual but must be the end result of contribution by all airmen to an ultimate body of sound conviction on which to progress.

Air Command and Staff College

Reference Notes

CHAPTER 2

1. Armstrong, H., Haber, H., and Strughold, H.: Aeromedical problems of space travel. *Journal of Aviation Medicine,* 20:383-417, 1949.
2. Armstrong, H. G.: Space medicine in the United States Air Force. (See 28, Chapter I thereof.)
3. Armstrong, H. G.: The medical aspects of the National Geographic Society—U.S. Army Air Corps Stratosphere Expedition of Nov. 11, 1935. *Journal of Aviation Medicine,* 7:55-62, 1936.
4. Ballinger, E. R.: Human experiments in subgravity and prolonged acceleration. *Journal of Aviation Medicine,* 23:319, 1952.
5. Bancroft, R. W., Coulson, C. K., Resendez, A. R., and Burkhardt, W. L.: Effects of explosive decompression on dogs during pressure breathing. School of Aviation Medicine, USAF, Project Report No. 21-02-075, Report No. 1, July 1949.
6. Benson, O. O., Jr.: The medical problems of flying. *XIII Congrès International de Médecine et de Pharmacie Militaires,* Paris, 1:227, 1951.
7. Beyer, D. H., and Sells, S. B.: Selection and training of personnel for space flight. *Journal of Aviation Medicine,* 28:1-6, 1957.
8. Buettner, K.: Bioclimatology of manned rocket flight. (See 28, Chapter VI thereof.)
9. Buettner, K., and Haber, H.: The aeropause. *Science,* 115:656-57, 1952.
10. Campbell, P. A.: Orientation in space. (See 28, Chapter V thereof.)
11. Clamann, H. G.: Continuous recording of oxygen, carbon dioxide and other gases in sealed cabins. *Journal of Aviation Medicine,* 23:330-33, 1952.
12. Fenno, R. M.: Man's milieu in space. *Journal of Aviation Medicine,* 25:612-22, 1954.
13. Gauer, O. H., and Haber, H.: Man under gravity free conditions. *German Aviation Medicine of World War II,* 1:641-44. School of Aviation Medicine, USAF, 1950.
14. Gaume, J. G.: Plants as a means of balancing a closed ecological system. *Journal of Astronautics,* 4:72-75, 1957.
15. Gerathewohl, S. J.: Personal experiences during short periods of weightlessness reported by sixteen subjects. *Astronautica Acta,* 2:203-17, 1956.
16. Gerathewohl, S. J., and Stallings, H. D.: The labyrinthine posture reflex (righting reflex) in the cat during weightlessness. *Journal of Aviation Medicine,* 28:345-55, 1957.

259

17. Haber, F., and Haber, H.: Possible methods of producing the gravity-free state for medical research. *Journal of Aviation Medicine,* 21:395-400, 1950.
18. Haber, F.: Bailout at very high altitudes. *Journal of Aviation Medicine,* 23:322-29, 1952.
19. Haber, H., and Gerathewohl, S. J.: Physics and psychophysics of weightlessness. *Journal of Aviation Medicine,* 22:180-89, 1951.
20. Haber, H.: *Man in Space.* Bobbs-Merrill Co., Inc., New York, 1953.
21. Haber, H.: *The Physical Environment of the Flyer.* School of Aviation Medicine, USAF, 1954.
22. Hanrahan, J. S.: The beginnings of research in space biology at the Air Force Missile Development Center, Holloman Air Force Base, New Mexico, 1946-1952. Air Force Missile Development Center, Historical Division Report, 1958.
23. Hanrahan, J. S.: History of research in subgravity and zero-g at the Air Force Missile Development Center, Holloman Air Force Base, New Mexico, 1948-1958. Air Force Missile Development Center, Historical Division Report, 1958.
24. Henry, J. P., Ballinger, E. R., Maher, P. J., Jr., and Simons, D. G.: Animal studies of the subgravity state during rocket flight. *Journal of Aviation Medicine,* 23:421-32, 1952.
25. Kooistra, J. A., Jr., Mitchell, R. B., and Strughold, H.: Problems common to the fields of astronomy and biology: a symposium. IV. The behavior of microorganisms under simulated Martian environmental conditions. *Astronomical Society of the Pacific,* 70:64-69, 1958.
26. Luft, U. C.: Physiological limitations in cabin environment and human adaptations. (See 53, Chapter XXI, pp. 567-74 thereof.)
27. Luft, U. C., Clamann, H. G., and Opitz, E.: The latency of hypoxia on exposure to altitude above 50,000 feet. *Journal of Aviation Medicine,* 22:117, 1951.
28. Marbarger, J. P. (ed.): *Space Medicine: The Human Factor in Flights Beyond the Earth.* University of Illinois Press, Urbana, Illinois, 1951.
29. Myers, J.: Basic remarks on the use of plants as biological gas exchangers in a closed system. *Journal of Aviation Medicine,* 25:407-11, 1954.
30. Ogle, D. C.: Address at Symposium of Southern Research Institute, 16 May 1957. *Medical Services Digest,* 8:2-8, September 1957.
31. Poppen, J. R.: Five years of space medicine. *Journal of Aviation Medicine,* 25:366-67, 1954.
32. Preston-Thomas, H., Edelberg, R., Henry, J. P., Miller, J., Salzman, E. W., and Zuidema, G. D.: Human tolerance to multistage rocket acceleration curves. *Journal of Aviation Medicine,* 26:390-98, 1955.
33. Schaefer, H. J.: Evaluation of present day knowledge of cosmic radiation at extreme altitude in terms of the hazard to health. *Journal of Aviation Medicine,* 21:375, 1950.
34. Simons, D. G.: Use of V-2 rocket to convey primate to upper atmosphere. Air Force Technical Report 5821, Wright-Patterson Air Force Base, May 1949.
35. Simons, D. G.: Methods and results of one year of balloon flights with biological specimens. *Journal of Aviation Medicine,* 25:380-87, 1954.
36. Simons, D. G.: Review of biological effects of subgravity and weightlessness. *Jet Propulsion,* 25:209-11, 1955.

37. Simons, D. G., and Parks, D. P.: Climatization of animal capsules during upper stratosphere balloon flights. *Jet Propulsion,* 26:565-68, 1956.
38. Simons, D. G., and Steinmetz, C. H.: The 1954 Aeromedical Field Laboratory balloon flights: physiological and radiobiological aspects. *Journal of Aviation Medicine,* 27:100-110, 1956.
39. Simons, D. G.: Problems common to the fields of astronomy and biology: a symposium. V. Manned balloon capabilities for astronomical observations. *Astronomical Society of the Pacific,* 70:69-74, 1958.
40. Stapp, J. P.: Human exposures to linear deceleration: I. Preliminary survey of aft-facing seated position. Air Force Technical Report No. 5915, Wright-Patterson Air Force Base, June 1949.
41. Stapp, J. P.: Human tolerance to deceleration: summary of 166 runs. *Journal of Aviation Medicine,* 22:42, 1951.
42. Strughold, H., Haber, H., Buettner, K., and Haber, F.: Where does space begin?: functional concept at the boundaries between atmosphere and space. *Journal of Aviation Medicine,* 22:342, 1951.
43. Strughold, H.: Life on Mars in view of physiological principles. Special Report, School of Aviation Medicine, USAF, March 1951.
44. Strughold, H.: From aviation medicine to space medicine. *Journal of Aviation Medicine,* 23:315, 1952.
45. Strughold, H.: *The Green and Red Planet: a Physiological Study of the Possibility of Life on Mars.* University of New Mexico Press, Albuquerque, New Mexico, 1953.
46. Strughold, H.: Atmospheric space equivalence. *Journal of Aviation Medicine,* 25:420-24, 1954.
47. Strughold, H.: The ecosphere of the sun. *Journal of Aviation Medicine,* 26:323-28, 1955.
48. Strughold, H.: The U.S. Air Force experimental sealed cabin. *Journal of Aviation Medicine,* 27:50-52, 1956.
49. Strughold, H.: Medical problems in orbital space flight. *Jet Propulsion,* 26:745, 1956.
50. Strughold, H.: Problems common to the fields of astronomy and biology: a symposium. I. General review of problems common to the fields of astronomy and biology. *Astronomical Society of the Pacific,* 70:43-50, 1958.
51. Sweeney, H. M.: Explosive decompression. *Air Surgeon's Bulletin,* 1:1-4, October 1944.
52. Ward, J. E.: The true nature of the boiling of body fluids in space. *Journal of Aviation Medicine,* 27:429-39, 1956.
53. White, C. S., and Benson, O. O., Jr.: *Physics and Medicine of the Upper Atmosphere: A Study of the Aeropause.* University of New Mexico Press, Albuquerque, New Mexico, 1952.
54. Wilson, A. G.: Problems common to the fields of astronomy and biology: a symposium. Introduction. *Astronomical Society of the Pacific,* 70:41-43, 1958.
55. Wood, E. H., Lambert, H. H., Baldes, E. J., and Code, C. F.: Effects of acceleration in relation to aviation. *Federation Proceedings,* 5:327-44, 1946.

CHAPTER 3

1. Armstrong, H., Haber, H., and Strughold, H.: Aero medical problems of space travel. *Journal of Aviation Medicine,* 20:383-417, 1949.
2. Buettner, K., and Haber, H.: The aeropause. *Science,* 115:656-57, 1952.
3. Fenno, R. M.: Man's milieu in space. *Journal of Aviation Medicine,* 25:612-22, 1954.
4. Haber, H.: *The Physical Environment of the Flyer.* School of Aviation Medicine, USAF, 1954.
5. Schaefer, H. J.: Exposure hazards from cosmic radiation beyond the stratosphere and in free space. *Journal of Aviation Medicine,* 23:334, 1952.
6. Simons, D. G., and Steinmetz, C. H.: The 1954 Aeromedical Field Laboratory balloon flights: Physiological and radiobiological aspects. *Journal of Aviation Medicine,* 27:100-110, 1956.
7. Strughold, H.: Space equivalent conditions within the earth's atmosphere: Physiological aspects. *Astronautica Acta,* 1:32-40, 1955.
8. Watson, F. G.: *Between the Plants.* Harvard University Press, Cambridge, Massachusetts, 1956.
9. Whipple, F. L.: Meteoritic phenomena and meteorites. (See 10, Chapter X thereof.)
10. White, C. S., and Benson, O. O., Jr.: *Physics and Medicine of the Upper Atmosphere: A Study of the Aeropause.* University of New Mexico Press, Albuquerque, 1952.

CHAPTER 4

1. Ballinger, E. R.: Human experiments in subgravity and prolonged acceleration. *Journal of Aviation Medicine,* 23:319, 1952.
2. Bierman, H. R., and Larsen, V. R.: Reactions of the human to impact forces revealed by high speed motion picture technique. *Journal of Aviation Medicine,* 17:407-12, 1946.
3. De Haven, H.: Mechanical analysis of survival in falls from heights of fifty to one hundred and fifty feet. *War Medicine: A Symposium* (ed. W. S. Pugh), 2:586. Philosophical Library, New York, 1942.
4. Edelberg, R., Henry, J. P., Maciolek, J. A., Salzman, E. W., and Zuidema, G. D.: Comparison of human tolerance to accelerations of slow and rapid onset. *Journal of Aviation Medicine,* 27:482-89, 1956.
5. Gauer, O. H., and Haber, H.: Man under gravity free conditions. *German Aviation Medicine of World War II,* 1:641-44. School of Aviation Medicine, USAF, 1950.
6. Henry, J. P., Ballinger, E. R., Maher, P. J., Jr., and Simons, D. G.: Animal studies of the subgravity state during rocket flight. *Journal of Aviation Medicine,* 23:421-32, 1952.
7. Henry, J. P.: Physiological laboratories in rockets. *Journal of Astronautics,* 2:22-26, 1955.
8. Preston-Thomas, H., Edelberg, R., Henry, J. P., Miller, J., Salzman, E. W., and Zuidema, G. D.: Human tolerance to multistage rocket acceleration curves. *Journal of Aviation Medicine,* 26:390-98, 1955.
9. Rothwell, W. S., and Sperry, E. G.: Escape from aircraft by downward ejection. *Journal of Aviation Medicine,* 24:322-27, 1953.
10. Seifert, H. S., Mills, M. M., and Summerfield, M.: The physics of rockets. *American Journal of Physics,* 15:1-21, 1947.

11. Stapp, J. P.: Crash protection in air transports. *Aeronautical Engineering Review,* 12:71-78, April 1953.
12. Stapp, J. P.: Effects of mechanical force on living tissues: I. Abrupt deceleration and windblast. *Journal of Aviation Medicine,* 26:268-88, 1955.
13. Stapp, J. P., and Hughes, C. D.: Effects of mechanical force on living tissues: II. Supersonic deceleration and windblast. *Journal of Aviation Medicine,* 27:407-13, 1956.
14. Stapp, J. P.: Human tolerance to deceleration. *American Journal of Surgery,* 93:734-40, 1957.
15. Stapp, J. P., and Blount, W. C.: Effects of mechanical force on living tissue: III. A compressed air catapult for high impact forces. *Journal of Aviation Medicine,* 28:281-90, 1957.
16. Stapp, J. P., and Lewis, S. T.: Human tolerance to aircraft seat belt restraint. *Journal of Aviation Medicine,* 29:187-96, 1958.
17. Webster, A. P.: High altitude–high velocity flying with reference to the human factors: IV. Opening shock of parachute descents. *Journal of Aviation Medicine,* 24:189, 1953.

CHAPTER 8

1. Campbell, B.: Research on the biological effects of the heavy particle cosmic rays. Holloman Air Development Center, Technical Report TR-55-8, December 1955.
2. Chase, H. B., Bliss, J. D. M., Straile, W. E., and Post, J. S.: Effects on the skin by cosmic ray heavy particles. Holloman Air Development Center, Technical Report TR-55-2, May 1955.
3. Chase, H. B.: Cutaneous effects of primary cosmic radiation. *Journal of Aviation Medicine,* 25:388, 1954.
4. Chase, H. B., and Post, J. S.: Damage and repair in mammalian tissues exposed to cosmic ray heavy nuclei. *Journal of Aviation Medicine,* 27: 533-40, 1956.
5. Chase, H. B.: Personal communication.
6. Eugster, J. A. G.: Effects on living tissues by primary cosmic ray particles. Report to European Office, Air Research and Development Command, February 1956.
7. Harlow, H. F., Schrier, A. M., and Simons, D. G.: Exposure of primates to cosmic radiation above 90,000 feet. *Journal of Comparative and Physiological Psychology,* 49:195-200, 1956.
8. Meyer, P., Parker, E. N., and Simpson, J. A.: Solar cosmic rays of February 1956 and their propagation through interplanetary space. *Physical Review,* 104:768-83, 1956.
9. Schaefer, H. J.: Exposure hazards from cosmic radiation beyond the stratosphere and in free space. *Journal of Aviation Medicine,* 23:334, 1952.
10. Schaefer, H. J.: Graphs and tables for the hit frequencies from heavy nuclei of the primary cosmic radiation: I. Hit frequencies for small specimens (drosophila, plant seeds, etc.). U.S. Naval School of Aviation Medicine, Project Report No. NM 001 059.13.08, June 1954.
11. Simons, D. G., and Steinmetz, G. H.: The 1954 Aeromedical Field Laboratory balloon flights: physiological and radiobiological aspects. *Journal of Aviation Medicine,* 27:100-110, 1956.

12. Simons, D. G., and Parks, D. P.: Climatization of animal capsules during upper stratosphere balloon flights. Presented at American Rocket Society, November 1955.

13. Simons, D. G.: Surface temperatures of animal capsules floating above 80,000 feet. Holloman Air Development Center, Technical Report TR-56-6, May 1956.

14. Simons, D. G., and Archibald, E. R.: Selection of a sealed cabin atmosphere. *Journal of Aviation Medicine,* 29:350-57, 1958.

15. Stone, W. S., University of Texas: Personal communication.

16. Tobias, C. A.: Radiation hazards in high altitude aviation. *Journal of Aviation Medicine,* 23:345-72, 1952.

17. Winzen, O. C., and Parks, D. P.: Operation Manhigh II. Presented at American Rocket Society, December 1957.

18. Yagoda, H.: Frequency of thindown hits by heavy primary nuclei in emulsion and tissue. *Journal of Aviation Medicine,* 27:522-32, 1956.

CHAPTER 9

1. Beyer, D. H., and Sells, S. B.: Selection and training of personnel for space flight. *Journal of Aviation Medicine,* 28:1-6, 1957.

2. Clark, B., and Graybiel, A.: The break-off phenomenon: A feeling of separation from the earth experienced by pilots at high altitude. *Journal of Aviation Medicine,* 28:121-26, 1957.

3. Crossfield, A. S.: Space travel symposium: A test pilot's viewpoint. *Journal of Aviation Medicine,* 28:492-95, 1957.

4. Henry, J. P., Eckstrand, G. A., Hessberg, R. R., Simons, D. G., and Webb, P. P.: Human factors research and development program for a manned satellite. Aeromedical Division, Human Factors Directorate, Headquarters Air Research and Development Command, Baltimore, Maryland, October 1957.

5. Mayo, A. M.: Space travel symposium: Some survival aspects of space travel. *Journal of Aviation Medicine,* 28:498-503, 1957.

6. Ogle, D. C.: Man in a space vehicle. *U.S. Armed Forces Medical Journal,* 8:1561-70, 1957.

7. Scott, T. H.: Intellectual effects of perceptual isolation. Unpublished Ph.D. dissertation, McGill University, Montreal, Canada, August 1954.

8. Simons, D. G.: Pilot reactions during "Manhigh II" balloon flight. *Journal of Aviation Medicine,* 29:1-14, 1958.

9. Stuhlinger, E.: Outlook to space travel. *The Scientific Monthly,* 85: 281-87, 1957.

10. Trites, D. K., and Kubala, A. L., Jr.: Characteristics of successful pilots. *Journal of Aviation Medicine,* 28:34-40, 1957.

11. Tupes, E. C.: Psychometric characteristics of officer effectiveness reports of OCS graduates. Air Force Personnel and Training Research Center, USAF, Lackland AFB, Texas, AFPTRC-TN-57-20 (ASTIA Document No. 098923), February 1957.

CHAPTER 12

1. Campbell, P. A.: Introduction to the problems of escape and rescue during space operations. To be published in Benson and Strughold (ed.): *Medicine and Physics of the Upper Atmosphere and Space,* John Wiley and Sons, New York, 1959.

2. Stanley, R. M.: Escape at launching and in the atmosphere from a space vehicle. To be published in Benson and Strughold (ed.): *op. cit.*

3. Haber, F.: Bailout at very high altitudes. *Journal of Aviation Medicine,* 23:322-29, 1952.

4. Haber, F.: Escape and survival at high altitude. School of Aviation Medicine, USAF, Project No. 21-1207-0006, September 1953.

5. Luft, U. C.: Physiological limitations in cabin environment and human adaptations, 567-74, in White, C. S., and Benson, O. O., Jr. (ed.): *Physics and Medicine of the Upper Atmosphere: A Study of the Aeropause,* University of New Mexico Press, Albuquerque, 1952.

6. Mayo, A. M.: Survival in space. The vehicle—combined requirements. To be published in Benson and Strughold (ed.): *op. cit.*

7. Petersen, N. V.: Rescue and retrieve space missions. To be published in Benson and Strughold (ed.): *op. cit.*

8. Ehricke, K. A.: Rescue from space by a secondary vehicle. To be published in Benson and Strughold (ed.): *op. cit.*

9. Stapp, J. P.: Human tolerance to deceleration: summary of 166 runs. *Journal of Aviation Medicine,* 22:42-45, 1951.

10. Preston-Thomas, H., Edelberg, R., Henry, J. P., Miller, J., Salzman, E. W., and Zuidema, G. D.: Human tolerance to multistage rocket acceleration curves. *Journal of Aviation Medicine,* 26:390-98, 1955.

11. Ballinger, E. R.: Human experiments in subgravity and prolonged acceleration. *Journal of Aviation Medicine,* 23:319-21, 1952.

12. Taylor, C. L.: Human tolerance for temperature extremes, 548-61, in White, C. S., and Benson, O. O., Jr. (ed.): *op. cit.*

A Glossary of Terms Related to the Human Factor in Space Operations

Compiled by

Dr. Richard W. Bancroft and Dr. Hans G. Clamann

Department of Physiology-Biophysics
School of Aviation Medicine, USAF

ablating materials. Special materials on the surface of a spacecraft that can be sacrificed (carried away, vaporized) during re-entry into the earth's atmosphere. Kinetic energy is dissipated and excessive heating of the main structure of the spacecraft is prevented.

aceto-carmine smears. A thin sheet of tissue cells smeared on a glass slide and stained with a red pigment to differentiate specific structures in the cells for examination under a microscope.

adenineless colonial strain of Neurospora crassa. A particular strain or culture of Neurospora that cannot synthesize adenine. It is nutritionally deficient and cannot grow unless adenine is added to the diet. See Neurospora.

aerothermodynamic border. Above an altitude of about 100 miles the atmosphere becomes so rarefied that there is no longer any significant heat-generating air friction or thermal influence on the skin or cabin of fast-moving vehicles.

afferent fiber response. The response of a nerve or nerve fiber transporting a stimulus in the form of a nerve impulse to or toward the brain (central nervous system).

agravic. The existence of no gravity. Theoretically, absolute agravic conditions in the true sense of the word do not exist in the universe. See zerogravity, weightlessness.

alkaline metal hydroxides. Chemical compounds characterized by being "OH compounds" of the "alkaline metals," which have the ability to absorb carbon dioxide from the air. These include potassium hydroxide,

KOH; barium hydroxide, $Ba(OH)_2$; sodium hydroxide or caustic soda, NaOH; calcium hydroxide, $Ca(OH)_2$; lithium hydroxide, LiOH; etc.

alveolar air. The respiratory air in the alveoli (air sacs) deep within the lungs. This air is composed of oxygen, nitrogen, carbon dioxide, and water vapor.

alveoli. The terminal air sacs deep within the lungs. The inhaled oxygen diffuses across the thin alveolar membranes (the walls of the air sacs) into the blood stream, and at the same time carbon dioxide diffuses from the blood into the alveoli and is exhaled through the lungs.

anacoustic zone. The zone of silence in space; the region above 100 miles altitude where the distance between the rarefied air molecules is greater than the wave length of sound, and sound waves can no longer be propagated.

analeptic drugs. Drugs that have a strengthening, invigorating effect by acting as a stimulant on the central nervous system. Restorative remedies.

angstrom. A special unit of measurement for specifying the wave lengths of light without the use of inconveniently small numbers. One angstrom is 10^{-8} centimeter (0.00000001 cm).

Anhydrone. A commercial trade name for the chemical compound magnesium perchlorate, $Mg(ClOH)_2$, used for water absorption. It has good efficiency but is explosive.

anoxia. A complete lack of oxygen available to the tissues within the body. This condition occurs at altitudes above 50,000 feet, for physiological reasons, even though there is still considerable oxygen in the atmospheric air.

asteroid. One of over 1500 minor planets which revolve around the sun mostly between the orbits of Mars and Jupiter. All are very small compared with the major planets. Ceres, the largest, is 480 miles in diameter; the majority are less than 50 miles; and some are about one mile in diameter.

baralyme. A commercial trade name for a type of carbon dioxide absorber, a mixture of calcium hydroxide and barium hydroxide.

"barber-chair." An adjustable type of seat that can quickly position the occupant from an upright seated position to a supine or semisupine position to increase his tolerance to high accelerations.

barium oxide (BaO). A chemical compound used for the absorption of water vapor.

bed height. The thickness of a layer of absorbing material or chemicals in the container in which the absorption process occurs.

bends. The formation of nitrogen bubbles, together with other biological gases, in body tissues and fluids, caused by exposure to reduced barometric pressure. It causes pain and discomfort in the arms, legs, and joints. The incidence of bends at high altitudes can be greatly reduced by denitrogenation (breathing pure oxygen) at ground level before ascent. See decompression sickness, dysbarism.

Bev (or BEV). One billion electron volts.

biatomic oxygen (O_2). The normal oxygen molecule, consisting of two oxygen atoms, which exists in the lower layers of the atmosphere. It constitutes 20.9 per cent by volume of the atmospheric air and is the essential agent in respiration.

biosatellite. An artificial satellite capable of orbiting through space, such as around the earth, which is specifically designed to contain and support man, animals, or other living material in a reasonably normal manner for an adequate period of time and which, particularly for man and animals, possesses the proper means for safe return to the earth. See **ecological system.**

breakaway phenomenon. See **breakoff phenomenon.**

breakoff phenomenon. The occurrence during high-altitude flight of the feeling of being totally separated and detached from the earth and human society. Also called the "breakaway phenomenon."

calcium oxide (CaO). A chemical compound commonly termed "quick lime" used for the absorption of water, but of poor efficiency.

capillarization. The degree to which the body tissues are supplied with the tiny, microscopic blood vessels (capillaries) that are vital for the exchange of biological gases, nutrients, and metabolites between the blood and tissue cells.

capsule. A small, sealed, pressurized cabin with an acceptable environment, usually for containing a man or animal for extremely high-altitude flights, orbital space flight, or emergency escape.

carbohydrates. A group of complex biochemical compounds, such as the sugars and starches produced by plants, that constitute a major class of food material for both plants and animals. Carbohydrates are basically composed of carbon, hydrogen, and oxygen in the ratio of $1 : 2 : 1$.

carcinogenesis. The origination or production of cancer.

cardiovascular reactivity. The response and function of the heart and blood vessels to various types of stress, such as exercise, acceleration, heat, and cold.

centrifuge. A large motor-driven apparatus with a long rotating arm at the end of which human and animal subjects or equipment can be revolved at various speeds to simulate very closely the prolonged accelerations encountered in high-performance aircraft, rockets, and manned missiles.

charge spectrum. The range and magnitude of electric charges with reference to cosmic particles at a certain altitude.

chlorate candles. Usually, a mixture of solid chemical compounds which, when ignited, liberates free oxygen into the air.

Chlorella algae. A species of algae. A microscopic, one-celled green plant found in fresh-water ponds. Because these plants contain the green pigment chlorophyl, they absorb carbon dioxide from the air and give off oxygen in the presence of light and thus can be used as biological gas exchangers.

chromosomal aberrations. Deviations or changes in the chromosomes, the small bodies in the reproductive portion of the cell which carry the inheritable characteristics.

closed respiratory gas system. A completely self-contained system within a sealed cabin, capsule, or spacecraft that will provide adequate oxygen for breathing, maintain adequate cabin pressure, and absorb the exhaled carbon dioxide and water vapor.

cold-pressor test. A test for measuring the response of heart and blood pressure to the stress of plunging an extremity (foot or hand) into ice water. Normal response is an increase in both heart rate and blood pressure.

corpuscular cosmic rays. Primary cosmic rays from outer space which consist of particles, mainly atomic nuclei (protons) of hydrogen and helium, positively charged and possessing extremely high kinetic energies. About

1 per cent of the primary cosmic rays consists of atomic nuclei of elements heavier than hydrogen or helium. See heavy cosmic ray primaries.

corpuscular radiations. See corpuscular cosmic rays.

cortical activity. The functioning of the areas for consciousness and awareness in the brain in response to sensory excitation.

cortical background activity. Activity involving the cortex of the brain, induced by the normally incessant sensory input during wakefulness.

cortical rest. A somnolent state of the cortex of the brain (the areas of consciousness and awareness) resulting from diminution or absence of sensory input.

cosmic ray primaries. See corpuscular cosmic rays.

cosmic ray secondaries. See secondary cosmic radiation.

crystalline lens. The biconvex, lens-shaped structure behind the pupil of the eye which serves to refract the rays of light entering the pupil and to focus them on the inner, nervous portion of the eyeball (the retina). Changes in convexity of the crystalline lens permit accommodation of vision for different distances.

cutting score. A critical test score or level of achievement used to divide a group of subjects into subgroups having specified predicted characteristics, such as the likelihood of success in a given situation.

d-amphetamine. A drug which stimulates the central nervous system and has been used successfully to sustain human proficiency. Known commercially as Dexedrine.

decompression sickness. A disorder experienced by deep-sea divers and aviators caused by reduced barometric pressure and evolved gas bubbles in the body, marked by pain in the extremities (shoulders, arms, legs), pain in the chest (chokes), occasionally leading to severe central nervous symptoms and neurocirculatory collapse. See bends, dysbarism.

denitrogenation. The removal of nitrogen dissolved in the blood and body tissues. In aviation, usually the breathing of pure oxygen for an extended period of time in order to prevent decompression sickness (aero-embolism) at high altitudes.

detachment. A particular state of isolation in which man is separated or detached from his accustomed behavioral environment by inordinate physical and psychological distances. This condition may compromise his performance.

diffusion process. The exchange of molecules in gas mixtures or solutions across a border line between two or more different concentrations, with reference to the difference in concentrations, the area for exchange, and time.

distorted angle fabrics. Material of a special, often basketlike weave suitable for pressure suits. Such fabrics permit a certain amount of flexibility when the suit is pressurized.

drag chutes. Various types of parachutes attached to high-performance aircraft. The parachute can be deployed, usually during landings, to decrease speed and also, under certain flight conditions, to control and stabilize the aircraft.

drogue recovery. Refers to a type of recovery system for space vehicles or space capsules after initial re-entry into the atmosphere by the deployment of one or more small parachutes to diminish speed, to reduce aerodynamic heating, and to stabilize the vehicle so that larger recovery parachutes can be safely deployed at lower altitudes without too great an opening shock.

dynamic closed-loop simulation runs. Experimental or training tests on the "man-machine" relationships, where man acts and reacts as an integral link in the control and reactions of the machine under the anticipated conditions that are to be encountered during actual operational situations.

dynamic pressure. Any pressure generated by the relative movement of a body or solid object against a fluid or gas, such as the windblast produced by movement through air. This dynamic pressure is commonly referred to as the "q."

dysbarism. A general term which includes a complex group of a wide variety of symptoms within the body caused by changes in ambient barometric pressure, exclusive of hypoxia. Characteristic symptoms caused by **decreased** barometric pressure (other than hypoxia) are the bends and abdominal gas pains at altitudes above 25,000 to 30,000 feet. **Increased** barometric pressure, as in descent from high altitude, is characterized by painful distention of the ear drums. See **bends, decompression sickness.**

dyspnea. Difficult or labored breathing.

ebullism. The formation of bubbles, with particular reference to water vapor bubbles and the boiling effect in biological fluids caused by reduced barometric pressure.

ecological system. An inhabitable environment, either created artificially, such as in a manned space vehicle, or occurring naturally, such as the atmospheric conditions on the surface of the earth, in which man, animals, or other organisms can live in mutual relationship with one another and their environment. Ideally the environment furnishes the sustenance for life, and the resulting waste products revert or cycle back into the environment to be used again for the continuous support of life.

 closed ecological system. A closed inhabitable environment, such as must be created and maintained within a manned space vehicle, that is designed to support life and which is completely independent of the outside conditions.

egocentric threshold of weightlessness. By extreme concentration of one's attention upon oneself, the subjective differentiation between weight and weightlessness.

EKG (ECG). Abbreviation for electrocardiogram, a graphic record of the heart's action traced by an electrocardiograph.

electro-encephalographic examination. The graphic recording of the electrical currents continuously produced by the brain. Traced as brain waves by an electro-encephalograph, the currents form patterns by which the normal or abnormal condition of the brain can be evaluated.

electrolyte. Any chemical substance that, when ionized in solution, conducts electricity. The proper proportion and balance between certain electrolytes (sodium, potassium, chloride, etc.) in body fluids and tissues are vital for normal body function.

electrophysiological studies. Measurement of the electric current and voltage that are produced by living tissue such as the heart (electrocardiogram) and brain (electro-encephalogram), to evaluate physiologic condition.

emissivity. The relative power (of a surface or a material composing a surface) to emit heat by radiation.

eosinophils. A type of white blood cell or leukocyte which stains a red color with eosin stain. Normally about 2 to 3 per cent of white blood cells but tending to decrease in the blood during stressful situations and thus usable as an index for stress.

epicotyl. The part of the stem just above the seed-leaves in seedlings.

ergometer. An instrument for measuring muscular work.

escape velocity. The speed a body must attain to overcome the attraction of a gravitational field, such as that of the earth, and thus theoretically travel on to infinity. The velocity of escape at the earth's surface is 36,700 feet per second or approximately 7 miles per second (25,000 miles per hour). For practical reasons a manned spacecraft would travel out through the earth's atmosphere at a lower velocity and then accelerate to escape velocity beyond in order to avoid unacceptably rapid initial acceleration and high skin temperatures from aerodynamic heating.

etiology. The doctrine of causes, particularly the causes and reasons for diseases.

extraneous sensory events. General, normal activity around a person, producing a more or less steady flow of "background" impressions such as noise (talking, street noise, etc.) and movement.

false-positive rate. The proportion of personnel denied selection for training because their expected performance was incorrectly predicted to be unsatisfactory.

fixation—block-confusion phenomenon. A three-phase, sequential occurrence in which the operator suddenly realizes that he is monitoring only one particular indicator. He then freezes or blocks and is powerless to act. This is followed by momentary confusion which can be so extreme that the operator does not know which control is associated with which indicator. With the termination of block and confusion (one or more seconds) the operator resumes his instrument scanning and attains his immediately previous level of proficiency.

freeze-out method. A method for controlling humidity by passing the moist cabin air over a cold surface, condensing and freezing out water vapor and possibly carbon dioxide.

frustration threshold. The point at which an individual feels or shows frustration over inability to achieve an objective.

functional reserves. The ability of the body to accomplish additional muscular activity and useful work beyond the normal level of activity of an individual.

g force. Force (inertial force) produced by accelerations or by gravity, expressed in gravitational units. One g is equal to the pull of gravity on the earth's surface (32.2 ft/sec^2) and thus refers to one's normal resting weight. See negative g, positive g.

glycogen. A starch-like, complex type of carbohydrate, formed from simple sugar (glucose) in the liver of man and animals. Glycogen is the principal form in which carbohydrate is stored in the body, mainly in the liver and muscles. Commonly called "animal starch." See carbohydrates.

gram calorie. A unit of heat, the amount required to raise the temperature of one gram of water (1 cc) one degree centigrade. Also known as "small calorie" or "standard calorie."

granuloma. A circumscribed collection of skin cells, resembling granulation tissue, surrounding a central point of irritation. A tumor or neoplasm made up of granulation tissue.

gravireceptors. Highly specialized nerve endings and receptor organs located in skeletal muscles, tendons, joints, and in the inner ear. Gravireceptors furnish information to the brain with respect to body position, equilibrium, the direction of gravitational forces, and the sensation of "up" and "down."

gravisphere. The spherical extent in which the force of a given celestial body's gravity is predominant in relation to that of other celestial bodies.

hardware. Specialized pieces of metal equipment or component parts engineered into a workable system, such as various items required in protective and pressurizing equipment necessary for survival or escape in space.

Harvard-type test. An exercise test for physical fitness and the efficiency of the heart. The subject steps up onto a platform 20 inches high and down again repeatedly until exhausted, usually within less than 5 minutes. The pulse rate is recorded before the test and at intervals afterwards, and a physical fitness index is calculated.

heat sink. A method or arrangement for heat absorption or transfer from one area (such as living space in a sealed cabin) to a more remote region of the vehicle.

heavy cosmic ray primaries. The positively charged nuclei of elements heavier than hydrogen and helium up to atomic nuclei of iron. These heavy atomic nuclei comprise about 1 per cent of the total cosmic ray particles and less than 4 per cent of the total positive charges.

hemodynamics. A branch of physiology concerned with the movement of blood through the heart and blood vessels, particularly with the pressure, volume, flow, and resistance relationships within the cardiovascular system.

Hg. Chemical symbol for the element mercury.

high-current-density systems. The process of electrolysis using electrodes of relatively small area with a direct electric current of high amperage.

histochemical. Chemical reactions within cells and tissues.

hydrostatic effects. The pressures exerted by a column of liquid (water, blood, etc.) under normal gravitational conditions on the surface of the earth or in a gravitational field during an acceleration. In zerogravity a column of liquid is weightless and these pressures cease to exist.

17-hydroxycorticosteroids. One of a complex group of vital hormones produced in the adrenal gland and profoundly influencing protein and carbohydrate metabolism in the body.

hypersonic. Mach 5 or greater. High-speed velocities five or more times the speed of sound. See **speed of sound.**

hyperventilation. Overbreathing. A respiratory-minute volume, or pulmonary ventilation, greater than normal. Hyperventilation often results in an abnormal loss of carbon dioxide from the lungs and blood, which may lead to dizziness, confusion, and muscular cramps.

hypoacoustic zone. The region in the upper atmosphere between 60 and 100 miles where the distance between the rarefied air molecules roughly equals the wave length of sound, so that sound is transmitted with less volume than at lower levels. Above this zone, sound waves cannot be propagated See **anacoustic zone.**

hypobaric. Low barometric pressure, particularly the low atmospheric pressure of high altitudes.

hypocapnia. Deficiency of carbon dioxide in the blood and body tissues which may result in dizziness, confusion, and muscular cramps.

hypocotyl. The part of the stem below the seed-leaves in seedlings.

hypoventilation. Underbreathing. A respiratory-minute volume, or pulmonary ventilation, that is less than normal.

hypoxia. Oxygen deficiency within the body. It may be brought on by scarcity of oxygen in the surrounding air or by inability of bodily tissues to absorb oxygen.

IF-8 ration. A type of in-flight box lunch or meal.

inert gases. All stable gases not participating in body metabolism and not reacting chemically at room temperatures (nitrogen) or at any temperature (e.g., helium and argon).

inertial orbit. The type of orbit described by all celestial bodies, according to Kepler's laws of celestial motion. This applies to all satellites and spacecraft providing they are not under any type of propulsive power, their driving force being imparted by the momentum at the instant propulsive power ceases. See Keplerian trajectory.

intrapleural space. The potential "space" between lungs and chest wall.

ionizing radiations. Any electromagnetic radiation of short wave length, such as X rays and ultraviolet radiation, causing ionization of gases and other substances. Neutral atoms and molecules are positively or negatively charged by these types of radiations. See also ionizing effect of cosmic particles under *secondary cosmic radiation*.

Keplerian trajectory. Elliptical orbits described by celestial bodies (and satellites) according to Kepler's first law of celestial motion.

limb of the earth. The edge of the earth at the horizon.

lithium chloride (LiCl). A chemical compound that may be used for water absorption.

mach angle cone. At sonic or supersonic speeds, the air striking the leading edges of an aircraft can no longer flow over the aircraft surfaces but is deflected sharply in straight lines at an angle away from the aircraft, thus forming a cone.

mach number. A number expressing the ratio of the speed of a moving body through the air to the speed of sound in the air. Thus, the speed of a moving object represented by this number. See **speed of sound.**

macrometeorite. A meteorite larger than a pea. Occasionally it exists as a great chunk of planetary matter.

melanophore. A cell containing black or very dark pigment.

meson. A fundamental particle, other than a proton, found in cosmic rays, which has a mass between that of the electron and the proton and may possess a positive or negative charge.

metabolic conversion. The variety of chemical steps and changes that occur in the body in the process of utilizing food and oxygen for the liberation of energy, the maintenance of life, and the breaking down and building up of body tissues.

metabolic reserves. The energy source stored in chemical form, such as carbohydrates, that can be efficiently mobilized and utilized by the body, particularly for muscular activity and work beyond the normal level of activity of an individual.

metabolites. A variety of biochemical compounds resulting from the metabolic breakdown process of nutrients within a living organism. See also *metabolic conversion*.

meteor safe wall. Refers to the protective blanket of atmosphere through which meteors only rarely can penetrate, instead being burned up and vaporized by friction with air molecules.

microbeam. The intense track of ionization caused by a heavy primary cosmic ray as it passes through air or other material before thindown and loss of energy.

microenvironment. The environment created and maintained within a very small space, such as a pressurized capsule or space suit, and sufficient to support life in a reasonably normal manner.

micrometeorite. A small meteorite or meteoric dust particle of less than about 1 to 2 mm in diameter, in the order of a grain of sand or fine powder, or smaller.

mission profile. The flight plan or operational pattern that is to be flown by an aircraft in relation to the designed operational performance such as speed, altitude, and distance.

mole. One mole (mol) of a substance is equal to the molecular weight of the substance in grams.

Munsell color chart. A special set of standard colors precisely graded as to difference in hue, vividness of hue, and brightness and used primarily for study of color vision.

mutagenic effectiveness. The degree of ability to cause inheritable variations of a striking character.

negative g. The opposite of "positive g." In a gravitational field or during an acceleration the human body is so positioned that the force of inertia acts on it in a foot-to-head direction, i.e., the headward inertial force produced by a footward acceleration. Example: flying an outside loop in the upright seated position. Standing on one's head equals one negative g.

neural pathways. Various possible courses followed by nerve impulses within the complex network of the nervous system.

Neurospora. A genus of mold (the red bread mold) used in the study of genetics and of biochemical changes produced by X-ray and other types of radiation.

nitrogen cycle. The exchange of nitrogen between animals and plants. Plants convert urea or nitrates to protein, animals digest protein and excrete its nitrogen content as urea, which is taken up again by plants.

oculo-agravic illusion (perceptual illusion). During subgravity and zero-gravity states, luminous targets seen in the dark appear to move and to be displaced in an upward direction.

orbital velocity. The speed a "circling" body (mass) must attain at right angle to the centripetal pull of a gravitational field in order to counterbalance it by inertial force and thus stay in orbit rather than escape the field of gravity or fall toward its center. For a circular orbit at any level in a gravitational field the orbital velocity is equal to 0.707 of the escape velocity (see) for that level, applied in a direction at right angle to the radius of the orbit. The closer a satellite is to the earth, for example, the higher its orbital velocity. The orbital velocity is 18,000 miles per hour for a circular orbit at 300 miles altitude. Since orbital velocity varies inversely with the distance from the earth, a satellite in an *elliptical* orbit (see inertial orbit) is at maximum velocity at its perigee (low point) and at minimum velocity at its apogee (high point), thus tending to surge around the earth in its orbit.

organic vapor. The vapor or gas that may evaporate from organic materials, such as hydrocarbons, alcohols, and volatile oils.

oscillographs. Electronic-indicating or -recording instruments usually employing cathode rays to act on a sensitized screen in a vacuum, similar to a television picture tube.

oxidizer. A chemical that supports the burning process, especially combustion of rocket fuel, by release of oxygen not otherwise present beyond the earth's atmosphere.

papilloma. A growth on the surface of the skin, such as a wart.

perceptual motor task. A task involving a motor (muscle) skill with special reliance upon sensory discrimination.

perihelion. That point on a planet's or comet's orbit nearest the sun.

photosynthesis. The building up of chemical compounds and substances by radiant energy (light). Usually refers to the ability of green plants to utilize the energy of light, aided by chlorophyl, for building up organic matter (sugar and starch) from water and carbon dioxide and liberating oxygen.

positive g. In a gravitational field or during an acceleration, the human body is normally so positioned that the force of inertia acts on it in a head-to-foot direction, i.e., the footward inertial force produced by a headward acceleration. Example: pulling out from an airplane dive in the upright seated position, or during a turn. Standing upright on the ground equals one positive g.

potassium superoxide (KO_2). A relatively unstable chemical compound which in the presence of water liberates free oxygen, forming potassium hydroxide (KOH), which in turn absorbs exhaled carbon dioxide from the air.

pressure suit. A garment designed to provide emergency protection against exposures to extremely low barometric pressures or the vacuum of space if cabin pressure is lost.

    full-pressure suit. An air-tight garment completely enclosing an individual, including hands, feet, and head, much like a diving suit, that can be fully pressurized with compressed oxygen to a maximum pressure of at least 3 psi (150 mm Hg).

    partial-pressure suit. A nonelastic garment tailored to fit skin-tight (arms, legs, trunk) with a helmet pressurized with oxygen. When the helmet is pressurized, the suit is drawn tighter and provides mechanical counter pressure over the body's surface.

primary cosmic particles. See corpuscular cosmic rays.

primary cosmic rays. See corpuscular cosmic rays.

proprioceptive stimulation. Stimulation originating within the deeper structures of the body (muscles, tendons, joints, etc.) for sense of body position and movement and by which muscular movements can be adjusted with a great degree of accuracy and equilibrium can be maintained.

psychomotor ability. Of or pertaining to muscular action ensuing directly from a mental process, as in the coordinated manipulation of an airplane's stick, rudder bar, and throttle.

range of indifference. The extent to which departure occurs from originally or initially tolerated standards of operation (as in reading a dial). Also, as a manifestation of fatigue, an operator's tolerance of, or indifference to, errors.

reaction pistol. A small, pistol-shaped rocket gun or jet gun, manually controlled, providing a possible means for propulsion and movement through space of an individual in a space suit or space capsule.

read-out indicators. Any type of indicating instrument from which meaningful information and data can be directly obtained and used.

real-time basis. The time actually involved in human or machine performance of an activity, exclusive of preparation, warm-up, rest periods, adjustments, eating, etc. For example, the time a computer is actually receiving data from a missile or satellite would be the real-time, whereas the computer might have been turned on and ready to operate for a much longer period.

refractory-like state. A biologic condition in which the nervous and muscular systems become less responsive to stimuli.

respiratory quotient (RQ). The ratio obtained by dividing the volume of exhaled carbon dioxide by the volume of oxygen taken up by the body from inhaled air.

retinal receptors. The optical portion of the retina; the light-sensitive endings of the expanded optic nerve that receive the visual light rays.

retrorockets. Component parts of a guidance and propulsion system for the purpose of diminishing the speed of any type of space vehicle by directing a rocket thrust directly ahead of the moving vehicle.

roentgen-equivalent-physical (rep). Units measuring a purely physical effect of radiation by the number of ion pairs produced per unit volume of target material per time unit.

satelloid flight. Powered satellite flight at altitudes below mechanical borders of the atmosphere.

secondary cosmic radiation. The energetic nuclear debris and ionization caused by the impact of primary cosmic ray particles on atoms and molecules of the upper atmosphere.

silica gel. Commercial trade name for a drying agent composed of a mixture of silicic acid and silicon dioxide in a colloid form, which can absorb large amounts of water.

sodium superoxide (Na_2O_2); also sodium peroxide. A very unstable chemical compound with explosive properties upon liberation of oxygen. Virtually abandoned as a possible source of oxygen for sealed cabins.

solar constant. The amount of energy from the sun falling on an area of 1 square centimeter just above the earth's atmosphere, equal to 1.92 gram calories per minute.

solar corpuscular rays. Cosmic radiation originating from the sun. See corpuscular cosmic rays.

space capsule. A small, completely sealed and pressurized cabin that is capable of maintaining an inhabitable environment, usually for one occupant, for a reasonable period of time, often designed for use both within and outside a space vehicle and with a controllable propulsion system. See space suit.

space simulators. Various types of closed chambers or cabins that can be hermetically sealed and in which human or animal subjects can be studied at ground level with regard to artificially maintained cabin environments and complete isolation under conditions as close as possible to conditions to be found in spacecraft (except weightlessness and true cosmic radiation).

space suit. A pressurized garment, either flexible or partially flexible, designed to protect an individual from the conditions encountered in the vacuum of space. A space suit must maintain a proper pressure environment for the occupant and protect him against extreme temperatures, accelerative forces, and ionizing radiations. In addition, a space suit should possess means for communication and propulsion and, if necessary, provision for food, water, and waste disposal.

space-time dilemma. According to Einstein's theory of relativity, time slows down increasingly in systems (for example, extremely high-performance spacecraft) moving at velocities approaching the speed of light, relative to other systems in space (for example, the earth). This slowdown of time is not apparent to the inhabitants of the moving system (the spacecraft) until they return to the system in space from which they started (the earth).

spatiography. The "geography" of space.

speed and altitude envelope. Maximum performance capability and range of an aircraft in relation to altitude and speed. The performance envelope can also include and be considered in terms of other parameters such as temperature and acceleration.

speed of sound. The speed at which sound travels through any medium, such as air or water. The speed of sound through air is used as a measure of velocity of high-speed aircraft and missiles, and is commonly called "mach." Sound travels through air at different speeds depending on the temperature of the air, but is essentially independent of the air pressure except at extremely high pressures (50 atmospheres) or extremely low pressures approaching a vacuum. In air at "standard sea level" conditions, sound travels at approximately 1100 feet per second or about 750 miles per hour.

spin table. A flat, round platform on which human and animal subjects can be placed in various positions and rapidly rotated, much as on a phonograph record, in order to simulate and study the effects of prolonged tumbling at high rates. Complex types of tumbling can be simulated by mounting the spin table on the arm of a centrifuge.

stagnation temperature. The temperature of the air on the surface of high-speed aircraft, particularly on the nose and leading edges of the vehicle, where the onrushing air is brought to a complete stop and all the kinetic energy of these resting air molecules is converted to heat energy. A close approximation of stagnation temperature (T_s) in relation to the speed (mach number, M) is given by the simplified equation: $T_s = 50\ M^2$ (°C) or $90\ M^2$ (°F). Within the earth's atmosphere, the stagnation temperature is independent of air density, or in other words, altitude, and for this reason a careful distinction must always be made between the temperature and the actual amount of heat.

steradian. In spherical trigonometry, the unit solid angle. The three-dimensional angle in the shape of a cone which covers an area on the surface of a sphere equivalent to the square of the radius of the sphere.

steroid content. The complex chemical compounds originating from some of the glands and being mostly fragments of hormones, which are an index of body functions.

striated muscle tissue. Refers to skeletal muscle tissue. The muscles that can be moved or activated voluntarily, such as the skeletal muscles of the arms and legs.

subcortical systems. The more primitive portions of the brain and the nervous system which regulate the unconscious, vital functions of the body (respiration, circulation, digestion, etc.) with connections to the more discriminating areas of the cortex.

subgravity. A gravitational environment that is less than the normal gravitational influence on the earth's surface; less than 1 g.

suborbital vehicles. Space vehicles which attain velocities insufficient to go into orbit.

succumbence. The condition of sinking, yielding, or giving way without resistance.

superoxide. A relatively unstable chemical compound containing more oxygen than normally exists in the more stable forms of the more reduced compound, thus providing a possible source of additional oxygen for breathing.

supersonic. Speed greater than the speed of sound. See speed of sound.

systolic/diastolic pressure. The highest (systolic) and the lowest (diastolic) blood pressure within the heart and great blood vessels produced by each full cycle of the contraction and relaxation phases of the beating heart.

tachycardia. Very rapid action of the heart.

thindown. The expenditure of heavy primary cosmic ray energy in ionizing the substance, normally air, through which it passes.

toxic derangement. Derangement of the brain or mental processes caused directly or indirectly by a poisonous substance, as well as the possible derangement of other cells, tissues, and organs of the body such as the heart, kidneys, liver, etc.

transverse acceleration; transverse g. The inertial force produced by an acceleration acting across the body, perpendicular to the long axis of the body, as in a chest-to-back direction. For example, the mild transverse accelerations during take-offs and landings in the upright seated position, and when in a prone or supine position during a pullout or turn. See positive g, negative g.

triphenyl tetrazolium chloride (TTC). A complex organic material on which heavy primary cosmic ray hits are indicated.

two-step Masters test. An exercise test for evaluating the function of the heart muscle by recording the electrocardiogram (electrical current output of the beating heart) before and after a period of exercise, consisting of stepping up and down a platform two steps high.

Van Allen phenomena. Refers to the belts of intense cosmic radiation surrounding the earth at very high altitudes, exceeding 600 miles. First reported by Dr. James A. Van Allen, Iowa State University, from measurements obtained from the two Explorer satellites in 1958.

vaporthorax. A condition characterized by the existence of large water-vapor bubbles in the intrapleural space between the lungs and the chest wall, occurring when an unprotected person (or animal) is exposed to altitudes above 63,000 feet, where the barometric pressure is less than 47 mm Hg and water at body temperature vaporizes from the liquid state.

ventilation. Biologically the aeration of the lungs and blood by breathing. The inhalation and exhalation of air in the process of respiration.

ventilation garment. A lightweight, specially designed garment that is integrated with the pressure suit for providing adequate evaporation and heat dissipation from the surface of the body by circulating dry air through the porous material.

viable. Capable of living or sustaining independent life. The state of being alive.

weightlessness. The weight of an object is the result of a gravitational force acting on a supported mass. Any object deprived of support and freely falling in a vacuum is weightless. An orbiting satellite above the earth's atmosphere is a special case of "free fall" and is also weightless. Within the earth's atmosphere it is possible, with powered flight, to fly a parabolic curve which in part is similar to the curve for free fall, creating a weightless condition. In this case, both inertial and aerodynamic forces are utilized to counterbalance the gravitational attraction of the earth. See **zerogravity.**

whole-body radiation. The radiations emitted from the entire body after being exposed to any influence producing radioactivity, such as X rays or high-energy cosmic particles.

X-class. The designation for types of experimental aircraft, rocket vehicles, or missiles. The symbol X stands for "experimental."

X-15. The experimental rocket plane being developed under USAF contract by North American Aviation, Inc., for the purpose of probing far into the upper atmosphere and studying flight characteristics under near-space or space-equivalent conditions as well as re-entry problems.

zerogravity. The complete absence of gravitational effects, existing when the gravitational attraction of the earth (or other spatial body) is exactly nullified or counterbalanced by inertial force. For example, during the proper parabolic flight-path of high-performance aircraft, or an orbiting satellite. See **weightlessness.**

APPENDIX II

A Reading List of Books on Astronautics

Compiled by
Dr. Raymond Estep

A. THE SCENE IN SPACE

Abetti, Giorgio. *The Sun,* 2d ed. New York: The Macmillan Company, 1957.
  A textbook. Usable by those having knowledge of basic physics and mathematics.

Clason, Clyde B. *Exploring the Distant Stars: Thrilling Adventures in Our Galaxy and Beyond.* New York: G. P. Putnam's Sons, 1958.
  A readable book for the layman containing descriptions of astronomical bodies and of their orbits.

Ellison, M. A. *The Sun and Its Influence: An Introduction to the Study of Solar-Terrestrial Relations.* London: Routledge and Kegan Paul, Ltd., 1955.

A factual study understandable by those having knowledge of elementary physics.

Hoyle, Fred. *Frontiers of Astronomy.* New York: Harper and Brothers, 1955.

The author, a mathematician at Saint John's College, Cambridge University, presents a highly readable account of the universe for the layman.

Kuiper, Gerard P. (ed.). *The Atmospheres of the Earth and Planets,* rev. ed. Chicago: University of Chicago Press, 1952.

Very technical and scholarly. By the Director of the Yerkes and McDonald Observatories.

Kurth, Rudolf. *Introduction to the Mechanics of Stellar Systems.* London, New York: Pergamon Press, 1957.

Of interest to the reader who has some knowledge of differential and integral calculus and of analytical geometry.

Moore, Patrick. *The Planet Venus.* London: Faber and Faber, Ltd., 1956; New York: The Macmillan Company, 1957.

A summary of what little is known about the planet and its physical aspects. Suitable for the general reader.

Peek, Bertrand M. *The Planet Jupiter.* New York: The Macmillan Company, 1958; London: Faber and Faber, 1958.

A survey of the slowly accumulated learning about the Great Planet, enlivened by the firsthand observation of the author, based on 15 years' experience as Director of the Jupiter Section of the British Astronomical Association.

Shapley, Harlow. *Of Stars and Men: The Human Response to an Expanding Universe.* Boston: Beacon Press, 1958.

Evidence for believing life exists in other worlds.

Strughold, Hubertus. *The Green and Red Planet: A Physiological Study of the Possibility of Life on Mars.* Albuquerque: The University of New Mexico Press, 1953.

An excellent biological examination of the significance of the green areas observable seasonally on the planet Mars. Highly readable but well-supported by technical detail.

Vaucouleurs, Gérard de. *The Planet Mars,* 2d ed. London: Faber and Faber, 1951.

For the general reader.

———. *Physics of the Planet Mars: An Introduction to Aerophysics.* London: Faber and Faber, 1954; New York: The Macmillan Company, 1955.

A lucid, professional study assessing past research in the light of current knowledge.

———. *Discovery of the Universe.* New York: The Macmillan Company, 1957; London: Faber and Faber, 1957.

An excellent narrative history of the development of astronomy from its origins to 1956. Compact and readable for the layman but rich in well-chosen detail. The author is a distinguished areologist at Harvard College Observatory.

Watson, Fletcher Guard. *Between the Planets,* rev. ed. Cambridge: Harvard University Press, 1956.

Asteroids, comets, and meteors described for the general reader in terms of size, composition, and movement.

Wilkins, Hugh P., and Patrick Moore. *The Moon.* New York: The Macmillan Company, 1955; London: Faber and Faber, 1955.

 A detailed description of the physical features of the moon. Wilkins is the Director of the Lunar Section of the British Astronomical Association.

B. SPACE OPERATIONS

Adams, Carsbie C., et al. *Space Flight: Satellites, Spaceships, Space Stations, and Space Travel Explained.* New York: McGraw-Hill Book Company, 1958.

 Discusses astronautics in terms of history, allied fields, and events of significance.

Alperin, Morton, Marvin Stern, and Harold Wooster (eds.). *Vistas in Astronautics: First Annual Air Force Office of Scientific Research Astronautics Symposium.* New York: Pergamon Press, 1958.

 A collection of 42 papers on such aspects of astronautics as re-entry, tracking and communications, environment and measurements, propulsion, orbits, and human factors, read at a symposium held at San Diego in March 1957 under the joint sponsorship of the USAF's Office of Scientific Research and the Convair Division of the General Dynamics Corporation.

Armstrong, Harry G. *Principles and Practices of Aviation Medicine,* 3d ed. Baltimore: The Williams & Wilkins Company, 1952.

 A standard reference work and textbook.

Bates, David R., and Patrick Moore (eds.). *Space Research and Exploration.* London: Eyre & Spottiswoode, 1957; New York: William Sloane Associates, 1958.

 Information for the general reader on rockets, satellites, space travel, space medicine, and space biology.

Beard, R. B., and A. C. Rotherham. *Space Flight and Satellite Vehicles.* New York: Pitman Publishing Corporation, 1958.

 Interplanetary flight in terms of present and future developments. Written for the reader having a basic scientific background.

Bergaust, Erik, and William Beller. *Satellite.* Garden City, N. Y.: Hanover House, 1956; London: Lutterworth Press, 1957.

 Covers most aspects of satellite flight from scientific uses to influence on society. Designed for popular consumption.

Bibliography of Space Medicine. Public Health Service Publication No. 617; Public Health Service Bibliography Series No. 21. Washington: U.S. Department of Health, Education, and Welfare; Public Health Service; and the National Library of Medicine Reference Division, 1958.

 A list of 381 references selected from the materials in the National Library of Medicine and from publications in the fields of aviation, aviation medicine, and astronautics.

Burgess, Eric. *Rocket Propulsion, with an Introduction to the Idea of Interplanetary Flight,* 2d ed. New York: The Macmillan Company, 1954; London: Chapman & Hall, 1954.

 Seeks to bridge the gap between technical and popular literature on rocketry.

————. *Frontier to Space.* New York: The Macmillan Company, 1955; London: Chapman & Hall, 1955.

A nontechnical discussion of the employment of rockets in upper air research.

―――. *An Introduction to Rockets and Space Flight*. London: Hodder and Stoughton, 1956.

An elementary volume designed for the general reader.

―――. *Satellites and Spaceflight*. New York: The Macmillan Company, 1957.

The story of the development of earth satellites in terms of construction, instrumentation, launching, communications, orbit, and future manned flight.

Carter, L. J. (ed.). *Realities of Space Travel: Selected Papers of the British Interplanetary Society*. New York: McGraw-Hill Book Company, 1957.

A variety of articles published since 1948 which discuss the history and development of astronautics, the biological and physical aspects of space flight, satellite vehicles, testing stations, and the future of space flight.

Clarke, Arthur C. *The Exploration of Space*. London: Temple Press, 1951; New York: Harper and Brothers, 1952.

A nontechnical basic study of the problems of space flight.

―――. *Interplanetary Flight: An Introduction to Astronautics*. London: Temple Press, 1950; New York: Harper and Brothers, 1951.

This review of the major problems (astronomical as opposed to technological) of interplanetary flight will probably be of more interest to the scientist or engineer in some field of rocket propulsion.

―――. *The Making of a Moon: The Story of the Earth Satellite Program*. New York: Harper and Brothers, 1957; London: Frederick Muller, 1957.

A portion of this volume is devoted to a discussion of various aspects of the earth satellite program, and especially to the U.S. Vanguard Project.

―――― and R. A. Smith. *The Exploration of the Moon*. New York: Harper and Brothers, 1954; London: Frederick Muller, 1955.

A four-stage assault on the moon is described and illustrated in 45 full-page drawings, 8 of which are in color.

Dornberger, Walter. *V-2*. New York: The Viking Press, 1954.

A translated history of German prewar and World War II rocket developments by the director of the Peenemunde Rocket Station.

Earth Satellites as Research Vehicles. Philadelphia: Journal of the Franklin Institute, 1956.

Seven papers and discussions presented in the Franklin Institute's symposium on "Earth Satellites as Research Vehicles" held in Philadelphia on 18 April 1956.

Epitome of Space Medicine. Randolph Air Force Base, Texas: School of Aviation Medicine, USAF, 1957.

A collection of 41 studies (10 research reports from the School of Aviation Medicine and 31 articles from scientific journals) on various aspects of space medicine.

Gantz, Kenneth F. (ed.). *The United States Air Force Report on the Ballistic Missile: Its Technology, Logistics, and Strategy*. Garden City, N. Y.: Doubleday & Company, 1958.

A collection of articles originally published in the *Air University Quarterly Review*. Supplemented by an extensive glossary to the text.

Gartmann, Heinz. *The Men Behind the Space Rockets*. New York: David McKay Company, 1956.

A nontechnical history of space flight (translated from German) told in biographical sketches of such pioneers in rocketry and astronautics as Ganswindt, Tsiolkovskii, Goddard, Oberth, Valier, Sänger, Zborowski, and von Braun.

Gatland, Kenneth W. *Development of the Guided Missile,* 2d ed. New York: Philosophical Library, 1954.

A nontechnical introduction to the field of guided missiles of interest mainly to the general reader.

——— (ed.). *Project Satellite.* New York: The British Book Centre, 1958.

A generalized treatment of the subject written for the layman.

——— and Anthony M. Kunesch. *Space Travel.* New York: Philosophical Library, 1953; London: Allan Wingate, 1953.

A nontechnical discussion of the many problems of space flight as they affect man and machine.

Guided Missiles: Operations, Design, and Theory. New York: McGraw-Hill Book Company, 1958.

A commercial version of *Air Force Manual 52-31* compiled in 1955 by the faculty of the Air Training Command's school for missiles at Lowry AFB, Colorado.

Haber, Heinz. *Man in Space.* Indianapolis—New York: The Bobbs-Merrill Company, 1953.

A readable book on the medical problems of space flight based on the author's long study in the field of aviation medicine in Germany and at the School of Aviation Medicine, USAF.

Haley, Andrew G. *The Present Day Developments in Space Law and the Beginnings of Metalaw.* New York: American Rocket Society, 1956.

An exposition on new concepts in space law presented at a meeting of the American Rocket Society held in November 1956.

Hogan, J. C. *A Guide to the Study of Space Law, Including a Selective Bibliography on the Legal and Political Aspects of Space.* Santa Monica, California: The Rand Corporation, 1958.

Primarily a list of 265 specific titles of articles and studies devoted to various aspects of space law, but also including comments on periodicals, books, and projects offering some treatment of the subject.

Krieger, Firmin. *Behind the Sputniks: A Survey of Soviet Space Science.* Washington: Public Affairs Press, 1958.

Based largely on translations of Soviet scientific articles published in Rand Corporation studies of 1956 and 1957, this volume was brought up to date by the addition of early press reports on the first sputnik.

Leonard, Jonathan N. *Flight into Space: The Facts, Fancies, and Philosophy.* New York: Random House, 1953; London: Sidgwick & Jackson, 1953.

A readable account for the layman.

Ley, Willy. *Rockets, Missiles, and Space Travel,* rev. ed. New York: The Viking Press, 1958.

This fourth edition (15th printing) of the work first published in 1944 as *Rockets* is an authoritative history of rocketry. It includes sections on U.S. upper air research programs and the Vanguard Project. The third and fourth printings of this edition contain two pages of preliminary data on sputnik flight.

——— and Wernher von Braun. *The Exploration of Mars.* New York: The Viking Press, 1956; London: Sidgwick & Jackson, 1956.

In the first half of this well-written book Ley describes the physical features and the orbit of Mars; in the second half von Braun presents a plan for reaching Mars by means of chemically fueled rockets.

Marbarger, John P. (ed.). *Space Medicine: The Human Factor in Flights Beyond the Earth.* Urbana, Illinois: University of Illinois Press, 1951.

A collection of papers on the medical problems of rocket flight read at a symposium on space medicine held in Chicago by the Professional Colleges of the University of Illinois in March 1950. Among the biologists, physiologists, and rocket specialists whose papers are reproduced are Wernher von Braun, Hubertus Strughold, Heinz Haber, Konrad J. K. Buettner, and Paul A. Campbell.

Moore, Patrick. *Earth Satellite: The New Satellite Projects Explained.* London: Eyre & Spottiswoode, 1955; New York: W. W. Norton & Co., 1957.

A review of developments in the field of rocketry and of plans for the launching of earth satellite vehicles written for the nonspecialist.

Oberth, Hermann. *Man into Space: New Projects for Rocket and Space Travel.* New York: Harper and Brothers, 1957.

A preview of the vehicles and the equipment of future space flight by the Hungarian-born pioneer of German rocketry.

Pendray, G. Edward. *The Coming Age of Rocket Power,* 2d ed. New York: Harper and Brothers, 1947.

A review of the history of rocket developments by one of the founders of the American Rocket Society.

Roos, Charles. *Bibliography of Space Medicine,* preliminary ed. Washington: National Library of Medicine, 1958.

A collection of 286 entries on various aspects of space medicine.

Rosen, Milton W. *The Viking Rocket Story.* New York: Harper and Brothers, 1955.

The story of the development and firing of the first ten Viking upper air sounding rockets at the White Sands Proving Ground as told by the project officer.

Ryan, Cornelius (ed.). *Across the Space Frontier.* New York: The Viking Press, 1952; London: Sidgwick & Jackson, 1953.

An expansion of a collection of articles first written for *Collier's* magazine on the launching and uses of an artificial earth satellite. The authors are Joseph Kaplan, Wernher von Braun, Heinz Haber, Willy Ley, Oscar Schachter, and Fred Whipple.

Sutton, George P. *Rocket Propulsion Elements: An Introduction to the Engineering of Rockets,* 2d ed. New York: John Wiley & Sons, 1956.

Largely devoted to a discussion of liquid-propellant rocket engines, this volume is of most interest to those having engineering or technical training.

Vaeth, J. Gordon. *200 Miles Up: The Conquest of the Upper Air,* 2d ed. New York: The Ronald Press Company, 1956.

A review of U.S. high-altitude research, with some preliminary information on plans for the Vanguard Project and a final chapter on interplanetary and interstellar flight.

Van Allen, James A. (ed.). *Scientific Uses of Earth Satellites.* Ann Arbor: University of Michigan Press, 1956.

A group of technical papers presented at a January 1956 meeting of the Upper Atmosphere Rocket Research Panel held at the University of Michigan.

Vassiliev, Mikhail V. *Sputnik into Space.* New York: Dial Press, 1958; London: Souvenir Press, 1958.

This English translation of an Italian translation of a Soviet study published in Moscow in 1955 has suffered in its multiple translations and in its title, for it contains relatively little on the sputniks. The original Russian title more accurately translates as *Travel into the Cosmos.* The volume may be of some value for its author's ideas on space travel subjects.

Von Braun, Wernher. *The Mars Project.* Urbana, Illinois: University of Illinois Press, 1953.

A brief semitechnical study of the possibilities of manned flight to the planet Mars.

White, Clayton S., and Otis O. Benson, Jr. (eds.). *Physics and Medicine of the Upper Atmosphere: A Study of the Aeropause.* Albuquerque: University of New Mexico Press, 1952.

A collection of 43 technical papers presented at the Symposium on the Physics and Medicine of the Upper Atmosphere held in San Antonio, Texas, in November 1951. Most of the papers were revised or rewritten before publication.

Williams, Beryl, and Samuel Epstein. *The Rocket Pioneers on the Road to Space.* New York: Julian Messner, 1958.

The contributions to rocketry and astronautics of Congreve, Verne, Tsiolkovskii, Goddard, Oberth, the German Society for Space Travel, the American Rocket Society, and the Peenemunde V-2 program.

APPENDIX III

The Contributors: Biographical Notes

Dr. Bruno Balke, M.D. University of Berlin, is Associate Professor of Physiology in the Department of Physiology-Biophysics, School of Aviation Medicine, USAF. From the beginning of World War II he was with the German Army in various theaters and in 1942 became head of the Department of Performance Physiology at the medical school of the Army Mountain Corps. In 1945 he was admitted as a University lecturer at Leipzig after presentation of a thesis on "Physical Efficiency of Man in High Mountains." Since 1950 he has been associated with Air Force advanced physiological research projects at the School of Aviation Medicine.

Dr. Richard W. Bancroft, Ph.D. University of Southern California, is Assistant Chief of the Department of Physiology-Biophysics, School of

Aviation Medicine, USAF. During World War II he served in the Air Forces in connection with studies in high-altitude physiology. Since 1950 he has been a member of the professional staff at the School of Aviation Medicine, where in 1958 he was appointed Associate Professor of Biophysics, Air University.

Major Charles A. Berry, M.D. University of California, is Assistant Chief, Department of Aviation Medicine, School of Aviation Medicine, USAF. His first Air Force assignment was in 1951 as Chief of Internal Medicine, Hamilton AFB. After aviation medicine resident training at Randolph AFB, he served as Deputy Command Surgeon, Caribbean Air Command, 1952-55.

Brigadier General Homer A. Boushey, A.B. in Engineering, Stanford University, is Director of Advanced Technology in the Office of the Deputy Chief of Staff for Development, Hq USAF. After completing his flying training he was graduated from the Air Corps maintenance engineering course in 1939, since which time he has held assignments with Air Force research and development activities, operational fighter units, and the USAF Headquarters staff. In 1941, as project officer for jet-assisted take-off development, he made the first rocket-powered flight in the U.S. In 1952 he went to the Wright Air Development Center, where he held positions as Chief of the Equipment Laboratory, Director of Weapon Systems, Chief of Staff, and Vice Commander. Later he became Deputy Director of Research and Development, Hq USAF.

Colonel Paul A. Campbell, M.D. Rushmore Medical College of the University of Chicago, is Chief of the Space Medicine Division, School of Aviation Medicine, USAF. During most of World War II he was Director of Research at the School of Aviation Medicine and at the close of hostilities he went to Germany as a member of the Air Staff intelligence team to study German Air Force research. He has written chapters for seven medical textbooks, two of which are on space medicine, and has served with the Air Force Office of Scientific Research as Special Assistant for Medical and Bioscientific Research.

Dr. Hans G. Clamann, M.D. University of Heidelberg, is Aviation Physiologist, Department of Physiology-Biophysics, School of Aviation Medicine, USAF, Randolph AFB. Born in Germany, he studied medicine at Goettingen, Munich, and Heidelberg universities. From 1929 to 1934 he was a fellow of the Emergency Society for German Sciences and research assistant at the Physiological Institute of Heidelberg and at the University of Wuerzburg. In 1935 he joined the Aero Medical Research Institute in Berlin, was promoted to rank of State Advisor in 1935, to Chief Medical Advisor in 1942, and later became Deputy Director. In 1947 he came to the School of Aviation Medicine, where he was named Research Fellow in 1951 and Professor of Biophysics in 1958.

Dr. Raymond Estep, Ph.D. University of Texas, is Historian in the Documentary Research Division of Air University's Research Studies Institute. At Air University since 1946, he has written a dozen book-length studies on international affairs, transportation, and air power. He is the compiler of the current selective bibliography published by Air University, *An Air*

Power Bibliography (through 1954) and its succeeding volume, which covers 1955-1956.

Brigadier General Don Flickinger, M.D. Stanford University School of Medicine, is Command Surgeon, Director of Life Sciences, and Special Assistant for Bio-Astronautics, Hq Air Research and Development Command. He was Medical Officer-of-the-Day at Pearl Harbor on 7 December 1941 and served in the China-Burma-India Theater. He became Director of Research, Internal Medicine Division, School of Aviation Medicine, in 1947 and later was Command Surgeon, Eighth Air Force. In 1951 he joined Air Research and Development Command as Director of Human Factors, then became Assistant Deputy for Development and Director of Research. In 1955 he assumed command of the Air Force Office of Scientific Research.

Lieutenant Colonel Kenneth F. Gantz, Ph.D. University of Chicago, is Editor of *Air University Quarterly Review*. His recently published science novel deals with the first flight of the United States Air Force to Mars.

Dr. Siegfried J. Gerathewohl, Ph.D. Institute of Technology, Dresden, is a staff member in the Department of Space Medicine, School of Aviation Medicine, USAF. In 1934 he affiliated with the German Army as a psychologist, transferring to the German Air Force in 1939 as aviation psychologist. He was Chief of the Psychological Assessment Center in Hamburg and during the last year of the war was adviser to the Aviation Research Institute of Munich. In 1946 he joined the staff of the Aeromedical Center in Heidelberg. He came to the United States in 1947 to join the School of Aviation Medicine.

Major Evan R. Goltra, M.D. Long Island Medical School, M.P.H. School of Public Health, Harvard University, is a student in the Advanced Course in Aviation Medicine, School of Aviation Medicine, USAF. Since his entry on active duty in 1949 he has served as field hospital commander, Fort Bragg, and with the Joint Brazil–U.S. Military Commission in Brazil.

Dr. George T. Hauty, Ph.D. University of Rochester, is a staff member of the Department of Space Medicine, School of Aviation Medicine, USAF. In World War II Dr. Hauty was for four years an Army intelligence officer in Alaska and the Aleutians. He joined the Department of Psychology, School of Aviation Medicine, in 1951 and the Department of Space Medicine in 1957, where he specializes in the effect of space conditions on crew efficiency.

Major General Lloyd P. Hopwood is Director of Military Personnel, Hq USAF. From 1938 to 1943 he held a variety of assignments in flying training; then after a tour in Air Force Headquarters he took command in 1945 of the rear echelon of the Eighth Air Force. In that organization he was successively Assistant Chief of Staff for Personnel, Chief of Staff, and Assistant Chief of Staff for Plans. Upon returning to the United States in July 1946 he headed the civilian institutions education program of Air University. After graduation from the Air War College in 1949 he was Deputy Director of Personnel Planning, Hq USAF. From 1953 to 1958 he was Commandant of Air University's Air Command and Staff College.

Major General Dan C. Ogle, M.D. University of Illinois College of Medicine, was Surgeon General, United States Air Force, from 1954 until his retirement in 1958. He joined the Army Medical Corps in 1929 and during World War II became Surgeon of the Fifteenth Air Force in Italy. After the war he transferred to the newly independent United States Air Force, assisted in establishing the separate Air Force medical service, and became its Deputy Surgeon General.

Lieutenant Colonel Burt Rowen, M.D. New York University College of Medicine, is Chief of the Human Factors Branch, Air Force Flight Test Center. Since February 1958 he has also been Human Factors Coordinator for the X-15 project. After his graduation from the School of Aviation Medicine, USAF, he went through the advanced flying school and flew with the 56th Fighter Group for a year before he returned in 1949 to the School of Aviation Medicine as an instructor.

Dr. S. B. Sells, Ph.D. Columbia University, has been actively engaged in research, teaching, and the clinical practice of aeromedical psychology for the past 10 years and has taught at Columbia University and the University of Texas. Until he recently joined the Department of Psychology, Texas Christian University, he was Professor of Medical Psychology and Chief, Department of Medical Psychology, School of Aviation Medicine, USAF.

Lieutenant Colonel David G. Simons, M.D. Jefferson Medical College, is Chief of the Aero Medical Field Laboratory, Air Force Missile Development Center. In 1947 at Wright-Patterson AFB he worked as project officer for rocket experiments in the physiological responses of animals to weightlessness. Since service in Japan as flight surgeon from 1950 to 1952, he has studied the biological hazards of primary cosmic radiation at altitudes of 85,000 feet and above, and supervised experiments on weightlessness. His balloon flight in Manhigh II, 19-20 August 1957, took him to an altitude of 101,000 feet.

Colonel John P. Stapp, Ph.D. University of Texas, M.D. University of Minnesota, is Chief of the Aero Medical Laboratory, Wright Air Development Center, where his aviation-medicine career began in 1946 in the Biophysics Branch. From 1947 to 1951 he made human crash deceleration studies with rocket sleds at Edwards AFB. In 1953 he was assigned to Holloman AFB Aero Medical Field Laboratory, where he directed Manhigh I and II balloon flights and rocket sled experiments to determine tolerance to windblast and supersonic escape decelerations.

Dr. Hubertus Strughold, Ph.D. University of Muenster, M.D. University of Wuerzburg, was for nine years Chief, Department of Space Medicine, School of Aviation Medicine, USAF, and is since October 1958 Advisor for Research at the same institution. A pioneer in aviation medicine, Dr. Strughold became director of the Aeromedical Research Institute in Berlin in 1935 and by 1945 was a colonel in the German Medical Corps. After the war he was appointed Director of the Physiological Institute, University of Heidelberg. In 1947 he joined the School of Aviation Medicine, USAF. Dr. Strughold has written a book describing Mars, *The Green and Red*

Planet, coauthored *Principles of Aviation Medicine* and an atlas on aviation medicine.

General Thomas D. White, United States Military Academy, is Chief of Staff, United States Air Force. For four years before his appointment in 1957 he was Vice Chief of Staff and for the two preceding years was Deputy Chief of Staff for Operations.

APPENDIX IV

Project Mercury and the National Space Program

Compiled by
Lieutenant Colonel Kenneth F. Gantz

First American into Orbit: Project Mercury
By the Editors of *Air Force* *

His name, rank, and serial number are unknown today, but within eighteen months to three years, the most precisely chosen test pilot in the history of flight will board a cramped, cone-shaped "cabin," probably at the Air Force Missile Test Center at Cape Canaveral, Fla., be strapped onto a form-fitting couch, and be blasted into an orbit approximately 150 miles above the earth. He will circuit the planet at an incredible 18,000 mph (once around the globe every ninety minutes). How many circuits he will make is a question that cannot be answered now; the probable maximum time of the mission would be twenty-four hours. But it is more likely that one or two successful orbits, then the crucial business of safe re-entry, will be the program.

Certainly *one* successful orbit and safe landing of the human pilot will be considered a monumental success by the managers of Project Mercury— the National Aeronautics and Space Administration, backed by the missile and medical know-how of the Air Force and other services.

If all goes well—and the talents of thousands of technical personnel combine to make that "if" as small as possible—the orbiting man will return

* Reprinted from *Air Force* Magazine, March 1959, by special permission. Copyright 1959.

safely to earth to tell his story. If he makes it, his historic journey will spell a giant *yes* to the question: Can a man endure the stresses of spaceflight, the awful increase in body weight during the acceleration upward, the sudden shift to weightlessness in orbit, the eerie isolation from his home planet, the decelerative stresses and fiery re-entry through the atmosphere as he and his vehicle hurtle earthward from nearly airless space to the lower layers where the friction of air against vehicle could vaporize him and his ship if they were unprotected?

The rocket that will take our American astronaut into orbit will be, according to best present estimates, the Convair-built USAF Atlas. Atlas has already made the orbital flight itself as the famed "talking" (but unmanned) satellite of late 1958.

The countdown for Mercury's monumental flight will go something like this:

The Mercury capsule, with the spaceman aboard, will sit on the top of the approximately eighty-foot-high Atlas missile. Inside his new "home" the astronaut, clad in a pressure suit and strapped into his seat, will recline back to the floor. If hardware recently developed at the Air Force's Wright Air Development Center at Wright-Patterson AFB, Ohio, is used, the seat will be something like a netted hammock and the restrainer will be a tight cloth across the spaceman's middle with an accordion-type "control" panel he can operate even under heavy g stresses.

The air in his capsule will consist of carefully mixed helium and oxygen plus other breathable gases circulated mechanically in his closed environment. The spaceman will probably have food and drink aboard, available for use during orbit and for the time he will wait to be picked up by the air-sea task force standing by for his recovery after re-entry. If he eats or drinks in orbit, it will be via devices such as suction tubes or squeeze bottles. This method is necessary because he and his capsule will be weightless in orbit.

Secured in his seat, the spaceman will be hooked up to a network of medical instruments designed to relay to the ground his every recordable physiological reaction. He will look at the world below him through a periscope device, and have radio contact—by voice—with the ground.

From the moment he enters his spaceship—the capsule to be built by the McDonnell Aircraft Corporation—a tense group of doctors and engineers and other technicians will be following his every reaction. The final countdown, unlike any other in missile history, will be under way.

Ground crews will make last-minute checks.

Then, finally the dramatic blast-off.

The next few split seconds will be vital. If anything seems to go wrong, ground control will touch off a mechanism to blast and parachute the astronaut to safety thousands of yards away from the fiery exhaust of the missile. An ambulance will rush to his landing point. What went wrong will be analyzed and reanalyzed, and the process will begin over again, days or weeks later.

If all goes well at blast-off, the astronaut will brace in his pressure suit for the seven or more g's he will have to take on his way up. The crushing pressure will push eyes and internal organs downward against the spaceman's horizontal axis. When the missile reaches orbital velocity of 18,000 mph, the man-carrying nose cone will be separated and will begin its orbit. Man and capsule will be weightless. The capsule will then be tipped by reactor jets in airless space to a horizontal attitude, and the spaceman inside will ride facing forward. The pitch, roll, and yaw of the capsule will be controlled automatically by "sensor" jets.

The descent from orbit will follow this procedure:

At a critical moment, precalculated on the ground so that trackers will be able to determine the landing area, the capsule will be somersaulted by jets (probably at a ground-issued signal) and then slowed by retrorockets to start its descent.

The astronaut will again be riding with his back downward. In strong contrast to the weightlessness of orbit, the g stresses—this time pushing *up* at him—may be even more hazardous than the pressures he took earlier.

As he curves downward toward the thicker layers of the atmosphere, a drogue parachute will be released to slow his descent and lessen the enormous frictional heat of capsule against air. With the drogue will burst out metal chaff to aid radar tracking of his descent. A heat-absorbing beryllium shield on the base of the capsule will protect him and his vehicle from vaporization. Once the capsule reaches lower altitudes where a conventional parachute can operate, another ground signal will release a large landing chute, eject the heat shield, and the man will come floating home. Ensuring his safe impact on land or water—and planners are now figuring on water—will be an inflatable bumper. The bumper will keep the capsule afloat as the astronaut awaits his rescuers.

From the moment the spaceman leaves orbit, his trajectory will be plotted to pinpoint his expected landing site as exactly as possible. It will be imperative to get to him with utmost dispatch, since the capsule will be limited in its ability to support his needs after he arrives home.

As of March 1958, the process to choose the man to perform the incredible mission described above is under way, under the technical management of NASA.

The NASA training program has made meaningful a quiet flurry of activity during recent months at such centers as the Air Force's WADC at Wright-Patterson AFB, Ohio, where since last November researchers have been putting finishing touches on screening programs for space volunteers. By late February, two screening programs—one to last five days, the other twelve days—had been completed, and by now one of them is probably in full play as an aid to the selection of the twelve-man team to be chosen from the thirty-six volunteers who in turn have been chosen from the nucleus of 110 Air Force, Navy, and Marine pilots called to Washington during February for briefings on the mission by NASA. From the final twelve-man team selected will emerge, just prior to the mission, the Mercury Astronaut who will perform the mission.

What will the screening be like? If WADC's plans are any indication, the thirty-six volunteers will be going through a regimen of thorough physical examination, deep psychiatric interviews, isolation chamber tests, subjection to centrifuge accelerations, performance tests in heat, noise, and pressure chambers. They will be measured by anthropologists, submit to cold water immersion of their feet to measure heart and respiratory toughness, take hard turns on automatic treadmills to check the limits of their constitutions. And they will probably take zerogravity rides in WADC's C-131B, whose roomy cabin allows actual floating in the air for brief periods.

Center for the twelve-man Mercury Astronaut team will be at NASA's Langley Research Center, Va., where they will be assigned to the Space Task Group. The project officer for NASA will be Robert R. Gilruth. The program will be under the general supervision of NASA's Dr. Abe Silverstein.

From their Langley headquarters, the group will return for intensive training at Wright-Patterson, at the USAF School of Aviation Medicine's Space Medicine Division at Randolph AFB, at missile test ranges, and, importantly, at Johnsville, Pa., where the Naval Air Development Laboratory's giant human centrifuge can take them on up-to-forty-g accelerations, sufficient to simulate re-entry shocks and buffetings. The Johnsville centrifuge has already been used extensively for the training of the Air Force's X-15 pilots.

Hardware development will proceed simultaneously with personnel training. Capsule mockups will be tested by technical teams, using short-range, solid-fuel boosters to take them through suborbital trajectories. As the McDonnell capsule proves out, more powerful boosters will take the mockups through longer range flights. Eventually animals (life-supporting containers for animals are under development at the USAF Division of Space Medicine at Randolph AFB, Tex.) will ride the capsules in ballistic trajectories. Final stages in the program will probably include animal launchings into orbit. And it is possible that Mercury trainees will take ballistic-trajectory rides also. Research along that line is also under way.

The capsule itself? Present design gives it the appearance of a truncated cone, or as some suggest, a television tube before you fit it into the cabinet. Seven feet across at the base, the capsule is expected to weigh about a ton. Both ends of the cone will be blunt and covered with heat-absorbent material, probably beryllium. The capsule will be about twenty-nine feet high, including its projecting hardware, antennae, and the like.

On the day Project Mercury becomes a reality, a man-machine complex of incredible precision will have been created. But of the two components, the man—and this is regardless of the success or failure of the mission—will be vastly the more important.

The Project Mercury Development Program Status Report as of 1 March 1959

Issued by
National Aeronautics and Space Administration

The NASA Space Task Group currently has under way five categories of development programs for the manned satellite project and has largely completed work in a sixth research area.

The program completed is the human support system, a form-fitting couch in which the astronaut will be supine during his flight. Through tests at Johnsville, Pennsylvania, it has been determined that the astronaut supported by the form-fitting couch can withstand many more g's, or forces of gravity, than will be experienced in the Project Mercury flight. As a matter of interest, a Navy officer (Lt. Comdr. Carter Collins) withstood approximately 20 g's in the NASA couch, more force than any human ever before has experienced.

The five development programs under way as of 1 March 1959 are:

1. Air drop tests, which are being conducted off the NASA's Pilotless Aircraft Research Station, Wallops Island, Virginia.

2. Reliability studies of the escape system, also at Wallops Island.

3. Wind tunnel investigations, at Langley Research Center, Virginia, and Ames Research Center, California.

4. Landing loads (impact) tests, in Langley's hydrodynamics laboratories.

5. Characteristics of the stability (drogue) parachute, in Langley's wind tunnels and at the NASA's High Speed Flight Station, Edwards, California.

An explanation of the test categories follows:

AIR DROPS

The terminal phase of the manned satellite project—safe recovery after the capsule re-enters the atmosphere—was an initial consideration of space scientists. Theoretical and experimental studies of this problem began nearly a year before the Space Task Group was formed by scientists at the Langley Research Center.

Essentially, the air drop program is designed to answer such basic questions as: What is the optimum altitude at which to deploy the recovery parachute? How reliable is the designed parachute system? What motions can the space pilot expect of the recovery parachute and the capsule during descent? What are the impact forces in both ground and water landings? How best can the capsule be recovered from the water?

Before the tests were started off Wallops Island, Langley scientists developed the system of ejecting models from the carrier, a C-130 Hercules transport. Ejection studies were conducted in the late summer of 1958 over the Salerno and Normandy drop zones at Fort Bragg, North Carolina, and over the deserted municipal airport at West Point, Virginia.

Full-scale models used as test vehicles are staged out of Langley, where capsules are loaded on the Hercules transport loaned to the NASA by Tactical Air Command. The test vehicle is dropped into a free fall from high altitude and is photographed in its descent by two T-33 chase planes. One plane is stationed at the same altitude as the C-130 and the other at the altitude where the recovery parachute will be deployed.

When the capsule impacts, two Marine HUS helicopters from Quantico and a crash rescue boat from Wallops Island go to the scene. One helicopter, directed by the other 'copter and the crash boat, retrieves the capsule by shackling a line to an eye located on the top of the test model.

Detailed studies are made from motion picture films taken by the T-33 jets.

ESCAPE TESTS

When the manned satellite is launched, it will have on top of it a pylonlike arrangement tipped with a small rocket system. In event of malfunction of the booster at any time during the flight up to staging, the small rocket can be triggered and it will carry the capsule and its occupant away from the booster. Normal deployment of the recovery parachute then will take place.

Reliability tests of the escape system and aerodynamic studies of the capsule-escape combination recently began at Wallops Island using full-scale models launched as payloads of research rockets. Scientists are determining from these studies the proper alignment of the escape rocket nozzles as well as the dynamic forces on the capsule and escape systems during launch and descent.

MODEL PROGRAM

Behavior of the capsule during flight is now being studied in the NASA's wind tunnels and at the Wallops Island station.

At Wallops, various-sized scale models are launched to determine stability characteristics, re-entry dynamics and afterbody heating. Models are subjected to a full velocity range—from mach 2 (twice the speed of sound) to more than 7000 miles per hour.

Studies in the fields of static stability, lift and drag, damping in pitch and allowable center-of-gravity positions for escape are being conducted in Langley's Unitary Plan Wind Tunnel and Eight-Foot Transonic Tunnel. The Eight-Foot Tunnel covers the mach .3 to mach 1.04 speed range, while Unitary duplicates velocities up to mach 4.5.

Static stability and damping in the mach 3 to mach 8 range are being studied in the Free Flight Tunnel at the Ames Research Center.

Stability characteristics in the mach 1.3 to mach 4 range are being investigated in Langley's Vibration and Flutter Tunnel; and in the 11-inch Hypersonic Tunnel, damping in the mach 7–10 range is under study.

Langley's stability tunnels—Spin, Free Flight and Full Scale—examine oscillation, dynamic stability at terminal velocity, and static and dynamic lift, drag, and pitching moments.

IMPACT TESTS

When the space capsule lands after its orbital flight, it will strike the water, or land, with a considerable force at 30 feet per second. Research is being conducted to determine the optimum shape of the leading face of the capsule to eliminate excessive deceleration forces on the occupant.

This problem is most acute in a ground landing. Although a water landing is planned, a ground impact must be investigated so that all possible contingencies can be anticipated.

In addition to leading face shapes, scientists are investigating crushable materials and are determining the degree of landing forces transposed to the capsule occupant.

Instrumented scale models are being dropped in water tanks and on hard surfaces at Langley from every possible impact angle, using a variety of structural materials arranged in various ways.

DROGUE PARACHUTE

Because the space capsule is a no-lift vehicle, provisions must be made to ensure steady flight in the atmosphere. It has been determined that the required stability can be obtained through use of a small parachute which will trail above the capsule as it descends. Since little research has been conducted on parachute behavior at high altitudes, NASA scientists must investigate dynamic pressure, loads, and operations characteristics in the range starting at the point where the drogue opens (about 70,000 feet) to the altitude where the recovery parachute deploys (about 10,000 feet).

This program involves research on snatch forces, which occur when the parachute package reaches the end of the shroud lines, and the shock forces, which are experienced when the parachute blossoms.

Dynamic pressure studies are conducted in Langley's wind tunnels, and the operational tests will be made at the High Speed Flight Station.

In the operational tests, the drogue system is taken to high altitude in an Air Force F-104 Starfighter over Muroc, California. From altitude, it will be dropped. Reliability, snatch-force, and shock-force studies will be made through telemetry and motion picture records.

The NASA's capsule drogue parachute testing program is expected to provide basic information not only for Project Mercury but also on operation of parachutes for all types of high-altitude missions.

The National Space Program

Excerpts from the Statement * of Dr. T. Keith Glennan,
Administrator, National Aeronautics and Space Administration,
Before the Committee on Science and Astronautics,
House of Representatives, 86th Congress, 1st Session

*   *   *   *   *

The probable material benefits of space exploration are both direct and indirect and may be applicable both to civilian and military activities. The first practical applications appear to be those of satellites to the problems of world-wide communications and of meteorological research and weather forecasting. The last satellite launched by the U.S.—the Atlas—demonstrated in dramatic fashion some of the potentialities of a communications satellite. This accomplishment is but the first step in a development expected to lead to an economically sound, wide-band, reliable, world-wide communication system. Such a system would permit the transmission of television programs, if the use of the system for such a purpose were considered desirable.

A meteorological satellite would enable world-wide observation of clouds and other aspects of weather as suitable methods and instruments are developed. At present there are available weather observations from a limited number of stations on the land masses of the globe and from a few ships at sea. The much greater amount of information from the world-wide coverage of the satellite would, when suitably processed, increase the accuracy of weather forecasts. Economic studies have shown very large dollar savings from relatively small improvements in accuracy. More accurate forecasts have tremendous economic implications for agriculture, food-processing industries, public utility companies, and numerous other industries.

There are other applications of satellites to more special uses, such as navigation and geodetic measurements. Beyond these we enter the realm of speculation and prophecy. We do not know the ultimate role of space vehicles in transportation any more than the few spectators of the early flights of the Wright brothers knew of our present jet transports that make the world a neighborhood. Some speculate that the moon and the planets represent a vast new physical frontier, a source of new material wealth, but

* [2 February 1959.]

at present this cannot be demonstrated. Suffice it to say that there are some clearly seen material benefits to human welfare from space exploration, and that there are others, probably more significant, hidden from our view. I am personally convinced that these now-hidden gains that will accrue from our national space programs represent future payoffs of incalculable value, very possibly outweighing greatly the investments that will be required.

I have referred to the goal of our national space programs as the opening of space to mankind. Such an aim embraces the many interests of man himself, the material and the spiritual. To explore space to gain additional knowledge about the universe in which we live; to open space to the travel of man himself; to open space as a demonstration of one's mastery of advanced technologies—all these reflect as in a mirror the insatiable curiosity of the human mind.

Our space science program is already providing much new knowledge about space that has led to the postulation of new theories about the earth and the environment surrounding it. And we have only begun to accumulate this new knowledge. High priority is being given to the study of energetic particles. In the immediate program, the interactions of high-energy particles with the earth's atmosphere and field will be studied intensively, and the types and energy of such particles and their spatial distribution will be measured. Of specific interest are the measurements of cosmic ray intensity in interplanetary space, time and latitude of cosmic ray intensity variations, composition and spatial extent of the great Van Allen radiation belts around the earth, cosmic ray energy and charge spectrums, and the nature of the particles producing auroras. Measurements will be extended as far as possible toward the sun and toward the outer reaches of the solar system, including the interactions of energetic particles with the atmospheres and fields of the planets.

These are but an indication of the broad program that must be undertaken in the years to come. In our selection of the scientific space experiments to be conducted, we look for advice to the Space Science Board of the National Academy of Sciences. This board of sixteen scientists is headed by Dr. Lloyd V. Berkner. It has already been helpful with reference to the immediate program for scientific exploration of the space environment. It also has in preparation a comprehensive report on the longer range scientific objectives with respect to the study of many physical phenomena relating to the moon, planets, and interplanetary space.

*   *   *   *   *

The President has assigned to NASA the development of the national space program.* In this effort we are working, of course, in closest coopera-

* [The Presidential order of 1 October 1958 transferred certain programs and projects already under way. These actions included, for example, a study contract the Air Force had with Rocketdyne Division of North American Aviation to determine the feasibility of undertaking development of a single-chamber rocket engine in the 1½-million-pound thrust class. Included also in these transfers were the Vanguard project and several Air Force and Army space probes then under the administration of the Advanced Research Projects Agency of the Department of Defense. Reserved to the Department of Defense by the Space Act of 1958 are "activities peculiar to or primarily associated with the development of weapon systems, military operations, or

tion with all other elements of our government, particularly with the Department of Defense. Our method has been to deal substantively with each of the major elements of the problem.

We have had to face up to the fact that we do not have available booster rockets sufficiently powerful to put into orbit or send on long journeys into space the size of payload required to obtain the scientific information that is needed. This fact is made no more palatable by realization that today and for some time to come the Soviets have rocket boosters permitting them to send into space payloads heavier than we can manage.

We need a whole family of new rocket boosters and upper-stage rockets that, used singly or in combination, will give us the amounts of thrust we need to accomplish our missions in space. Because these boosters of varying capabilities are necessary for both civilian and military space programs, NASA undertook the development, with DOD, of an integrated program aimed at correcting this situation as soon as is humanly possible.

This program is based on a minimum number of rockets that will be used as building-block units in combination to meet expanding mission requirements. By midsummer of next year, a new, second-stage rocket engine, when used with an Atlas, will permit us to put approximately 6000 pounds of payload into orbit, or send about 1000 pounds of payload as far as the moon. Another rocket engine now being developed, also for use as the second stage of vehicles using the Atlas or Titan booster, will have been completed by early 1961—little more than two years from now—which will enable us to put 8000 pounds of payload into orbit and send a 2000-pound payload to the moon. NASA and DOD are working together in the development of these and other upper-stage rocket motors.

Clustering existing big rocket motors will provide a first-stage booster having a thrust of 1½ million pounds by 1962. Engines of this cluster, procured under DOD auspices, are now in production, and the engineering on the total power package is well advanced. It will permit us to put 10 tons of payload into orbit and to send two tons of payload into deep space, far beyond the moon.

Development of a single-chamber rocket booster designed to deliver one to one and one half million pounds of thrust is also being pushed, to bring it to a stage of usefulness inside of four years. Within two years thereafter we believe we will have learned how to cluster four of these giant rocket motors to provide a first-stage booster with 6 million pounds of thrust. It will lift 75 tons of payload into orbit.

Another problem area—that of guidance and control—requires particularly heavy emphasis both in planning and implementation. Development of midcourse and terminal guidance systems is clearly also necessary. Above all, simplicity and reliability must be built into these systems. Our principal task at the moment is to acquire information about the space environment—and this calls for reliability in getting our instruments aloft, whenever and wherever we may want to make our measurements.

Still another problem—to expand our capacity for tracking and data acquisition—is now well on its way to solution. Additional stations will be

the defense of the United States (including the research and development necessary to make effective provision for the Defense of the United States)...."]

established in this country and abroad. These stations may be manned, in some instances, by nationals of the countries where they are to be located. Still further expansion of these networks will be required, as time and our programs move forward together.

Perhaps the most difficult of our problem areas is our understanding of the capabilities of man himself in this new and exciting adventure into space. While much progress has been made, intensive effort is required to assure us that the men who volunteer for space flights possess the physical and mental capabilities to withstand the rigors of flight in space.

Whatever the problems we may encounter in this particular area, I find it difficult to believe that we shall fail in our efforts to surmount them.

To focus all of these research and development activities and give them real meaning—to sharpen the determination with which we tackle these problems—we have undertaken Project Mercury, an attempt by this nation to send man into space. Last month NASA chose the McDonnell Aircraft Corporation of St. Louis to design and produce the prototype of a capsule to carry the man in this project.

Selection of the pilot-astronauts has already begun. Initially we will need a dozen men, chosen with greatest care from a group of volunteers. The group will be totally involved for many months in a program of rigorous training for the first orbital space flight.

Although this first orbital flight by our modern Mercury will surely be a pioneering venture, we are determined that the risks to the pilot will be no greater than those experienced during the first flights of a new, high-performance airplane. As in such airplane flights, the astronaut will play a vital role in the Mercury project. Repeated flights of the space capsule, first carrying only instruments and later animals, will have tested and proved the practicability of the final phase of Project Mercury—manned satellite flight—before it is undertaken.

I have referred to one other aspect of Project Mercury as being, in my opinion, of the utmost importance. Sending man safely into space is an arm-stretching, mind-stretching undertaking that thrills every one of us, and demands from every one of us the very best we can muster. It is a focal point for all our energies, all our enthusiasms, all our determination. It will result in much earlier development of the technology needed for other difficult space missions.

Index